FROM FLYING HORSE TO MAN IN THE MOON

FROM

Flying Horse

TO

Man in the Moon

A History of Flight from Its Earliest
Beginnings to the Conquest of Space

HENDRIK DE LEEUW

Illustrated

ST MARTIN'S PRESS · NEW YORK

To The Boy Scouts of America

3.30

CONTENTS

ILLUSTRATIONS

FROM FLYING HORSE TO MAN IN THE MOON

YESTERDAY'S DREAM

The flight of birds has been the envy of man from the dawn of history. Mystified by the ease with which birds soared through the air, the ancients have left for posterity descriptions of winged gods, winged beasts, bird-drawn vehicles . . . and flying horses. The ancients sensed that the distant horizons they sought could only be reached through flight.

At first these ancients recorded their yearnings and innermost feelings by means of the written word. Translating their words into deeds, they fastened artificial wings onto themselves in the hope that they could fly in the air not unlike birds. Ancient man also believed that he could solve the mystery of the flight of birds on the assumption that since man and fish were able to swim in water, birds could do the same through the air. This idea was erroneous, as high speed photography proves.

How it is possible for birds to fly has been the subject of investigation and research by countless probers. But to this very day no man-powered effort to fly like a bird has been successful. Why? Because unassisted human muscle power has been incapable of effecting sustained flight. It has been found that the muscles a bird uses to fly in most cases makes up a third or more of the weight of the whole bird, which is in itself a powerful engine, whereas the muscles of a human being available for the movement of limbs are too weak themselves to sustain much flight.

Delving deeply into the arcana of earliest flights, we find that doves and pigeons have been employed as message carriers for more than 2,500 years. Organized pigeon postal services have been in use in China and in the Middle East since the 8th Century. In ancient Greece pigeons were used to report the winners in the Olympic Games. Greek sailors made use of birds in the fifth century B.C. to send messages home to their folk, that all was well or that they could be expected home very soon. Carrier pigeons were also used by the Crusaders, and many centuries later Australia and New Zealand used them in their postal carrying service.

In classical times the Greeks and Romans firmly believed that their gods and deities could fly, as evidenced by the legends of Hercules, who was borne heavenward by a flying chariot, and of Mercury, who used winged sandals to fly into the heavens. The Old Testament story relates how the Prophet Elijah was carried to heaven in an aerial chariot, and Ovid's oft-mentioned legend of the adventures of Daedalus and Icarus is truly the classical myth of aviation.

And so while romance and religion left countless legends about man's urge to soar aloft in the clouds, the idea of human flight captured the imagination and thought of a great many people and dreamers for centuries to come. As these thoughts, ideas and experiments grew, they bred a new crop of dreamers and pioneers, who in their turn left enough suggestions to set other creative minds at work.

Skimming through centuries of time and space, it came to pass some time around 250 B.C. that one deep thinker, named Archimedes, hit upon a scientific discovery involving the principle of the flotation of bodies in liquids or gases. This discovery was to play an important part in the history and development of aviation. To arrive at the principle of his discovery, let's start with the problem that had concerned man, which was to discover some method whereby he could move about in the air freely and defy the laws of gravity. There were two fundamental ways in which this could be accomplished: (1) By floating about in the "air ocean" just as a fish rises to the surface or sinks in the water, a process called *aerostation*. In other words, the machine attempting this had to be lighter than air; (2) To take advantage of reactions developed by the rapid movements of bodies through the air, a process called *aerodynamics*.

This lighter-than-air flight depended upon the simple principle that "a body, when immersed in a fluid, would float, if the weight of the fluid it displaced were greater than the weight of the body itself." In other words, if the body weighed more than the amount of fluid it displaced by its own bulk, it would sink. For example: Let us take a large bag or balloon and inflate it with hot air or gas of a density less than that of the surrounding air. It displaces a volume of air whose weight is greater than the total weight of the bag or balloon. Because of this difference it floats skyward. If, on the other hand, the air creates what is now commonly referred to as aerodynamic lift, it is the very force that makes lighter-than-air flight possible.

Thus the idea that objects and bodies could be made to float upon the air's upper layers, just as boats can be made to float upon water, has been in the inventive minds of philosophers and scientists for a great many centuries. Certainly the publishing of their speculations on the subject must have had a profound influence on the course of aeronautical accomplishments and doubtless, in time, led to the creation of the practical balloon.

Thus earlier aviation history opens when some seven centuries ago a Franciscan friar, Roger Bacon, a most learned man, and a foremost scholar of his time, pondered about the great achievements that still lay ahead. The writings of this famed and remarkable man probably contained the first really sensible ideas on aviation. He scoffed at the then prevalent notion that man could fly by attaching wings to his body, although he was a staunch believer nonetheless in the theory that man could fly. Bacon held to his belief regarding the physical appearance of the earth. He also believed the atmosphere to be a fluid, like water, and thought that it must have a surface high above the earth. He therefore felt that if man could build a mechanical contraption to float in the air, it would be possible for man to reach that surface, actually float across the sky, and make a descent at a designated spot. He thought that if a very-finely-made sphere of thin metal could be constructed and filled with some lighter-than-air substance, it would enable man to soar and float in that atmosphere. There was one fly in the ointment, however: He had no idea of what this substance really could be, but he did conclude that it would be necessary to fill the sphere with what he called "liquid fire." He may have had in mind a gas lighter than air, something like today's hydrogen or helium.

Having conceived an idea predating that of the balloon, Bacon may have been the first human being to evolve a practical method of flying. Had he gone a bit further in his experimentation and suggested fixed wings and an engine to drive a propeller, he would have established the fundamental principles of flying—what makes an airplane take to the air. It was left for the famed Wright Brothers, however, seven centuries later, to work all of this out and produce the first successful, controllable flying machine.

Spanning some 250 years in time brings us to the year 1542,

when Leonardo da Vinci, that great figure in earlier aeronautical pioneering and achievement, was born in Florence. Artist of rare attainments, evidenced by such masterpieces as *Mona Lisa* and *The Last Supper,* universal genius—gifted sculptor, musician, architect, anatomist, engineer, and scientist—he was also a man of extraordinary physical strength. He was reputed to be able to bend heavy metal bars over his knee and twist horseshoes out of shape with his bare hands. Yet so gentle was this great man's nature that he used to roam the streets of his beloved Florence buying caged birds in order to set them free. It was undoubtedly his great love of birds, together with his predilection for scientific matters, that stimulated his interest in the art of flying.

Da Vinci devoted countless hours to the study of the flight of birds, the structure of their wings and tails, and the muscles controlling all these parts. Calling his mathematical knowledge into play, da Vinci made an estimate of the strength of the various parts of the bodies of the birds, measuring them with comparable sections in the human body. His manuscripts advocated the streamlining principles in aircraft construction, which he illustrated by his drawings of an aerial propeller, a cleverly conceived parachute (called by him a "fall-breaker") and a helicopter. However, he got no further than the making of pen-sketches. But his written observation that "an object offers as much resistance to the air as the air does to the object" was in itself a forerunner of Newton's law that "to every action there is an equal and opposite reaction." Sir Isaac Newton (1642-1727) was the father of the Third Law of Motion and the Law of Gravity, with which present day airplane and missile scientists are so vitally concerned.

Da Vinci's design for a helicopter, a craft that would rise straight up into the air, consisted of a helix driven by a spring mechanism. Trying it out, he is said to have remarked, "If it is turned at great speed, this helix will be able to form a screw in the air and climb high." John William Lieb, an American mechanical engineer, remarked, "Leonardo da Vinci needed only a practical motor. If he had had that, the airplane would have been invented centuries earlier than it was."

It is not at all unlikely that at least one great man living today is able to trace his own life's work to the findings of da Vinci, for soon after the turn of the 19th century a Russian woman showed her young son a print of da Vinci's helicopter design. This boy was

Igor Sikorsky who has made the development of the helicopter his life's work. To Sikorsky goes the distinction of having made the helicopter the practical and very useful vehicle it has become and is to this very day.

— 2 —
LIGHTER-THAN-AIR CRAFT

The first scientific attempt to create a lighter-than-air vehicle probably occurred in 1670, when the Jesuit monk, Francesco de Lana, drew a design for an airship. He had been pondering the questions why it was that smoke rose skyward and whether there were gases that were lighter than air. He also wondered whether such a gas, when bottled up in a container, would cause the container to float about as a cork floats on water. He was firmly convinced that, were he to remove the "air" from a spherical container it would surely rise. Having that in mind, he visualized a vacuum balloon consisting of four copper spheres, in the belief that the weight of the metal of such a sphere would be less than the weight of the air that could be removed from inside the sphere, with the result that the empty spheres would rise. There was, however, one flaw in his calculation. He did not realize at the time that the external pressure on the spheres would cause them to collapse when the air was removed. It would have been necessary to carry ballast to control the ascent and to permit air to enter the spheres to descend, which is the principle that controls the balloon.

The only one who may have been successful at flying during the 17th century was the French inventor Besnier. He constructed a kite capable of lifting a man, and it is believed that he actually did fly. This man was ahead of the mechanical know how of his time, for mechanics had not yet reached the point of being able to put his idea into practice.

This brings us to another milestone in aviation's earlier history, even if, in a sense, the event did not have any direct connection with aviation. This discovery occurred in 1766, when Henry Cavendish, an English chemist, displayed a special interest in the study of vapors. One day, while pouring oil of vitriol on slabs of zinc, iron and tin, he produced some strange new gas, which proved to be 14½ times lighter than air. It was given the name "hydrogen" by Lavoisier, in 1790. No one had believed that Cavendish's discovery had any real significance, nor had any one been interested enough to experiment with it. Had this been done, it might have led to the discovery of the balloon, a distinction that was postponed for the brothers Joseph and Etienne Montgolfier; for it was their experiments and subsequent discoveries that laid the foundation for lighter-than-air flight.

— 3 —
PIONEERS OF BALLOONING—THE MONTGOLFIERS

The real pioneers of the art of ballooning were Joseph and Etienne Montgolfier, paper makers of Annonay, France, whose ballooning experiments and flights took place between 1740 and 1810.

The idea for the discovery came to brother Joseph, after reading an article by the chemist and physicist clergyman, Joseph Priestley, relating to his experiments with different kinds of air. Joseph became so absorbed in the details of this Englishman's disclosures that, seated one day before the fireplace in his shop, he kept studying the flames as they eddied up the chimney. It dawned upon him that these vapors seemed lighter than air because they kept going up. He then filled a paper bag with smoke, to see whether the bag would rise. It did, and that led to the brothers' experiments with balloons. They next placed a small receptable at the bottom of the bag, so that the smoke could be kept at a certain temperature, and the bag rose higher.

Having thus far done their experimenting indoors, the Montgolfiers decided to try the same thing outdoors, with the result that the bag (or balloon) rose as high as 100 feet. Growing more and more enthusiastic, they decided to hold a public demonstration at Annonay on June 5, 1783, during which their balloon rose about 6,000 feet and landed 7,600 feet away from the spot where it had started.

The Montgolfiers became the heroes of all France. Their balloons became known as Montgolfiers, and the era as "BALLOONO-MANIA." Looking for even greater honors, the Montgolfiers decided

The flying horse of Greek mythology.

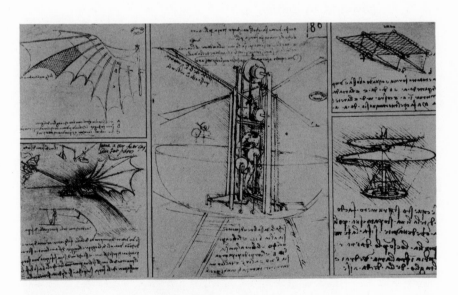

Drawings of flying machines by Leonardo Da Vinci. Upper left: structure of an artificial wing; lower left: a flying wing; center: flying machine with four wings moved by hand; upper right: wing; lower right: helicopter.—BIBLIOTHÈQUE DE L'INSTITUT DE FRANCE

Frontispiece from *L'Homme dans la Lune*, 1666, showing a flying machine powered by birds.

An artist's conception of an aerial vessel lifted by balloons being used for an interplanetary voyage, 1744.

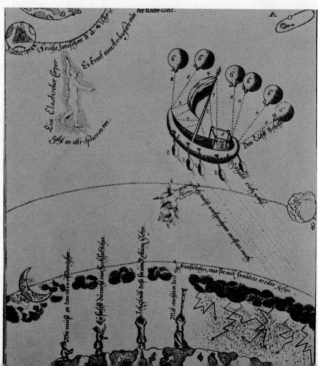

An early Montgolfier balloon, 1780.—BOAC

Lilienthal's 1893 glider, now in the Aviation Museum, Chalais-Meudon, France.—AIR FRANCE

to try out the invention of Cavendish by using hydrogen gas. To make sure that their discovery received official recognition, they forwarded a certified account to the *Académie des Sciences* in Paris, where their achievements, despite criticisms from many skeptics, created a sensation. They soon met with competition, however, when the noted physicist J. A. C. Charles, a distinguished member of the Académie, entered the ballooning picture. By using hydrogen entirely, he created a balloon, called the Charlière, believed to be the better and safer of the two.

A public demonstration by the Montgolfiers took place on August 27, 1783, at the *Champs de Mars,* in Paris, an event that had a particular interest to Americans as well, for among the thousands of gaping spectators was Benjamin Franklin, the then highly popular and "airminded" envoy of the rebellious American States to France. Observing the activities from the window of his carriage, Franklin showed a more than ordinary interest in the proceedings—which should not come as a surprise, since Benjamin Franklin not only had been tinkering with kites, but had flown one in a thunderstorm thirty years before, in Philadelphia.

But there were others who were not as enthusiastic about all this ballooning business. When one of these skeptics turning to Franklin, asked, "What's the use of such a balloon?" Franklin replied with the laconic question, "Of what use would be a new-born baby?" When Louis the Sixteenth, King of France, asked the Montgolfiers to stage a demonstration for himself and the royal family, they not only consented most readily, but constructed a balloon entirely of linen, and decorated it in lively colors and designs most pleasing to the royal family. Attached to the bottom of the balloon was a basket which puzzled the King greatly. When the monarch asked what this basket was for, Etienne removed the canvas cover, which had hidden a bleating lamb, a frightened rooster, and a quacking duck. These animals actually became the world's first aerial passengers.

When all was in readiness for the flight, the straw and wool beneath the large gallery were ignited and the tethering ropes were cut, and the balloon with its menagerie was carried aloft. Gracefully rising over the Versailles Palace, it came down after a successful flight of eight minutes, a mile-and-a-half away. The animals came out of the ordeal without a scratch.

The stage now was set for the first aerial balloon flight by man.

This honor fell to the King's historian, Pilatre de Rozier, who made the ascent on November 21, 1783, but who unfortunately became the first air fatality in history. Crossing the English Channel from Boulogne to England with his companion P. A. de Romain, on the 15th of June, 1785, his hydrogen-filled balloon burst into flames twenty-five minutes after take-off, killing both men.

Balloonomania had taken Europe by storm. Everybody tried this newest craze, although most ascents were failures. The best remembered flight was made by Jean Pierre Blanchard, a mechanically inclined man who, long before the Montgolfiers had produced their first balloon, had devised a flying machine, though with disastrous results. Disappointed, he went to England, where he met John Jeffries, an American physician who had settled in Britain after the American War of Independence and who consented to finance his undertaking. This led to a Channel crossing on January 7, 1785, which became one of the classics in ballooning history. After a long, insalubrious crossing, they finally landed twelve miles from Calais in the tree tops of the Guines Forest, where the populace found them clinging desperately to the branches. Once liberated, they were given a wild celebration in Calais (where the balloon's basket may still be viewed in the museum) and a monument was erected marking the spot where they landed so unceremoniously. The French King later presented Blanchard with a purse of 12,000 gold *Livres,* and a life pension of fifty pounds a year.

A year or so later, Blanchard decided to transfer his activities to the New World, where he made many ascents. One of these, in Philadelphia in 1793, was witnessed by General George Washington. Remaining in America for two years, Blanchard is best remembered for his ascent during which he parachuted a dog, a cat and a squirrel back to earth safely—probably the first parachute drop made in the New World.

Ballooning had by now become an accepted step in science, and balloon races became the order of the day. The only drawback was that captive balloons were entirely dependent on the whim of the elements. Soon the cumbersome, highly inefficient and dangerous hot-air Montgolfières became a rarity, and the hydrogen-filled Charlières took their place as the generally accepted vehicles for human transportation. The first motor-driven dirigible balloon was built and flown by Henri Giffard in 1851. The earliest use of balloons for military purposes is said to have occurred at Maubeuge, on June 2, 1794, when the first company of French *Aerostiers* rose in a hydrogen-filled balloon to observe the enemy's position.

Another ballooning milestone was passed on September 5, 1862, when the British balloonist, Henry Coxwell, accompanied by his friend the astronomer James Glaisher, rose to a height of at least 29,000 feet over Wolverhampton. Both pioneers suffered not only from a lack of oxygen, but from freezing cold. Their plight became so desperate, in fact, that Glaisher was almost frozen, while the sturdier Coxwell not only had a tough job keeping his friend alive, but had to manipulate the balloon's valve cord with his teeth, thus forcing the balloon to descend by slow stages.

Ten years later Paul Haenlein of Germany managed to make an ascent in a semi-rigid, cigar-shaped craft, in which a gas engine, used for the first time, enabled him to reach a speed of *ten* miles an hour. A flight of no less importance took place in Paris, in 1858, when the French balloonist-photographer Nadar (Feliz Tournachon)—to whom I shall refer in later chapters—took the first aerial photograph with a successful *daguerreotype* of a Paris rooftop scene. Not to be outdone, E. William Black made use of aerial photography in some scenes of Boston, in 1860.

Surpassing all these were the adventures of Thaddeus Sobieski, Constance Lowe and John Wise, who had been flirting with the grandiose idea of a balloon crossing of the Atlantic. They built a mammoth balloon, with a cabin-like basket for passengers and a thirty-foot steam-powered life boat, and named it the *City of New York*. It was equipped with a helicopter screw to facilitate the ascent and descent. Since they had difficulty securing hydrogen in New York, they decided to transfer the huge contraption to Philadelphia, where they began their flight on the very day that the steamship *Great Eastern* dropped anchor in New York.

Disaster struck once more. Torrential rains and terrific winds burst the huge bag and demolished their balloon completely.

Having had his fill of disappointments, Lowe, known generally as Professor Lowe, abandoned his Atlantic crossing idea and constructed another huge balloon instead, with which he successfully drifted sixty miles, proving that he could make use of a western wind. This he followed up with a second trip from Cincinnati, floating more than 800 miles to the South Carolina coast. But then something happened that he had not counted on. The Civil War had broken out, and the poor professor was captured as a Yankee spy. Securing his release with no little difficulty, and returning to Cincinnati, he received a commission to organize and head what then became known as the United States Army Aeronautics Corps. This Corps, made up of seven captive balloons, was manned by highly competent and trained aeronauts, and had a generous supply of hydrogen-generating equipment.

Making close to 3,000 ascents, Lowe not only reported the movement of the Confederate Forces to General McClellan's Army of the Potomac, but he chalked up his greatest success at the Battle of Fairoaks, where the Union Army was saved from destruction by his most accurate reports.

When the Confederate Army got wind of the fact that the Federals made use of balloons with such remarkable success, they, too, began the construction of one balloon, in complete secret, even though General Longstreet reported the lack of suitable material in his despatch as follows: "While we were longing for the balloons that poverty denied us, a real genius arose for the occasion and suggested that we send out and gather silk dresses in the Confederacy and make a balloon." Some of the ladies in Richmond donated their silken petticoats for the bag's fabric, while others devoted their time to sewing them together. And thus the balloon was ready for use in the "Seven Days Campaign." As gas was to be had in Richmond, the patchwork ship was filled there, then securely tied to a locomotive on the York River Railroad and run to a suitable spot where it was sent aloft. Unfortunately, the commander transfered the bag to a steamer on the James River, where it was captured by the Federals when the ship was stranded on a bar one day.

After the end of the Civil War, Professor Lowe gave up ballooning, opened an observatory in California and devoted himself to the study of astronomy.

Another balloonist who provided real history-making copy was the Swedish explorer S. A. Andree, who tried to cross the North Pole by balloon. His plan was to drift across the Pole with a combination of trail ropes, and he figured on a target somewhere in the Bering Strait. And so Salomon August Andree, accompanied by Nils Strindberg and Knut Fraenkel, departed from Dane's Island, Spitsbergen, the last civilized outpost south of the North

Pole, on July 11, 1897, in a balloon christened by him *Ornen* (*overnen*, or Eagle) to start the drift across the Pole. His expedition met with disaster, however, and, except for one carrier pigeon and five floating buoys, which were washed ashore in 1899 and 1900, the courageous Andree and his companions disappeared over the Arctic wastes, never to be heard from again.

More than thirty years went by before this Arctic mystery was solved, the first clue to the fate of the missing balloonists coming on August 8, 1930, when sailors from the Norwegian sealer *Brootvaag* went ashore on White Island. There they spotted an aluminum lid and a dark object protruding from a snowdrift. After some digging, they uncovered Andree's canvas boat, some rusty scientific instruments, and human bones bleached as white as the snows that had covered them for those many years. But that was not all; they also came upon a weather-beaten diary which had belonged to Andree. There also was ink in the men's fountain pens, paraffin in their primus stove, and a log book.

Thus was the true story of Andree's fateful expedition revealed. We learned, how due to leaking gas they were forced to descend very close to the Pole, at a spot two hundred miles to the north. The diary also gave details of a hard and distressing trek on foot back toward Spitsbergen. It also revealed how they had stopped at White Island completely exhausted, how one by one they died, with Andree the last to go. This also made the last entry in their diary, doubtless just before Andree lost consciousness. The Norwegian sailors also found some tins containing Andree's undeveloped photo negatives which, of course, were greatly deteriorated. But despite the almost impossible task of bringing these negatives back to life, Swedish experts succeeded in developing them, so that twenty prints became legible.

Relics of his fateful expedition may still be seen in the small Andree Museum at Grenna, Andree's birthplace, a fitting monument to the courage and indomitable spirit of this intrepid Swedish explorer and aeronaut.

Hot air balloons, used 178 years ago by the brothers Montgolfier in France and later abandoned as impractical, have staged a comeback in the United States, according to a despatch from Sioux Falls, North Dakota, dated July 21, 1961.

The large, new type balloon, developed in Sioux Falls, now uses propane gas instead of the straw that was burned by the

Montgolfiers, and a new lightweight plastic material is used for the bag. It is the very simplicity of these new balloons that has engaged the attention not only of the Army, but also of Naval authorities.

Flanked by tanks of propane fuel not unlike that used for cooking in homes the pilot is suspended—as it were—in a trapeze-like chair. If the pilot desires to rise, all he does is to open a valve wide, and he closes it part of the way when he wants to descend.

The Navy showed interest because it envisaged using such a balloon during amphibious operations, while it might also be handy for lifting heavy loads, including tanks. The Army evinced interest in this new small hot-air balloon, because of its ability to lift and carry great weights over ravines or difficult terrains, to hoist flares over battlefields, and hold these flares for extended periods.

— 4 —

THE SEMI-RIGID DIRIGIBLES

The semi-rigid dirigible took its place in aviation history at a time when Europe as well as America was becoming more and more airminded.

In France, the brothers Paul and Pierre Lebaudy (sugar refiners) constructed a more-or-less-successful powered dirigible in 1902, making a flight in it from Moisson to Paris, a distance of 38½ miles, on November 12 of that same year.

In America, Thomas Scott Baldwin, an experienced balloonist, trying hard to find the right kind of motor for his dirigible, finally had one made by the Curtiss Company of Hammondsport, New York, which made it possible for his airship to be completed. The United States Government subsequently commissioned the construction of such airships, which continued in use until other contenders for the supremacy of the sky entered the field.

There is little doubt that much credit for man's conquest of the air is due Count Ferdinand von Zeppelin (1838-1917), an army officer who became interested in military ballooning when he fought on the side of the Union in America's Civil War with a German Army Corps. Having completed plans for his first 420-foot-long airship—the LZI—in 1893, the Count devoted his entire life to the construction of airships.

After Zeppelin had used up his private fortune, he was successful in interesting King Wilhelm of Württemberg as well as some private capitalists in his initial endeavors. And, being the sort of man who did not believe in letting the world in on all he knew, he carried on his work in the utmost secrecy in a hangar floated on pontoons and anchored in Lake Constance near Friedrichshafen. It was here that he built the largest airship of the time, a veritable monster, measuring 420 feet. By 1914, the first year of World War I, some 26 Zeppelins had been constructed, and had made 800 voyages all over Europe, carrying a total of 14,000 passengers.

The Lake Constance works were destroyed by the RAF in 1943, at the very time when the Germans had finished construction of the LZ-72, with which they had planned to bomb New York.

Of course much abuse had been leveled at this great builder, mainly because of his war exploits, and Count von Zeppelin had plenty of competition while he was constructing his brainchildren, the pride of Lake Constance. About the time that von Zeppelin was busy with his pets, Alberto Dumont, the Brazilian playboy, was making Europe, and France in particular, airminded. An accomplished engineer, son of a rich Brazilian coffee planter, and known far and wide for his eccentric ways, emaciated figure, odd hats, and high stiff collars, Dumont is said to have brought not only skill, but plenty of charm to the new field of aeronautics.

Having settled in the "City of Light," where he became a most familiar figure on the Parisian boulevards, a fine motor racing enthusiast, and extremely well-liked by the French military authorities, Alberto Dumont designed and flew 14 small airships, and crash landed or wrecked one or two on the Parisian rooftops or among the trees of the Bois de Boulogne. Flying one day from Saint-Cloud, to and around the Effel Tower and back, he won the 125,000-franc prize offered by Henri Deutz, a member of the French Aeroclub, to the first aeronaut making such a trip in 30 minutes. As an illustration of the eccentricity of this remarkable man, Dumont on one occasion simply deflated his balloon, packed up everything—balloon, accessories and what not—into the passenger basket and, stowing the whole business on his back, traipsed nonchalantly back home.

On another occasion he flew from the airdrome to his home, a feat that necessitated his traveling between rows of buildings with a drag rope trailing through the streets. Upon arrival at his home on the Rue Washington, he had the servants hold on to the ship, while he went inside to have breakfast. When he had finished, he climbed into the airship and flew it back to the airdrome.

Great Britain was also building dirigibles and balloons in those days, but her first rigid airship, the RI-M, was destroyed in 1911, even before it could be tested. Using wood and steel, instead of duralumin, Great Britain then built the R-34, and after a series of trial flights she completed her transatlantic voyage from east to west, with passengers, and crew of 61, plus a stowaway, probably the first aerial stowaway in history. Commanded by Major G. H. Scott and the U. S. Navy's Lt. Commander Zachary Landsdowne (who later lost his life in the Shenandoah disaster), the 670-foot airship landed at Roosevelt Field, after a voyage of 108 hours, and 12 minutes, in the first lighter-than-air transatlantic crossing.

After the Armistice, Germany had quite a number of Zeppelins in active duty or under construction. Some of these were turned over to France, England and Italy, one was dismantled and shipped to Japan; and six others, with the exception of the *Bodensee* and *Nordstern,* which were left in active duty, were destroyed in their hangars by German personnel in 1919.

Despite the fact that these lighter-than-air airships had been such an offensive instrument in the hands of the Germans during the war, the Allies went posthaste into the construction of these monsters. But one disaster after another made the traveling public extremely apprehensive as to whether these ships really provided the answer to the passenger service. The hydrogen gas with which the German airships were supplied also created a terrible fire hazard. Helium, which could be obtained only in the United States, provided the one safe lifting power.

After the death of Count von Zeppelin, all that he had created now was left to a group of men who were imbued with one desire —to carry on in the tradition of the grand old man. Among this group was Dr. Hugo Eckener, one of the greatest of airship designers; another was Karl Arnstein who, transferring his activities to America, assisted people over here in manufacturing the airship.

Eckener set to work on the 776-foot-long LZ-127, better known as the *Graf Zeppelin,* which made her maiden trip on September 18, 1928. Commanded once more by Dr. Eckener, this famous aircraft set out on a cruise to the Arctic from Friedrichshafen in 1931, carrying a group of guests and scientists from all over the world.

Collecting valuable scientific data from the Arctic regions, she covered more than 312,000 miles during a six weeks' cruise. The owners then placed her in the regular passenger service between Germany and South America, where she completed a trip every three days.

Under Dr. Eckener's direction was built the LZ-19, better known as the *Hindenburg,* whose successful crossings seemed to fulfill all the expectations of the builders. Still there seemed to be something radically wrong with all of these Zeppelins, which used hydrogen as a lifting gas. This newest monster, more than three city blocks in length, capable of attaining a speed of 84 miles an hour, was a stable and well-soaring ship. Cooking aboard was done by electricity. There were accomodations for crew and 70 passengers. All well ventilated and heated cabins were inside ones, containing lower berths, sinks with hot and cold running water, upholstered chairs and window seats. During the summer of 1936, the Hindenburg's average time for the crossing from Frankfurt to Lakehurst, N. J., was 60 hours.

Meanwhile, in the United States, the Goodyear Zeppelin Corporation had been awarded a contract by the United States Navy for the construction of two large airships, one of which, called the *Akron* and christened by Mrs. Herbert Hoover on August 8, 1931, met a terrible fate when she plunged into the Atlantic off the New Jersey coast. Of the 70 persons aboard, only 3 were rescued. The other, the *Macon,* found a watery grave in the Pacific on February 12, 1935, because of structural failure in the main frame. Only two of her crew of 84 lost their lives. The world had barely recovered from the shock of an English tragedy when the ZR-2, built in England, broke in two and burst into flames falling into the Humber River near Hull, with a loss of life of 26 British and 16 American officers and men, when a semi-rigid airship called the *Roma* (bought by the U. S. Army from Italy and built by Umberto Nobile) also met a tragic end. While on maneuvers and about to land at Langley Field, it struck some high-tension wires. Thirty-two men perished in the fire, while 11 were able to jump to safety.

Despite possible disasters, work on the construction of these ships continued. America was hard at work on the ZR-I at the Naval Aircraft factory in Philadelphia. This was the first home-made rigid dirigible. Leaving her hangar on her maiden flight on September 3, 1923, the graceful airship was flown to the Pulitzer Air Races at Lambert Field, St. Louis, where she was christened *Shenandoah* (Daughter of the Stars) by Mrs. Edwin Denby, wife of the Secretary of the Navy.

All this took place in the era of wonderful nonsense. It was the age of "Flaming Youth." Jack Dempsey was still the undisputed heavy weight champ of the world. Radio was in its infancy. The whole United States was stirred up in those days by airship fever. Many chambers of commerce pleaded with the U. S. Navy to have the new battleship of the air fly over their cities. Babies were named after her. Even the ultra-conservative President Calvin Coolidge, ordinarily not one to jump into hasty adventures, approved the airship's flight over the North Pole. Mooring masts were built all over the land, even in Alaska. Ships at sea were also equipped with mooring masts, should the Shenandoah decide to come home to roost. The North Pole scheme took the country by storm, and such famous explorers as Stefansson, Captain Bob Bartlett and others heartily approved the plan. The spring of 1924 was the time set for the undertaking.

The airship itself, 680 feet in length, was a handsome looking vehicle. Her twenty gas cells were filled with helium, a new gas refined from a mineral product accidentally discovered by none other, of course, than a Texas oil digger. Lighter than hydrogen, helium also was safer, as it would neither ignite nor explode.

By January 16, 1924, the *Daughter of the Stars* had made 14 voyages, totalling 10,000 miles. As she was moored to her mast on the evening of that very day, violent gusts in the open field at Lakehurst struck the colossus with such an impact that a portion of the ship's nose was torn off, releasing her from the coupling that held her to her mast. With some of her crew still aboard, her officers having already landed, she shot up into the dark stormy heavens.

In the control car was Captain Anton Heinen, a former wartime Zeppelin commander engaged by the United States government to teach our officers the art of dirigible navigation. Machinists also were at their posts in six engine gondolas, when suddenly Captain Heinen felt an abrupt cessation of the constant vibration of wires. This could only mean one thing, that the ship had broken loose from her moorings.

As the huge ship reeled off into the dark, Captain Heinen started up all her motors, swinging her around so that she would be able at least to ride with the heavy wind. He despatched a message, when over Mitchel Field, that the wind was blowing too hard to permit her to land, and disappearing over Staten Island, she finally made it while still bucking the 75-mile-an-hour gale, battered but still hale, with two compartments caved in, a hole in her bow, and half the steering gear torn away. Damage to the ship was quickly repaired, and many successful flights were logged in the succeeding months.

Then Lt. Charles Rosendahl, one of the most capable of airship men, was sent to inspect the ship in preparation for her delayed North Pole adventure, the *Shenandoah's* next voyage of importance, scheduled for early September, 1925. While out for a test cruise on that bright sunny autumn day, she encountered a severe electrical storm over the state of Ohio. A gust-driven rainstorm pelted her. Then came a loud, cracking sound as the duralumin girders began to buckle. She dived, nose downward, in a swift, uncontrollable descent, which was her last. Only a few of the ship's crew managed to escape. Among the 14 that perished was Lt. Commander Zachary Landsdowne, the very man who had come across the Atlantic on the R-34, to be given command of the fateful *Shenandoah*, "Daughter of the Stars."

About the time that Lt. Commander Landsdowne was busily engaged in preparation for the *Shenandoah's* flight, plans also were under way in another part of the world for the first serious attack on the North Pole by air. The splendid performance of the *Los Angeles* had attracted the attention of Captain Roald Amundsen, the immortal Swedish Arctic explorer who, accompanied by the wealthy American sportsman, Lincoln Ellsworth, had made several unsuccessful attempts to reach the North Pole by plane. Then, in the spring of 1925, the discoverer of the South Pole, accompanied by Ellsworth, Leif Dietrichson and Hjalmar Riiser-Larsen, attempted a flight across the Polar sea in two Dornier seaplanes. Forced to make a crash landing on the ice pack, they were given up for lost for nearly a month. After one of their Dorniers was repaired, it made a most difficult take-off with all four men aboard. No sooner had Amundsen and his party returned safely to Spitsbergen, than he was already planning another flight, this time by airship. Riiser-Larsen made the suggestion that they try to secure the N-I, an Italian semi-rigid dirigible built by Umberto Nobile, considered an ideal vehicle for such an expedition.

Soon the wheels were set in motion for this new adventure. Visiting Amundsen in Bundefjord, near Oslo, Nobile informed him that Mussolini not only would sanction this undertaking, but would donate the army airship N-I, provided the enterprise be undertaken under the sponsorship of the Italian Government, and fly her colors. This condition was, of course, refused by the sensitive and patriotic Amundsen, who regarded the flight a Norwegian-American venture. Nobile then made a new proposition, by which Mussolini agreed to sell the ship outright for $75,000, an offer that was quickly snapped up. There followed now a lot of dickering about who was to be the expedition's leader, and who was to issue the orders. Settling this argument to each other's satisfaction, it was agreed that Amundsen would be the leader whereas Nobile, who was after all thoroughly familiar with the renamed *Norge,* would act as assistant pilot and be permitted to take an Italian crew with him.

Setting out from Rome on April 10, 1926, and making stopovers at Toulon, Oslo, and Leningrad, where the ship underwent some overhauling, the party finally put in at Kingsbay, Spitsbergen, where they learned to their dismay that Admiral Richard E. Byrd and pilot Floyd Bennett had been there ahead of them and had already returned, having completed a successful flight by plane to the North Pole and back to the United States. Instead of abandoning his own expedition, Amundsen decided to take the airship over the Pole anyway, and then continue across the Arctic Sea to Alaska, a total distance of 2,700 miles.

Heading north into a graying mist, the *Norge* reached the North Pole on the morning of May 11th. The flags of Norway, the United States and Italy were dropped, as per pre-arrangement. Then, running the *Norge's* engines at full speed, and continuing south over limitless expanses of ice and terrain that had never been seen by man before, the group landed at Teller, Alaska, on May 14, 1926.

The flight across the top of the world was one of the most daring and important adventures in history, for on it many thousands of square miles of ice lands were explored for the first time. It was finally learned that no great land mass lay between the North Pole and Alaska. Amundsen and Ellsworth left by dog sled for the 55-mile trip to Nome, while Nobile and most of the crew remained to dismantle the *Norge.* The first authorized story of their polar expedition appeared in the New York *Times,* and later in a book, *The First Flight Across the Polar Sea,* in which Amundsen and Ellsworth declared that for the commander of the airship "a better selection could hardly have been made than Nobile." Nobile, on the other hand, wrote a long account of the trip for the *National Geographic Magazine,* in which Amundsen's contribution to the expedition was minimized. This was followed up by two long and violent articles by Amundsen in *World's Work,* in which he accused Nobile of everything from incompetence to cowardice.

When Nobile announced that he was setting out on a second polar trip, Amundsen and many of his countrymen predicted that the affair would turn into a fiasco. How correct their prediction was, Nobile's disastrous trip later proved.

— 5 —

THE LOSS OF THE *HINDENBURG*

The great air ship *Hindenburg,* the German people's pride, went to her doom on her 64th crossing as she was landing at Lakehurst, New Jersey, May 6, 1937. She suffered a death toll of 22 crewmen, 13 passengers, and one member of the ground crew. Ten thousand mourners, including the usual thrill seekers, attended the rites for the 28 European victims, on May 11, Pier 86, at the foot of West 46th Street.

The *Hindenburg* had suspended her flights during the winter of 1936-1937, but the United States Government had permitted her to make 18 trips during the spring of 1937.

On the day of the disaster, the Hindenburg had been on a sight-seeing cruise over New York. Thousands of people, lined up from the Battery to the Bronx, had craned their necks to see this monster, this wonder-ship of the sky, the biggest battleship then afloat. As the big ship, with huge black Nazi swastikas on her fins, was making a turn over the Empire State Building, many of her 97 passengers could be seen watching the large crowds below from the ship's promenade deck.

This sixth day of May was an eventful day, especially for the Borough of Brooklyn, as the Dodgers—then in seventh place in the National League—were battling the Pittsburgh Pirates at Ebbett's

Field. Below the *Hindenburg* a barrage of shrill whistles and deep moans from tug boats and ships were the harbor's discordant lullaby of welcome to this master of the sky. When the huge monster hove out of sight, and the crowd had been thrilled by a view of the "safest aircraft ever built," people went back to work.

The ship had been insured with Lloyd's of London for 500,000 pounds sterling. Her commander was stocky Captain Ernst Lehmann. On the bridge of the control car was Captain Max Preuss, who handled the ship's navigation with great skill. On the promenade deck was Birger Brink, a reporter for the Stockholm *Tidningen,* on his first trip to New York.

Significantly, there had been plenty of safety measures. Matches had been confiscated. The air in the fireproof smoking room was kept at high pressure to repel any stray hydrogen. The catwalks were covered with rubber. Crewmen wore suits that were free of buttons and metal, and all ladders were rubber encased. The four 100-horsepower motors that drove the ship at a dead air speed of 84 miles an hour required no ignition. They used crude oil that would not burn.

Down below, on the flat, sandy scrubland at Lakehurst, the members of the press were anxiously awaiting the ship's arrival. They had been there very early as her landing had originally been announced for about 8 A.M. Then, at four o'clock in the afternoon, up went a shout: There she is! Commander Charles Rosendahl, commandant of the Lakehurst Air Station, had received a despatch from the cautious Pruess that he did not like the dark storm clouds that had been hovering, and that he preferred to stay aloft and cruise about for some two or three hours.

By 6:22 P.M. the ceiling was 200 feet. Visibility was five miles, and the wind was blowing northwest. The ship was cruising now at the rate of 8 knots. Lehmann climbed into the control car. A few minutes after seven o'clock Rosendahl recommended immediate landing. It had begun to drizzle.

It seemed to many, however, that the ship was making too sharp a turn. At an altitude of 200 feet the ship headed into the wind toward the landing party. The first landing rope, over 400 feet long, was thrown down, and a moment later a second rope hit the wet sand. Sailors picked up the line and pulled it toward one of two little railway cars on circular tracks. By this time most of the passengers, highly impatient because of the long wait, had lined up for inspection in the main lounge. Sixteen U.S. Customs men started from the mooring mast toward the motionless ship, followed by health officers.

And then . . . an ominous quiet. There was something in the air that no one could explain. The motors were turning over silently, slowly—as the ship hung about 75 feet above the ground.

It was exactly 7:25 when, suddenly, a flame burst from the top of the ship. The explosion, starting with the first burst of flame, grew louder and louder. Suddenly the ship's tail dipped. The bow then shot way up.

Beneath the flaming ship hundreds of men in landing crew and customs uniforms were dispersing fast but running with great difficulty in the wet sand. It took but 34 seconds for the bow to crash to earth. Now the entire ship was engulfed in flames. It seemed that the passengers could be saved only by a miracle in that mass of flaming hydrogen. Passengers began to drop like ants from the ship.

Fire engines, ambulances, first-aid trucks from near and far raced to the scene. Captain Lehmann was so badly burned that he could hardly have survived. The hangar of the airship was a madhouse. Newsmen were frantically struggling with this most dramatic of all stories, the like of which they had never experienced in all their newspaper careers.

The cause of the holocaust? As Captain Lehmann is said to have explained it later: Lightning. Nobody was able to interview any one. In Berlin, Dr. Hugo Eckener was being given the sad tidings by a New York *Times* correspondent. About five hours later, at midnight, Lakehurst Naval Air Station was in position to appraise the damage. The excitement of those horrendous hours had abated somewhat. Funeral directors had set up an improvised morgue in the building.

Never in all history had there been a disaster that had hit the world with such impact as this one. President Roosevelt sent a message of condolence to Chancellor Hitler. It should be recorded here that there had been great bitterness in Germany because the United States had steadfastly refused to sell the non-inflammable helium to the German Zeppelin Company. With the death of Captain Lehmann the death toll rose to 36. The destruction of the *Hindenburg* brought to an end the short, though brilliant era of these giant Zeppelins.

Then came the last voyage home of the 28 victims of the disaster. Uniformed German storm troopers stood at attention. The swastika was flown from the head of each coffin. The troopers' right arms were stiff and uplifted in the Nazi salute. The Horst-Wessel song was sung. Then the coffins were placed aboard the *Hamburg* for the final journey.

Hitler refused to permit other commercial flights, so the original *Graf Zeppelin*—the newest ship of the Zeppelin concern which had made a test flight on September 14, 1938—was dismantled in March 1940, and two months later the hangars at Frankfurt were blown up.

This did not mean the end of the lighter-than-air travel business, however, because of the existence of another formidable weapon—the Blimp—which had chalked up impressive performance records in perfect safety.

In the ensuing 14 years, the Goodyear Airship Fleet, flying 4,183,470 miles without a single hitch, carried hundreds of thousands of passengers. The United States Navy joined the Goodyear Company in making the blimp the safest and most durable aircraft in the sky.

These tough ships, never over 385 feet in length, operated as a most successful means of defense during the Second World War, turning back a great many German subs and sea wolves bent on raiding allied shipping. It is safe to say that not one single allied ship was sunk when the convoys were guided and protected by these blimps. During the last years of World War II, these rather ungainly looking vessels also cleaned out mines from the waters south of France, preceding the oncoming allied invasion.

Today, these reliable old friends the blimps have been put, unceremoniously and without sentimentality, into mothballs, excepting the one or two which have been preserved as historical curios.

— 6 —

GLIDER PIONEERS

Having disposed in a general way of the part played by balloons and dirigibles in the aeronautics picture, let's now turn history back to those days when pioneers, scientists and adventurers tried their hand at finding out what were the forces that made aeronautics tick.

The greatest force in aeronautics, before such men as Lilienthal, Montgomery and the Wright brothers came on the scene, may well have been the scholarly Yorkshire baronet Sir George Cayley, born in 1771, one of the most analytical minds in aviation's earlier history.

When young, like many boys of his age, Cayley took a keen interest in balloon ascents, especially those by the Montgolfiers. A story is told that one day he surprised his schoolmates by appearing on the playground with what he called a flying top, a clever little device consisting of a wooden spindle upon which a spool-like block could be rotated by winding a string around the block and then giving the string a sudden pull. A three-bladed propeller made from sheet metal rested upon the spool, loosely held by two pegs. They permitted the rapidly-spinning propeller to fly off as soon as the spool was rotated fast enough.

Young Cayley made a number of these tops, including one which spun about ninety feet into the air. From that time on George Cayley devoted most of his time to the study of aeronautics. Grasping the scientific principles of aerial travel, Cayley predicted, or rather anticipated, the coming of an elongated balloon of the rigid type so effectively used in the 20th century.

He constructed a glider from wood and cloth, casting it away from him at the top of a hill and into the wind to take full advantage of the wind's lifting force. He realized that it would be necessary to create more wing area, but that longer wings would make the model more sluggish. With his discovery that by using two wings he could double the lifting capacity, the idea of the first biplane was born.

Like many other inventors and pioneers Cayley became deeply interested in winged flight, and being very fond of birds, he made a thorough study of their flight and behavior. He realized that man's pectoral muscles were too weak to sustain him in the air as wings support a bird. He realized that man would have to be equipped with an engine to do the wing-beating for him. He discovered, however, that this idea was not correct either, because the upward thrust of the wing by the engine might also send the flyer downward.

Closely observing the antics of birds, Cayley noticed how they soared long distances without even flapping their wings by simply twisting and dipping them. So he constructed a mechanism formed like the body of a bird and attached wings of the same material across it. He managed to sail this contraption for quite a distance. He then made another much larger glider, with an even longer wing equipped with a double set of wings, one pair above the other, which became the first biplane in history. He now tried it from the top of a hill, from which it glided with perfect steadiness for quite a distance. He then built one to carry a man and his coachman, trying it out from the crest of a hill; it soared along on a level with the hilltop. This glider became the ancestor of gliders and airplanes known to us today.

The first one to investigate the center of pressure, Cayley also realized the importance of streamlining and that a tail plane was necessary for longitudinal stability and control. Suggesting the creation of biplanes, triplanes, two- and three-deckers, Cayley made the following prophetic prediction in his writings: "I feel perfectly confident, however, that this noble art of flying will soon be brought home to man's general convenience, and that we shall be able to transport ourselves and families, and their goods and chattels, more securely by air than by water, and with a velocity of from 20 to 100 miles per hour."

Toward the close of his fruitful life, Cayley devoted his attention to heavier-than-air flight by constructing a model of what he called an aerial carriage, a contraption with two propellers and four rotating wings. It was a sort of helicopter, built in such a way that its revolving wings could carry it straight up to any desired height. He never perfected this model, however, before his death.

Throughout the 19th and 20th centuries, inventors and air-minded people carried on Cayley's tradition which was to lead, in time, to the first successful powered airplane.

Another man, imbued with vivid imagination and flair for promoting, named William Henson, had also been stung by the flying bug. He not only had a sound idea of a small steam engine, but of a plane, that came very close to the general conception of our present-day airplane. The Ariel, or Ariel Steam Carriage, turned out to be a monoplane with double surface wings and a combined tail-plane elevator, which could be moved up and down and spread out like a bird's tail. It fell down, however, on one detail: the inventor had failed to provide the machine with lateral stability by way of a dihedral angle, which had been Cayley's principal theory. In fine, the Ariel was unable to sustain itself in the air. Becoming discouraged, Henson chucked the whole job, and in disgust emigrated to the United States where, settling on a Texas ranch, he died in 1888.

The second half of the 19th century witnessed a burst of activity among glider and airplane designers. The inventors who made real gliding possible may well have been John J. Montgomery, an American, and the German Otto Lilienthal, who both conducted successful gliding experiments.

Montgomery, a professor at Santa Clara College had, together with his brother, been busying himself at home in a hayloft secretly assembling a gull-like contraption out of sticks and bits of cloth. Loading it onto a cart one early morning, the brothers took it up in the hills behind San Diego, where, due to misjudgment in landing, the machine crashed and was damaged beyond repair. Montgomery built a man-carrying glider in the early nineteen-hundreds, with which he made a number of flights from the steep hillsides near San Juan, continuing his experiments until he was killed in 1911, when one of his machines collapsed in the air.

Six years after John Montgomery had soared through the air on a motorless winged contraption, the German Otto Lilienthal performed a similar feat in his native Germany, and he is credited with having been the first to have successfully flown in a glider. When Otto and his brother Gustav were very young they constructed small glider models and sailed them about the yard of their home at Anklau in Pomerania. Later, when Otto was only 13 years old, he and his brother constructed some wing-like frames, and covered them with linen remnants their mother had given them. Otto then attached them to his shoulders and hands. Then, running to a nearby hill, he jumped as high as he could while flapping his arms. Discovering that these wings were of no earthly benefit, he decided that the secret lay in the feathers, so he began collecting all the feathers that he could lay his hands on. But when he had glued them onto the wings with tar, the befeathered wings did not do the trick either.

The French-German War of 1870 intervened, and once this was over, Otto devoted himself to studying the flight of birds, especially that of the sleek air-riding storks, whose ability to glide with motionless wings had greatly intrigued him. This led to the publication of his book *Der Vogelflug als Grundlage der Fliegekunst,** which became one of the classics of the science of aeronautics.

Turning his attention now to biplane gliders, Otto made his first real glide in 1891. His glider was a most unique contraption. It was made of peeled willow saplings and cotton cloth, and had been given several coats of wax to make it airtight. It had arm rests to sustain the weight of his body, while his legs were dangling below. He believed that by sliding his body backward or forward along the arm rests he could move his craft up or down, and by swinging his legs in a desired direction, he could turn it to either side. In other words, he could "bank" it as this maneuver is called.

Launching himself from a springboard, Lilienthal tried out his glider in the garden. Then, after several tries, he went to the nearest hill, where he made a number of successful flights. Accompanied by a friend, he began taking longer hops, during which he became quite adept at utilizing the air currents.

Constructing a biplane glider with an 18-foot span and wing area of 200 square feet at first, he made a year later what may be called a fixed wing glider, with flapping wing tips and a mechanism driven by a cylinder of compressed carbonic gas with a hand-operated valve. Believing this glider could keep him aloft for about four minutes, Lilienthal was now sure that he was ready for the big test. Witnessed only be his assistant, and taking off in a gusty wind from a high hill near Stollen, on August 9, 1896, Lilienthal attained a height of 50 feet while in full flight. But then the wind suddenly abated. This caused the glider to nose downward, which plunged him to the ground with a sickening crash. Removed from the wreckage with a broken spine, Otto died the following day. His last words were: "Sacrifices must be made."

Thus this glider pioneer came to his end, leaving a host of disciples to carry on his work, one of whom was the British Percy Pilcher, who not only had been a steady observer of Otto's experiments at Gross Lichterfelde, but had flown Otto's gliders on many occasions. But he met an almost similar fate. He was trying to get his own glider, the *Hawk*, off the ground as it was being towed by a team of horses, when a bracing wire broke. The glider was but thirty feet off the ground, and it crashed. Badly injured, Pilcher died two days later.

* "The flight of birds as the foundation of the art of flying."

Now let's see what the rest of the world was doing in the glider business.

Pilcher, Lilienthal and Montgomery had given their lives to the cause when they were at the height of their pioneering careers. Octave Chanute was no longer young but over sixty, when he began his aeronautical endeavors.

Another one of the gropers, a man whose name was to go down in the aerial hall of fame and who was considered by many one of the greatest Australians that ever lived, was Lawrence Hargrave, one of the most fascinating figures in the history of aviation. His adaptation of the humble kite was to be fundamental to the main development of the powered plane.

Born in England in 1850, son of John Fletcher Hargrave, who practiced at the Bar in London until 1856 when he migrated to Australia, Lawrence Hargrave stayed behind to continue his education. He, too, came to Australia in 1866. Apprenticed at first to an engineering firm, then working as an assistant at the Sydney Observatory, he was almost at once drawn to the study of air currents. Fired with ambition to solve the problem of human flight, Hargrave decided to make this his life's work.

He commenced his experiments with monoplane models. Between 1892 and 1900 he concentrated his attention on box kites and curved surfaces. Hargrave's attitude of mind was best expressed in a statement he made in 1890: "The writer thinks the act of invention to be a sort of inspiration and a pleasure that the individual does not seek to be rewarded for undergoing." Always afraid that a patent would restrict the use of his inventions, Hargrave refused to patent them but rather published his discoveries to the world. He felt that he had enough means to keep himself in comfort, and his love of his work meant more to him than all the wealth in the world.

The theory of the flapping motion of the wings of birds formed the basis of the means of propulsion in all of Hargrave's earlier works. Reverting to the study of the soaring of birds in 1899, Hargrave discovered that many sea birds were not entirely dependent on a head wind to enable them to soar, but rather derived sufficient energy from the power of the waves in apparently still air. He observed that the closer the bird came to the water's surface, the firmer and more inelastic would be the uplift of the rising air. The bird appeared to feel the surface with the tip of its lower wing.

Believing that a very light engine was essential for flight, he invented the rotary engine, the first engine suitable as an efficient unit for an aircraft—although no one had any notion of the immense importance of his invention at that time. This engine, consisting of a compressed air motor in which the cylinders revolved about a stationary crankshaft, formed the basis of some of the best of the earlier aero-engines in Europe, like the French-made Gnome, the engine that made the first flights possible.

It is an historic fact that the Wright Brothers asked Hargrave's permission for the use of his invention, to which Hargrave is said to have replied, "My inventions and discoveries are for humanity." Santos Dumont, who made the first public flight in France, also used Hargrave's box kites as a pattern for his own aircraft. Although Hargrave's name may have been largely forgotten, he was a vital factor in the history of world aviation, because he brought flight past its experimental stage. His priceless models are carefully preserved in Munich, Germany, for he deeded all his ideas to Germany so that a great many students might profit by them. Ironically, the bullet that killed his own son in World War I came from a plane he, himself, helped to pioneer.

The initiative in aeronautics was about to pass from Europe to the United States, where a vast industrial expansion was in progress. American engineers were busily working on every phase of applied science, and great attention was being paid to aerodynamics.

One man who had a most productive hand in America's glider and aviation history in those days was the French-born Octave Chanute (1832-1910) who, having been brought to the new world when he was six, was destined to become one of America's most prolific and eminent engineers. Although he had been interested in aerial exploration for quite a while, it was not until he reached the age of 60 that Chanute became impressed by Lilienthal's work. He began to collect every bit of information here and abroad about aeronautics. He published *Progress in Flying Machines* in 1894 which, to this very day, is a prized collector's item and one of the bibles of aeronautics. He encouraged the Wright Brothers and lauded the accomplishments of Hargrave of Australia. He also gave the Wright Brothers practical suggestions about the biplane construction.

He made 300 glider flights down the sand dunes of Lake Michigan, near Miller, Indiana, and continued his glider experiments until 1902, when he considered himself too old to pilot a plane.

Another American who also did his bit in developing scientific aeronautics, even though he was not always successful, was the astronomer and mathematician, Professor Samuel Pierpont Langley, of the Smithsonian Institute. Obsessed with flying, although already well in his fifties, Professor Langley had made more than thirty glider flights with elastic-band-driven models based on a small aircraft created by the Frenchman Pénaud. Calling his models *Aerodromes,* his one aim in life was to produce a successful powered model and a full-sized aircraft.

At the time when America went to war with Spain, Langley is said to have flown one of these aerodromes for a quarter of a mile at a speed of 30 miles an hour. Often kidded for what a great many people termed his childish pranks, the Professor let nothing interfere with his experiments. He was a most persistent individual, because he believed in what he was doing. One day the government asked him to design a full-sized aerodrome, for which they gave him a grant of $50,000 to do the work.

Like so many of the other experimenters before him, he also suffered from the lack of a gasoline motorcar engine light enough to serve his purpose, until Charles Manley, his assistant, managed to produce the first full-sized 53 HP power aero-engine. Langley then designed a model consisting of two sets of main planes attached in tandem, with a tail plane and fin in the rear, and the engine located between the two sets of wings. Langley suffered one defeat after another, however, because instead of running his aerodrome along a rail, as the Wright Brothers did after him, Langley decided to catapult his contraption from a houseboat in the Potomac River. He did this three weeks before the Wright Brothers had started their historic series of exploits.

The end of the Langley story is that, after the members of the press had had the time of their lives howling over this earnest man's defeats, he decided to give up trying, which added another name to the long list of heartbroken pioneers.

— 7 —

THE WRIGHT BROTHERS

The 17th of December, 1903, became a red letter day in the history of aviation. A most important event took place that was also to sway the history of the entire world: the crowning achievement of heavier-than-air flight. It was the work of Orville and Wilbur Wright, a devoted and highly religious-minded pair of ingenious and quietly confident workers.

However, the story of the miracle that took place on December 17, 1903, had actually begun long before that historic date. It had begun, in fact, twenty-five years earlier when the Wright Brother's childhood interest in flying had been aroused by the gift of a toy helicopter. This small toy, the gift of a loving father to his two young sons, may have started it all. Their loving father was the United Brethren Bishop Milton Wright who, together with his daughter Katharine, lent his sons undivided support. The year was 1878.

Fourteen years had passed since Bishop Wright had presented his sons with the little helicopter model. The memory of this fascinating toy, supported by their kite-flying experiments, kept the boys' dream of flying alive. As they grew to young manhood the persistent vision shared by them grew even stronger. They felt that this must not be an idle dream, they must make it come true.

In these early nineties, America was in the midst of the bicycle craze. Everyone who could afford it owned a bicycle of some sort and belonged to a bicycle club. Since the bicycle craze was growing, the Wrights did the logical thing. They set up a bicycle shop next door to their home. This was December, 1892. Their reputation for straight dealing spread about town, and soon scores of cyclists began to pedal their way to the Wright bicycle shop.

While Orville and Wilbur were engaged in handling their ever-growing business, Octave Chanute was experimenting with his contraptions on the sand dunes at Lake Michigan. The Wrights read Chanute's *Progress of Flying Machines* with great interest, and it spurred their resolve to undertake actual flights of their own at an early date. Reading everything that had been written on the subject, they hastened the start of their own experiments. They began their own series of kite and glider tests, an approach to the construction of a man-carrying glider, in July, 1899. As a result of these tests, they concluded that the speed and volume of wind flowing around the wings of a glider were the key to sustained flight, and that further tests must be made in an area where the prevailing winds blew strong and steadily.

After a careful study of charts and metereological data sent them by the U.S. Weather Bureau, they picked Kitty Hawk, in North Carolina, as the site for their glider tests. Then, after some correspondence with Joseph Dosher, in charge of the Kitty Hawk weather station, they decided to make a personal inspection. These boys never left anything to chance.

And so, on the bright early fall day of September 6, 1900, Wilbur left Dayton for his first visit to Kitty Hawk, a name that was to become as world-renowned as their own.

It might also be of interest to mention at this juncture that, after carefully observing the soaring flights of buzzards, Wilbur stumbled across what resulted in one of his key inventions. He noticed that when the birds were rocked to one side by a gust of wind, they would right themselves by increasing the angle of incidence of the dropped wing. This seemed to give them more lift and enabled them to level off. It was this experience that was responsible for the birth of the idea of the wing "warping" control or "ailerons." Patented by them afterwards, it became one of the essential controls of all aircraft to this very day.

But let's go back to their experience at Kitty Hawk, where the inhabitants welcomed them with neighborly kindness. Here the brothers set up housekeeping in a tent on the site that Wilbur picked as their testing ground. The one thing that amazed these young men from the lush farmlands of their own midwest was the sand—nothing but acres of sand—millions of tons of sand blown up in heaps from the sea.

The crude engine they constructed left much to be desired; its sputtering and coughing jogged the frail craft into sideslips on each succeeding flight. They continued to develop greater skill, however.

Their first flying attempt, undertaken on December 14, was unsuccessful because their machine jumped the greased rail from which they had intended to catapult into the sky. They repaired a broken wing in a jiffy and on the morning of December 17, while a small audience of neighboring fishermen and a Mr. A. D. Etheridge of the Kitty Hawk Coast Guard Station were watching, Orville stretched himself in prone position across the lower wing of the biplane.

It was a bitter-cold day. Incredulous until the last and shivering as they faced the biting wind from the bleak Kill Devil sand dunes, the spectators tried to follow the movements of the two pioneers, but all they could see was the frail-looking wooden biplane with its linen-covered wings. Then came the historic moment which would mean success or failure. Hoisting the signal once again, Orville waved to his brother to remove the blocks from the front of the skids. The noisy engine set the frail craft a-shuddering. Grabbing hold of the controls, Orville slipped the release wire, and off he went, as the *Flyer* rose eight to ten feet into the air. She wavered. She steadied, and then she rose, as John T. Daniels of the Coast Guard clicked the camera. And so the *Flyer* was airborne at last at thirty miles an hour, before she again plowed her wing into the sand, as Orville grunted from the shock of the landing.

There had been no fanfare, no feature story, no stir or comment from the papers except a short paragraph about this event. It would be some time before the American public would actually know what had taken place on that cold, wintery day at Kitty Hawk. As written by Orville later: "This flight lasted only 21 seconds, but it was nevertheless the first in the history of the world in which a machine carrying a man had raised itself by its own power into the air in full flight, had sailed forward without reduction of speed and finally landed at a point as high as that from which it started."

— 8 —
AFTER KITTY HAWK

There had been little aerial activity in Europe after the turn of the century, but a decided change took place after Octave Chanute gave an illustrated lecture at the Aeroclub in Paris about the Wright Brothers' flights and his own. The effect of all this was climactic. The European flight picture took a definite turn, and

French aeronauts began to give Americans a real run for their money.

Captain Ferber, who had also been tinkering with gliders, now began building his own improved Wright-type glider, which became the incentive French pioneers had been waiting for. Ferber lost his life, however, while piloting a plane made by the famous Voisin brothers, in 1909.

As more and more reports about the Wright Brothers' powered flight began to filter through, they were treated with extreme reservation by the French pioneers. The American newspapers which had been skeptical, too, of the Wright Brothers' achievements, now grew more enthusiastic, and the Scientific American, which had poked fun in its January, 1906, issue about the Wright Brothers' achievements, said three years later that "in all the history of invention there is probably no parallel to the unostentatious manner in which the Wright Brothers of Dayton, Ohio, ushered in their epoch-making invention of the first successful aeroplane flying machine in the world."

Meanwhile European pioneers bestirred themselves—men like Leon Delagrange who was to become in time one of France's aviation aces, or Louis Bleriot, a prosperous manufacturer of motorcar lamps, who, greatly interested in aviation, decided to abandon the biplane for a monoplane. This machine, nicknamed *Canard,* had paper-covered wings, a fuselage and monoplane elevator in front, and the propeller and a large vertical rudder in the rear. Bleriot next hit upon a completely novel type of monoplane by placing the fuselage, tractor airscrew in front, and the mainplanes, elevators and rudder in the rear. This plane, in fact, became the "mother" of all monoplanes the world over.

Returning once more to the Wrights, they flew for the first time in public in 1908, and while brother Orville kept fascinating the Americans at home, brother Wilbur caused a veritable sensation in Europe. He gave a demonstration at Le Mans, where a monument has been erected to him—the pioneer of flight, whom the world once scorned.

Attired as always in familiar cap and stiff collar, and perched in upright position on the wing of the plane, Wilbur pulled the release wire, slid down the track, and brought his two-seated plane up into the air on its maiden flight in France. And while the press was gaping, Wilbur gave a remarkable performance, banking, circling and finally coming in on his skids for a perfect landing. The enthusiasm of the huge crowd was indescribable. Former die-hards were dumbfounded. French and foreign flying men acknowledged that they had never seen anything like this brief but astounding exhibition. As he watched the flight, Bleriot is reported to have remarked, "The Wright machine is indeed superior to our own," while Sir Robert Baden Powell of the Boy Scouts made the prophetic statement that Wilbur Wright was in possession of a power that would control the fate of nations.

In America, where the United States War Department had at first been lukewarm to the Wright's vehicle, it now broke the ice and made a contract with the Wrights on the 3rd of March, 1908, and invited them to come to Washington to discuss the possibilities of their vehicle as an instrument of war. Orville submitted specifications for a military plane, for which the authorities agreed to advance $25,000 provided the plane was able to carry a pilot and one passenger on a sustained flight over a distance of ten miles at a speed of 40 miles an hour. The Government furthermore agreed to pay $2500 more for each additional mile of speed, an offer that was readily accepted. This plane was completed by the time that Wilbur returned from France.

The first test took place on September 9, 1908, followed by another on September 17 at which Lt. Thomas E. Selfridge of the U.S. Signal Corps was a passenger. During a series of complete circles over the Fort Meyer parade grounds, a wire snapped off near the hub and caught in the propeller when the plane was hardly 100 feet up. As this low altitude made a landing impossible the plane took a dive and crashed to the ground. Selfridge lost his life in the accident and Orville suffered a broken thigh that disabled him for many months.

The wrecked plane was rebuilt and powered with a 25 HP four-cylinder motor built by the Wrights themselves, and then tested again in July, 1909. Flying a course averaging 5 miles, from Fort Meyer around a marked balloon, located on Shuter Hill, and return, Orville bettered the specifications exacted by the Government, so that he won not only the $5,000, but a bonus over the contract price. This initial success set them up in business, and the Wrights began building a plant for the manufacture of planes and engines at Dayton. Meanwhile Wilbur returned to France to live

The historic flight at Kitty Hawk, December 17, 1903. Orville Wright pilots, Wilbur looks on. —BOAC

Orville Wright.

Wilbur Wright.

Bleriot landing at Dover, England, after crossing the English Channel on July 25, 1909.—BOAC

Bleriot and his wife after the historic Channel crossing.—BOAC

Glenn Curtiss at Lake Keuka, N.Y., in a Curtiss A-1 Triad, the first naval airplane.—CURTISS WRIGHT

up to a contract he had entered into with France and the Astra Company that also led to contracts with Italy and Germany.

They subsequently built their first hydroplane, with canoe attached to the undercarriage, which was flown by Wilbur from Governor's Island around the Statue of Liberty over a course of 19½ miles.

To illustrate the curious attitude of people about the business of flying, the story is told that, while the Wrights were making flights with the new plane at Simms Station, Dayton, a characteristic example of a doubting public occurred. In order to make the flights in little or no winds, most of the flying was done in the early morning or late in the afternoon. In spite of the early hour, as the plane was rolled out of the shed a strange looking man used to drive up in a cart, which he parked alongside the roadside near the field. Here this fellow and his cart would remain until the flights were completed and the plane was wheeled back into the shed. The driver then would shake his head, turn the horses and cart around toward Dayton, and drive away. The man? An undertaker. And the wagon? A hearse.

Later, when the American press could find hardly enough words in praise to fill their newspaper copy, and the American Government was no less laudatory, President Taft presented the Wrights with medals of the Aero Club of America and later with the Congressional Medal of Honor.

Wilbur succumbed to scarlet fever in Boston, in 1912, and Orville, who never quite overcame the shock of his brother's death, died on January 30, 1918. He had given his consent by this time to have the most famous aircraft in the world—the *Flyer*—returned from London's Science Museum, where it had been sent in 1928 (because of a court case brought by the Wrights apropos of a patent infringement by Curtiss). The *Flyer* then was placed on permanent exhibition in the National Museum in Washington.

It is interesting to record that some months ago one Elmo Peale Pickering was honored because he was the first to have operated a radio from an airplane, on August 4, 1910, as he flew a Wright Brothers B. Model biplane from Mineola to Manhattan Beach, and return, non-stop. On this one-hour trip, made at a thousand feet altitude, he sent dits and dashes to two beach stations, three steamships, and a station located on a New York City rooftop. Believing himself to be the last surviving pupil of the Wright

Brothers, Mr. Pickering claims that it was brother Orville who instructed him at the Wright airplane factory in Dayton, Ohio, and that he had only 7 hours of flying instruction before making that flight.

Another event of historical interest was the flight of the 32-year old Galbraith Perry Rogers, the first man to have flown from Sheepshead Bay Racetrack to the Pacific Ocean in a Wright biplane, in September, 1911. This flight had been sponsored by J. Ogden Armour, who had financed the project to publicize a new soft drink, Vin Fizz. After 49 days, 68 stops and several accidents, Rogers finally landed at Pasadena. Five months later he was killed in a California air crash.

Now scientists everywhere were busy as bees, inventing, copying, and let's admit it, often infringing the work of those inventors and pioneers who had preceded them. In France, the Brazilian Santos Dumont had set the pace, followed by such pioneers as Voisin, Bleriot and others.

The world still regarded flying as the work of crackpots and airplanes as toys. There undoubtedly existed sufficient reason for people to think so, because, if one looks at the machines of those days—crates they were called then—crashes were the order of the day. Safety measures and instruments used by airmen of today were then totally unknown. Flights were usually made at dawn or sunset, and if a pilot wanted to ascertain for example whether the weather was alright for flying, all he did was to light up a cigarette, and if the smoke rose straight up the weather was considered favorable.

But fly they did, as witnessed by the first aerial meet held at Rheims, in 1909, in which such aviators as Latham, Paulhan, Cockburn and the American Glenn Curtiss took part. In those days of daredevil aerial activity, inventions and records also rose by leaps and bounds. First came the invention of the Gnome in engine construction and the development of the rotary conceived by the Australian Hargrave, that lifted the aircraft out of its infancy stage past the terrors of early flying. As this engine was air-cooled besides, the use of the old type tank and radiator was abandoned.

Next, the brothers Charles and Edouard de Nieuport constructed a monoplane, in 1910, in which particular attention was paid to the fuselage, framework, and streamlining and in which the tandem cockpit was built in such a manner that only the head of the pilot and passenger could be seen.

Then came the creation of the more modern type of helicopter by Louis and Jacques Breguet, even though their machine made no free flight. The honor for the first helicopter to lift man into space should go to Cornu, who built his in 1907. Finally, the Frenchman Henri Coanda constructed his own type of jet aircraft, which he took up at Issy-les-Moulineaux, in April, 1910.

In those earlier days of aviation the industry added the names of Henri and Maurice Farman to its roster. Like the Wright brothers, these pioneers began as bicycle manufacturers, while brother Henri was also an expert engineer and motorcar racer. Though of English birth, they were Frenchmen and, curiously enough, unable to speak a word of English. Henri won the Grand Prix d'Aviation for the first triangular flight of one kilometer (2-1/5 mile) in his Voisin, while brother Maurice took up his first passenger, Leon DeLagrange, who again had the extreme pleasure of taking up a Madame Therese Peltier, the world's first woman aerial passenger.

France began to earn her aviation laurels in real earnest when Louis Bleriot took off from Baraques on the French coast, on July 25, 1909, at four in the morning to land his monoplane at Dover Castle half an hour later, winning thereby the 1,000 pounds *Daily Mail* prize. Having crashed at least 50 times, and with each airplane crash spurring him on to even greater efforts, Bleriot had made the discovery that propeller driven planes with the engine located in the nose of the machine proved to be the best.

Bleriot's historic channel flight also struck an ominous note in Europe in those days, causing the famous airman, Sir Alan Cobham, to remark that "the day that Bleriot flew the English Channel also marked the end of our insular safety and the beginning of the day when Britain must seek another form of defense beside her ships."

The year 1910 proved one of feverish activity in aeronautics all over the continent. The first flight to the Orient and India was copped by the English pilot Keith Davies, which led to Lord Northcliffe's new *Daily Mail* offer of 10,000 pounds sterling for the first flight from London to Manchester, provided it was done in 24 hours, an offer that had gone begging since 1906.

The two fliers throwing their hats in the ring were the Englishman Claude Grahame-White and the Frenchman Louis Paulhan, with Paulhan winning the contest after a hot pursuit by Grahame-White. This flight took place during the night, something unheard of in those earlier days of flying, with Grahame-White using a motorcar headlight for illumination. Subsequently going to America, where he won several aerial contests, Grahame-White was the first pilot to land on Pennsylvania Avenue outside the White House to make a long-intended call on the President, something that greatly appealed to the sports-loving Americans.

During these eventful years before World War I, test pilot and designer Geoffrey de Havilland, and Sir Thomas Octave Murdoch Sopwith, of yachting fame and creator of the Sopwith fighter plane, also scored marked successes. One of the greats in English aviation and creator of the historic FE-I, the Farnborough Experimental No. I, Sir Thomas Sopwith not only established the British flight-endurance record of 108 miles in 3 hours, 11 minutes, but flew from Eastchurch, England, to Tirlemont, Belgium, a distance of 169 miles, in 3 hours, winning the Baron de Forrest prize of 4,000 pounds sterling.

The mails were carried by plane for the first time in England between Hendon and Windsor, on September 9, 1911. Two years later the famed Sopwith Tabloid plane was produced, and the Schneider Trophy for seaplanes was established.

A year earlier, Lt. C. R. Sampson had created quite a sensation when he succeeded in taking off in a small biplane from a platform erected on the warship HMS *Africa*, which actually turned the warship into an aircraft carrier. To keep the record straight, Sampson's flight was predated by E. B. Ely, when he flew from the shore of San Francisco to the cruiser *Pennsylvania*, on January 17, 1911, and back again to shore.

— 9 —

GLENN CURTISS AND ANTON FOKKER

We all know that the airplane was not invented by any one single inventor or experimenter, but was rather the result of the progressive efforts of countless, dauntless pioneers, many of whom lost their lives in the attempts. An incredulous world, less skeptical after the invention of the Wrights, began to regard the "birdman" as an accomplished fact.

One of these "birdmen" was Glenn Curtiss, who won the first leg of the Scientific American's trophy flight for the first pre-announced and officially witnessed flight of 1 kilometer in his own machine over the serene valley at Hammondsport, New York, in July, 1908. Four years earlier Glenn Curtiss had installed a Curtiss motor in the airship, the *California Arrow,* the first navigable airship to have made a circular flight in America.

Born on May 21, 1878, in the hamlet of Hammondsport, Glenn Curtiss' life was patterned after that of the Wrights in one respect. It had given him the best possible preparatory course, for his future destiny began with his experience as a bicycle racer and as the designer of the fastest motorbikes in the world. This also developed his interest in mechanics. Except for a short stint with the Eastman Kodak Company during his formative years, his budding genius came to the fore when he commenced creating combustion motors.

Under the sponsorship not only of the famed scientist Dr. Alexander Graham-Bell, but also of Mrs. Graham-Bell, who financed his undertakings, particularly that of the Chanute-type of biplane glider with which the first flight in New York State was made, Curtiss decided to produce a heavier-than-air machine. With this airplane, the *June Bug,* he made a public flight on July 4, 1908, which marked another advance in the world's aviation industry. Now followed a series of experiments with the *White Wing,* equipped with the Curtiss-made engine, and with the *June Bug,* built entirely to Curtiss specifications—although it was generally believed that the wing-tip ailerons infringed on the patents of the Wright Brothers. Turning his attention now to the creation of his *Silver Dart,* Curtiss won the prize offered by the Aero Club of America with this plane for being one of the first four pilots to fly a full five-eighths of a mile in America.

But the flight that was to make the name of Curtiss even more renowned took place in 1910, as the result of the offer made by Joseph Pulitzer, owner of the New York *World,* of a prize of $10,000 to be paid to the first aviator completing the nonstop trip between Albany and New York along the Hudson River route. Another stipulation was that the flight was to take place during the then-held Hudson-Fulton celebration. Curtiss won the event.

Another event that added to Curtiss' fame took place at Rheims' aviation meet, where he competed against a field of 40 aircraft, including the Wrights, Voisins, Farmans, Bleriots, Antoinettes, Renault-Pelterie, Ariels, Breguets, Kluytmans and Fernandez. Here Curtiss won the speed record of 47-48 miles an hour.

Curtiss' life had been no bed of roses. The Wright Brothers had sold their patent claim to a group of wealthy and influential men, and Curtiss was being hounded day and night by law suits and injunctions.

Under the auspices of the Curtiss Exhibition Company, Curtiss established America's first open flying school in September, 1910, at Hammondsport, followed by others at San Diego and Miami, Florida, to which flocked serious students of aviation, beside parachute jumpers and stunt men looking for a novelty. Most, however, were primarily anxious to learn how to fly. Significant, too, is the fact that the first official air mail in the United States was carried by Captain Paul Beck of the U.S. Army in a Curtiss machine.

The late Rodman Wanamaker sponsored the first flying boat, called *America*, designed by Curtiss for a transatlantic flight. It was to be piloted by Commander J. Porte, one of the pioneers of seaplane flying, who had been waiting in this country to pilot the airplane monster across. Returning to Britain when the war broke out, his report about the *America* proved so flattering that it induced the British Government to order similar craft from Curtiss.

Curtiss had also worked on army tractors in 1913, which were to become later the world-famous *Jenny*, a tractor monoplane flying boat. A year later the first J. N. or "Jenny military tractor" designed by Curtiss for the U.S. Army was completed. These became the best known machines in the world, and were flown by thousands of pilots during World War I.

All armies engaged in World War I were well stocked with fighting aircraft of some sort. The Russians considered themselves fortunate in having Major A. P. de Seversky as a military pilot, and the Germans were no less favored at having the ingenious and resourceful Dutchman, Anthony Fokker in their camp. Having offered his airplane ideas to America, France, Britain and Italy without any takers, and being in Germany when the war broke out, Fokker was enticed by the Germans with lucrative offers, with the result that "Tony" Fokker produced his world-famous craft for that country until the end of the war.

Born in Java, in 1890, Anthony Herman Gerard Fokker had tinkered with aircraft already in his teens, although nobody would have thought that a boy with such eccentric ideas would produce some day the world's fastest and deadliest aircraft. He was like the other boys in his youth, adept at climbing trees like a Javanese monkey, picking up nails with his toes, and doing all the adventurous things so beloved by the young. He built a model railway track that took up the whole of the downstairs floor space, invented a system of automatic switches, and electrified the whole of the line. He made gas engines, steam engines, a "puncture-proof" tire, and even built an extremely seaworthy canoe at the age of twelve. In 1910 he built an odd-looking monoplane, even though he had never seen a plane in the air. His knowledge was practically all self-taught.

At the outbreak of the war young Fokker began building monoplanes for the Germans which soon became a menace to the Allies. When the Germans downed a French plane equipped with a crude contraption for shooting machine gun bullets through the propeller which deflected the bullets without damaging the propeller, they asked Tony to study the idea, and to try to produce something more serviceable. Up to that time it was the best invention of its kind, although many bullets were wasted.

So Tony got busy, and within a week he had perfected a synchronized machine gun that would shoot bullets through the propeller without the need for deflectors. Thus did the menace of Fokkers to the Allies grow. Paving the way for the German air aces, Fokker's invention helped make it possible for Baron von Richthofen—Germany's greatest war ace—to down no fewer than 80 enemy planes before being killed in an air duel himself.

Fokker's gear was first used by two German aces—Oswald Boelcke and Max Immelman, two of Germany's top military pilots, and the loss to Allied planes continued until during a dense fog the French were fortunate enough to bring down on one of the French airdromes a German plane equipped with the synchronizing gear. The Allied engineers then went to town. They copied and even improved the gear, after which the fully-equipped Sopwiths went into action, in 1916. This marked the beginning of the end of the domination of the German *Fliegentruppen.*

— 10 —

AIR ACES OF WORLD WAR I

World War I gave birth to a new race of daring men, reminiscent of the chivalrous Knights of the Middle Ages—the Air Aces. The reason for this was not far to seek, because war fliers became a most privileged section of the armed forces.

War pilots were used in Germany to heighten the morale of the folks at home, and feted wherever they showed their faces. Pilots of one nation admired and respected the flying exploits of those of another. They were always ready to honor the fallen, to drop notes and apprise one another of the death of a comrade, or to drop messages of challenge or congratulations. Hence a strange camaraderie developed that was hard to explain.

France thus would proudly remember her ace Rene Fonck, who chalked up 75 victories, or the semi-invalid Guynemer who was shot down eight times and was killed later, and the no-less-daring Nungesser, who was to vanish later in an attempted Atlantic flight and who had suffered so many wounds that he claimed there was not a bone in his whole body without an aluminum clip.

Germany did not lag far behind, claiming her Red Baron Manfred Freiherr von Richthofen, that country's greatest war ace, accredited with eighty victories and as renowned in Great Britain as he was in his native land. But the most chivalrous and respected of the German fliers was Hauptmann Captain Oswald Boelcke, the first to have tried Fokker's destructive gear, with which he scored forty victories before being downed himself in an air collision.

The United States, too, had had her share of war heroes because when War I broke out a small group of wealthy Americans, then cutting it up in Paris, almost at once offered their services to France. Though few nations willingly accepted foreigners in their fighting forces, it became possible in the case of these men through the famous French Foreign Legion. Hence William Thaw, Bach, and Bert Hall, followed later by many others, were permitted to form the famed Lafayette Escadrille under the leadership of Norman Prince, Kiffin, Rockwell and Victor Chapman, joined later again by Lufberry, America's outstanding ace, who was killed in action on May 19, 1918.

Doing first yeoman service in Flanders, then transferred to the French Flying Corps, the corps later adopted the title Lafayette to create a French atmosphere and give it added distinction. Rockwell was wounded on May 24, 1916, and a few days later Chapman was killed. Then the Escadrille tasted its first bitterness. Rockwell, who continued to fly, was the next one to fall, and Prince was killed in October, so that by March, 1917, only one of the original seven Americans remained in the squadron. By the end of the war, 40 gallant Americans, flying under the Indian-head banner of the Escadrille, had given their lives for France and the Allied cause.

At the outset of the war Eddie Rickenbacker, one of our foremost motorcar racing drivers, went to France as General Pershing's chauffeur. But even the honor of driving for the Supreme Commander of the American Army did not bring him the excitement he craved. Looking for a change and as soon as it could be arranged, Eddie, or "Rick" as he was popularly called, joined the 94th Pursuit or "The Hat in the Ring" Squadron and, sooner than he expected, became its Flight and Squadron Commander. Demonstrating a complete understanding of the requirements for a successful air leader by always leading and never driving his pilots, Rick never asked them to do anything he would not do himself. Leading his men fearlessly, he always safeguarded the less competent aviators. His daring and skill in handling planes and guns were shown in the fight in which his first enemy plane was brought down.

Accompanying another pilot more experienced at that time than himself, Rickenbacker followed the other plane, watching his every move. He realized that there must be an enemy plane somewhere near, but he still could not see it. Soon the German plane dove in sight, and both he and his companion pilot made a dive at it. Rickenbacker, with throttle wide open, was soon in the lead. The German dove his plane, too, but Rickenbacker gained on it and trained his sights on the cockpit of the German plane before firing his first shot. He could see the tracer bullets streaking into the plane's tail. Then, raising the nose of his plane slightly, he watched the stream of fire rise up to the pilot's seat. The plane swerved from its course, indicating that the rudder was no longer directed by hand. Pulling up his plane, Rickenbacker watched the other as it continued at a terrific speed, finally striking the ground at the edge of a wooded area inside allied lines. And so the Germans not only had one less pilot, but were also short one of their latest pursuit planes.

Thus America's ace scored his first air victory. . . .

This chronicle about the achievements of our American aces would not be complete unless the heroic feat of Lt. William White Jr., of the 147th Squadron, were included, which stands as one of the war's greatest sacrifices. The story is told of how during the aerial fighting around Metz, a formation of 'Spads' was sent out to destroy an enemy balloon. En route toward the balloon, 8 Fokkers from Richthofen's Flying Circus were encountered by Lt. William White Jr., of New York, who was leading the combat. The Germans seemed at first to center their attack on him, but during the general melee that followed, White turned in time to see the concentration of the attack shifted to the rear plane of his formation. Realizing apparently that if the fire of one of the enemy's planes was not stopped his pilot would be doomed, he made a quick zoom, a half turn, then plunged toward the German plane without even attempting to use his machine gun. He flew straight into the Fokker, and the two planes, locked together, fell into the Meuse River far beneath the scene of the fight.

While America had her roster of outstanding fighting units, and France boasted her *Cigogne* (stork) squadron or Escadrille Lafayette, no one could forget the achievements of the British RAF No. 60 squadron, which counted among its outstanding aces Major Micky Mannock, a legendary figure worshiped by his co-fighters and generally regarded as the top fighting leader this air war had produced. Ruthless in action, with 73 victories to his credit, and supreme master of tactics, Mannock was killed during the last year of the war. He received a Victoria Cross posthumously.

Britain, Canada and their allies could lay claim to many other aces, including Captain Albert Ball, whose name will go down in history as the very first great British Ace. Born at Nottingham, England, in 1896, he enlisted in Kitchener's mob while still a boy. Transferred to the RFC, he set the world talking with deeds of daring for which he received the highest honors a country could bestow. He was happiest when his plane was in the air, and when he failed to return at last, his score was 43 planes and one balloon shot down within a year. The end had come suddenly at the height of his fame. He took off on May 7, on what was to be his last patrol. Exactly what happened on that tragic flight will always remain a mystery; all that is known is that he never returned. Days of anxious waiting passed until Wolff's German Agency made the following announcement: "Lt. Lothar von Richthofen has brought down a triplane piloted by Captain Ball, his 20th victory." He was buried in the German war cemetery at Abbeoulin, near La Bassée. Perhaps the name that has lingered longest in the memory of those who remember the war deeds of these airmen is that of Captain W. Leefe Robinson, V. C., the first man to bring down a Zeppelin over British soil, a feat he performed at the age of 21. Born in Southern India, traveling extensively in Russia as a lad and entering Sandhurst at the outbreak of the war, Robinson became an aerial observer. He was wounded over Lille, and once recovered, he learned to fly and became attached to various English stations for night raids.

On the night of September 2, 1916, an air raid was made by the Zeppelins on London, and Captain Robinson went up to help beat off the raiders. He engaged one airship, which escaped, and seeing immediately ahead a second raider of the skies, he braved the accurate gunfire from the anti-aircraft defenses on the ground, and carried on a running fight with the heavily-armed Zepp. The airship threw out black clouds of smoke in an endeavor to shake him off, as its machine gunners kept up an intensive attack. But as always Leefe Robinson stuck to his self-imposed task. When he thought the moment to strike was right at last, he dived from a height of 10,000 feet straight at the intruder pumping streams of lead into it. In an instant the Zepp burst into flames and fell to earth a blazing broken mass a few miles from London's northern suburbs. Ironically enough, Leefe Robinson did not die while fighting the enemy, but succumbed after a few weeks' illness as a result of influenza. Another glorious and unforgettable fighter was the Canadian Lt. Colonel W. A. Bishop, whose war exploits, started in 1917 as a member of the Canadian Expeditionary Forces, include 72 victories. The official account of this great ace's feats, for which he was awarded the Victoria Cross, makes thrilling reading.

Sent out to work independently, Captain Bishop flew first of all to an enemy airdrome. Finding no machines about, he flew to another field three miles south-east, which was at least 12 miles the other side of the line. Seven machines, some with their engines running, were on the ground. He attacked these from about 50 feet, and a mechanic, who was starting one of the engines, was seen to fall. One of the machines got off the ground, but Bishop fired 15 rounds into it at very close range, after which it crashed. Then a second machine took off, into which he fired 30 rounds at a 150-yard range, and it fell into a tree. As two more planes rose from the airdrome, he engaged one of them at a height of 1000 feet, emptied the rest of his drum of ammunition into the fourth hostile plane, and then flew back to the station. Four hostile scouts followed 1000 feet above him for about a mile but they would not attack. After Bishop had run up a score to 72 planes, he was relieved from the fighting force and very wisely sent back to assist in training new units, where his experience was of incalculable value. Thus he survived the war and lived for some years as the Ace of Aces.

Major Barker's fighting career had many things in common with that of Colonel, later General, Bishop. Both were Canadians who began their military careers in the cavalry. Billy Barker, as he was affectionately called by his friends, was a man of fine physique who, at the age of 20, enlisted in the Canadian Mounted Rifles, served with them in France as a private until 1915, and then transferred to the RFC. After serving as an observer for six months employed chiefly in artillery observation duties, Barker returned to England to learn to fly. He must have had many an opportunity to handle the "stick" as an observer, and he proved such an able pupil that he flew solo after but one hour of dual instruction.

Nineteen seventeen saw him back at the war flying two-seaters, once more on artillery observation and reconnaissance duties. His machine was a famous Camel, and his fearless tactics soon resulted in one more of his many decorations. His squadron, of which he now was a Flight Commander, was moved to the Italian front and over the Alps, where the ace soon became the terror of the Austrian pilots. He had an experience about this time that made a lasting impression on him, when he shot down an Austrian observation balloon. Leaping for safety with their parachutes, the two balloon observers were already half way to the ground when the blazing wreck of the falling balloon enveloped them in its folds, bearing them down in a sheet of flame. Barker was so upset by this ghastly spectacle that he never attacked another balloon. "I do not fight men who cannot fight back," was his terse comment.

Barker's hair-raising exploits did much to lift the drooping morale of the Italians and cause discomfort to their opponents. He once attacked a group of six German Gothas, broke up the formation and sent one down in flames, after which he was personally presented with the Italian silver medal for valor by the Italian king. Playing havoc with the enemy forces in the air and on the ground during the early months of 1918, victory after victory fell to his all-conquering guns. He was badly wounded in October in a fierce encounter against an overwhelming number of enemy scouts. Wounded in both legs and his thigh, and with one arm smashed by explosive bullets, he fought on until he had accounted for six of his adversaries. Fainting from pain and loss of blood he succeeded in guiding his disabled machine back to the airdrome, where he crashed.

After many months in the hospital, where he endured over 20 operations, he slowly regained consciousness and life to learn that for his last, inspiring battle he had been awarded the Victoria Cross. He retired from the RAF with the rank of major, and was promoted later to Colonel in the Royal Canadian Air Force. While he was flying a civil airplane near Ottawa on March 2, 1930, his engine failed and he crashed to the ground. This gallent ace had made his last flight.

One of the most romantic German aces of the war, about whom more stories have been woven than about any other flying airman, was Baron Manfred von Richthofen. His exploits and those of his famous 'Circuses' have become a legend. Before the war von Richthofen was a typical Prussian officer of the Uhlans, whose regimental cap he wore until his death. After seeing service on the Russian front, he was transferred to the Imperial Flying Corps on the western front. Vain but always fair, never once forgetting that he was a scion of a noble German family, a relentless and rather inhuman killer who in battle was a dangerous foe, Richthofen brought down 80 enemy planes. Treating his prisoners courteously after a fight, he gave such assistance as was possible to make their confinement easier to bear. When given command of a squadron, Richthofen identified his plane by painting it brilliant red, which became famous along the entire front battle line. Later all his squadron's planes were painted in brilliant colors, and the group not only became known as Richthofen's Circus, but moved with great speed along the entire front. Since Richthofen was accustomed to drop notes on allied airdromes telling of the fate of their allied airmen he had shot down, it was only natural that when he was downed by a comparatively unknown allied pilot, the Royal Flying Corps not only dropped a message on the German airdrome advising them of his own fate, but showed their respect for this greatest of German pilots by covering his grave with flowers and erecting a beautiful monument. Thus he passed, feared in battle but respected as a man and honored accordingly in death.

During the month of April, of the year 1917, Richthofen shot down 30 machines. Toward the end of the war and of his career he did not dog fight with his Circus, but usually sat above it, picking off stragglers. Whereas most of his flying was in an Albatross, he later used a Fokker triplane, the same type of vehicle in which he was killed by Captain Roy Brown of Toronto, on April 21, 1918.

Richthofen once admitted that he had never looped-the-loop or indulged in unnecessary acrobatics in his life, while the great secret of his long success probably was his outstanding ability to hit what he shot at. He used to make a collection of silver mugs upon each of which he inscribed the number of a victory and the date.

The Richthofen Circus, or *Jagdtafel* as it was called, was known for some curious superstitions, one of which was the habit of greeting its members employed, such as *"Hals und Beinbruck,"* which means, "May you break your neck and legs," whereas their *"Glück Auf"* (Good luck) would have turned any German ace pale with fright, because calamity would surely follow. No one would fly on the day any one greeted him this way, nor would he permit himself to be photographed. However, Richthofen broke this rule himself, as did Boelcke, both of whom were killed afterwards.

The first real ace of the war, and an ace even before the term was coined, was Lt. Max Immelmann. An officer in the Imperial Flying Corps when the war broke out, he lost little time in making himself known to his enemies. During the early, critical days of September, 1914, a German Taube appeared over Paris, dropping bombs in the streets. With the bombs came the following brief note addressed to the people of Paris and published in the Paris papers the next morning: "People of Paris, surrender. The Germans are at your gates. Tomorrow you will be ours"; signed "Lt. Immelmann, Air Scout." Immelmann continued his raids for some days, and his name appeared next in the papers on October 2, 1915, when a communique was issued by the German authorities that Lt. Immelmann had shot down a British airplane for his 4th victory, the first notice of this kind that had ever been published in the history of the world.

It is said that Immelmann was the creator of some special type of air fighting, with what has since become known as the "Immelmann" turn. His combat method was to pull up as if he was going to loop-the-loop, and then, turning sideways over the vertical end, come out in the opposite direction. This simple way of gaining height and at the same time reversing direction took a lot of allied aviators by surprise until the trick became known, when his score declined rapidly.

Immelmann was an egotistical man, arrogant and intolerant of those beneath him in social status or military rank, a typical aristocrat of the German pre-war military clique. But he was an exceptionally fine soldier, daring and utterly fearless. The Fokker monoplane gave Immelmann his great chance as an air-fighter, when one after another of the allied planes fell under the guns of his speedier craft. Discovering the advantage of a surprise attack, Immelmann learned the trick and value of diving out of the sun and using the clouds for cover. Making a profound study of unsuspected "blind spots" in the opposing two seaters, he knew the wisdom of holding his fire until he was within effective range. Before Immelmann's death in air combat, he had imparted a good deal of his knowledge to Oswald Boelcke, who took up flying despite the fact that the Army had rejected him because of lung trouble. Hauptman Oswald Boelcke, Germany's second ace and a friend of Immelmann, though a horse of a different color, had learned so much of the art of air dueling from the latter that he not only equalled his master's score but surpassed him, in spite of the fact that air victories were always hard to confirm.

Boelcke was different from Immelmann in many ways, because he was a gentleman in every sense of the word, a sportsman to the core. A kindhearted man, Boelcke killed his enemies with real regret, and never owned that love of killing that was the mark of distinction of Baron von Richthofen. He much preferred shooting a machine down over his own side of the line, and then entertaining the pilot in his mess. The story of his encounter with a derelict machine in the air with the pilot dead at the stick has been repeated with bated breath in every flying corps billet and messhall on the western front.

It happened this way (as told by Floyd Gibbons in his book dealing with the death of Baron Manfred von Richthofen): "One day he attacked a Martinsyde scout and poured in a burst from such a range that the pilot must have been killed instantly. The unlucky 'tinsyde' continued to fly on even keel in wide circles, making no attempt to retaliate or escape. Boelcke studied the machine in amazement. Presently, very cautiously, he flew nearer and the solution became apparent. The pilot was crumpled up in his seat and his last convulsive action must have been to grip the joystick in such a position that the machine remained in steady flight. Boelcke continued his patrol, and on the return journey they passed the Martinsyde still circling on its ghostly course and the German leader dipped his wings in salute—an action which speaks louder than words."

Boelcke fought his last fight on October 28, 1918, when the fame of his Circus was at its very height.

No less a group of glorious and unforgettable fighters were the French aces of World War I, among whom Captain René Paul Fonck has been singled out as the Premier Ace of France. He had planned to be an engineer until the aviation bug bit him. Flying when the war broke out, he rceived his pilot's certificate in 1915 and joined the Escadrille C. Caudros 47, on the reconnaissance and photographic detail.

He lost no time making a name as a daring and able pilot. His exploits took him over the lines dailly for more than seven months, and he often handled his two-seater under the most trying circumstances. Attacked by two Rumplers in August, 1916, Fonck forced one of them by sheer pluck and brilliance behind allied lines, for which he was awarded the military medal. Soon after, when his escadrille proceeded to the Somme for the big offensive, Fonck was picked out by the British for his daring. Accepting combat anywhere at any time, regardless even of enemy superiority, Fonck became a byword and was made a Chevalier of the French Legion of Honor.

On September 15, he downed the German pilot Wisseman, who was reputed to have shot down the great Guynemer, Fonck's friend and brother ace. Truly an artist in the air, Fonck had a method totally different from that employed by other air aces—that of rushing head-on at an adversary regardless of enemy fire. His ability to grasp all the rudiments underlying the theories of aerial combat was almost uncanny. His studiously careful method of attack may be demonstrated by the fact that he had never been wounded, nor had his plane been hit by a bullet, until he had downed his 32nd plane.

On one of his patrols, Fonck encountered a two-seater Rumpler flying along at 24,000 feet and minding its business. Flying a SPAD, a plane much easier to handle in the air than the Rumpler, Fonck managed to maneuver his position in such a way as to stay out of range of his opponent's guns, until he had readied himself for the attack. Then, with the coast clear, diving his machine and pulling it up under the Rumpler's tail, Fonck emptied his machine guns into the German's cockpit and gasoline tank. Turning over, the Rumpler dropped like a wounded bird from about 20,000 feet to the ground, followed by Fonck, who landed nearby, anxious to learn the identity of the enemy pilot. The German's papers revealed him to be Wisseman, the very one who had shot down Guynemer.

As Fonck's victories far exceeded those of any allied pilot, he rightfully earned the sobriquet Allies' King of the Air. Trained for combat as he would have been for any athletic event, Fonck won his victories by sheer coolness, perfect fitness, confidence, abstinence and caution, plus the ability to judge the right moment to strike. With all that he never as much received a single scratch.

Another French hero was the immortal Captain Georges Guynemer, Knight of the Air. Still a schoolboy during the early days of French mobilization, Guynemer did his best to enlist in the infantry but was rejected because of his slight build and extreme youth. Within a year, though, he was to become the hero of all France. His exploits and final disappearance were little short of miraculous, and Guynemer has gone down in French history as the greatest hero of the first world war.

Shot down eight times, Guynemer once returned with his plane riddled with holes from bullets which must have missed him by inches. He painted red circles around the bullet holes, and his plane soon carried more red paint than its original buff.

After his first big victory he was transferred to the famous Escadrille Cicogne (Stork escadrille), which then was flying the Nieuport, the best fighting vehicle in the world war at that time. He had one of his many miraculous escapes in September, 1915, when, accepting combat with a large formation of enemy planes, his own plane was put out of action. Unable to maneuver, and floating down towards the enemy trenches, he ran the gauntlet of machine gun fire from hostile aircraft. Dropping lower and lower, he glided over the enemy's support trenches and was pelted by a sea of murderous fire and hurtling metal. French infantrymen saw the tattered and torn Cicogne crash in a shell hole in no-man's land, and poured blindly over the parapets, regardless of enemy's fire, to carry their beloved ace to safety.

While the Battle of Verdun was raging Guynemer scored victory after victory in the Spad he was then flying, on the side of which was painted in large white letters *Vieux Charles.* After he had shot down 19 enemy craft with the *Old Charles,* it was taken to Paris and exhibited to the hero-worshipping French, who showed their appreciation by decorating it with flowers.

During the Battle of the Somme his wing was smashed by anti-aircraft shells and, with his Spad out of control, all that Guynemer could do was await the inevitable end. The machine crashed and buried its nose deep into the mud, but when the horrified soldiers arrived to carry the ace's corpse away, they found Guynemer standing there calmly surveying the wreck.

Guynemer scored his 53rd and what also turned out to be his last victory on August 20, 1917. The French military authorities now asked him to take a well-earned rest, but he refused. "They would think I have stopped flying because I have received all the decorations France can give me," was the reason he gave. He was obviously a very sick man, and though he still took to the air he was unable to secure another victory. Luck seemed to have deserted him. Then, on September 11, 1917, he took off again for a patrol—one from which he never returned. Soon after leaving the airdrome at Dunkirk he was seen in combat with an enemy aviator above Ypres. This was the last authentic record of his activities.

As indicated previously, it had been the German custom to publish the names of airmen falling within their lines, and in Guynemer's case one would have thought that the Germans would have only been too anxious to let the world know that one of their own airmen had downed the ace of aces.

Ten days passed. No news of Guynemer. A few days later information drifted in from intelligence sources that a German pilot named Wisseman had written to his mother that he had shot down Guynemer. Bringing pressure to bear through the Swiss

Red Cross for recovery of Guynemer's body, Germany replied that he had been buried at Poelcapelle. When Poelcapelle fell into the hands of the British a few days later, there was no sign of his grave. In reply to further inquiries the German authorities stated that all trace of Guynemer's body, and his machine, had been obliterated by British artillery, something that was hard to swallow. Thus Guynemer's body lies in an unknown grave.

In an account by Germany's war ace, Ernst Udet, a very down to earth resumé is given of one duel the Germans had with Guynemer that came to an almost unbelievable end. Udet, at that time the flight commander of Jagdstaffel 15, or the Black Cross Circus, consisting of four planes, tells how he took off very early one morning at a time when he would have the sun at his back. There had then been a great deal of activity along the entire front, and he saw long rows of captive balloons which looked like a string of oversize sausages against the summer sky. As these bags greatly annoyed him, he decided that something had to be done about them. So he flew higher, he thought, than he had ever soared before. The altimeter showed 15,000 feet. The air there was thin. It was very cold.

Suddenly he sighted a hostile machine which, in the distance, looked like a tiny water beetle, while from another direction a small object rapidly approached. He recognized it as a Spad, an enemy fighter on the prowl for trouble seekers like himself. Bracing himself in his cockpit, he realized that he was in for a fight. The two planes met at the same altitude. The other fellow's machine was painted light brown. Soon they were circling around each other playing for an opening. From below they must have looked like two big birds indulging in springtime frolics. Udet knew, however, that it was to be a game of death. The first pilot to get behind the other's back would be the winner.

At times, he said, they passed so near to each other that Udet could see every detail of his adversary's face visible below the helmet. On the side of his opponent's plane, he said, there was a stork and two words painted in white. The fifth time that he flew past him, so close that he even felt the draft of his propeller, Udet managed to read one word—*Vieux*. Thus it dawned on him that it must have been Charles Guynemer's insignia. And what was more convincing, there existed only one man in the world able to handle a machine as Guynemer did.

Udet tried every trick he knew—turns, loops, and sideslips—

but Guynemer followed each movement with lightning speed, so that Udet realized that Guynemer was more than a match for him. Not only did he have a better machine, but he was the superior duelist. Still the German felt he had to carry on. To turn away now would be fatal. He then went into a steep turn and, for just one moment, he said, he had Guynemer at the end of his sights. He squeezed the trigger. There was no response—his gun had jammed. Holding the stick in his left hand, he hammered at the gun with his right, but his efforts to clear the stoppage proved unavailing.

For a moment, then, Udet considered the possibility of escaping. But with such an opponent that would surely have been inviting disaster. In a few seconds Guynemer would be on his tail and could shoot him down with the utmost ease. So they flew in circles, and then "for eight minutes we kept flying 'round each other," Udet said. They were the longest eight minutes he had ever experienced.

Then, suddenly, Guynemer looped and flew on his back over Udet's head. At that moment Udet relinquished hold of the stick and hammered with both hands at his machine gun. It sometimes worked, he said. However, Guynemer had observed his actions and realized that Udet was his helpless victim. He again passed close over Udet's head, and then, to the German's great surprise, he raised his arm and waved. Immediately afterwards he dived away toward the west, in the direction of his own lines. Udet flew back stupefied. He staunchly believed that Guynemer had proved that even in modern warfare there was still something left of the knightly chivalry of bygone days. "And," added Udet, "I lay this belated wreath on Guynemer's unknown grave."

Another name that has forever remained in the Frenchman's memory is that of Charles Nungesser, the dearly beloved French ace, a prince of pilots, nicknamed the Hussar of Death, who sacrificed his life in his last endeavor to bring more glory to France. Charles Nungesser had been in search of adventure all his life. As a young man he went to the Argentine Pampas where, a crack shot with pistol and rifle, he hunted wild game. Then, when his beloved France was in danger, he dropped all his Argentine interests and returned to his country to go to war.

Assigned at first to the Second Hussars, a regiment that was not active enough for him, he had himself transferred to the 148th Infantry, where he braved enemy fire on many occasions. One day, when the Germans had completely surrounded his company, the French commander picked out young Nungesser to try to secure aid at the risk of German rifle and machine gun fire. After many perilous escapades his gallantry saved the day, and he became known as the Hussar of Death. He adopted as his insignia a white coffin against a black background, a candle on each side of the coffin, and a skull and crossbones.

Wounded many times, but always recovering, Nungesser felt he bore a charmed life. Bones were so cruelly damaged in many parts of his body that they had to be removed and replaced with aluminum plates. It was even said that part of his skull had been replaced by a metal section.

After he had been wounded 17 times, the military authorities pressed him to take his discharge, which he refused to do. He kept hobbling about the airdrome with the help of a cane, flying when and where he felt inclined. At the close of the war he had chalked up a total of 45 planes and balloons, officially confirmed, and ranked third on the French honor list of aces.

The first nonstop transatlantic flight with passengers was made by Jean Assolant and René Lefèvre, on June 13, 1929, from Old Orchard, Maine to Comillas, Spain. The passengers were Armand Lotti who financed the flight, and Arthur Schreiber, a stowaway discovered after it was too late to turn back.

— 11 —

EARLY LONG-DISTANCE FLIGHTS

In the postwar days of 1918, when large numbers of planes had become available and many a former army or navy pilot was able to get hold of an Avro, Jenny or Caudron, the barnstorming and stunt flying era began. As these men formed circuses and gave exhibition flights, more and more people became airplane conscious. There was hardly a carnival or fair at which some daredevil airman did not thrill the gaping populace with a breathtaking performance. Wing-walking, sky writing, flying wing to wing, climbing from plane to plane and dog fights were the order of the day. And though some were killed in these exhibitions, others lived to fly another day. Many went in for cross-country flying.

In those earlier days of aviation, airlines were being established all over the globe and their planes manned by first class pilots. They needed to prove that traveling by plane was perfectly safe. As the air became more and more airplane crowded, governments began to take a hand, with the result that government experts met in Paris, in 1919, to arrive at some measure of international control. Accepted flying standards became recognized by every civilized nation.

The airplane began to take its place in national and international life. A period of record breaking was close at hand, because every first class pilot was out to break previously-attained records of time, endurance, distance and altitude. Let's trace now the spectacular developments and records that were made in those earlier days.

America initiated the first commercial airmail service between New York and Washington, followed by the New York-Cleveland route with the Curtiss JC-4s, Jennys. A special Communications Wing was formed in Great Britain, in December, 1918, to carry British government officials from London to Paris. And when the Curtiss Company built the first airplane specially designed for mail service, in 1920, a network of airmail route was established throughout our land.

The big aviation prize was still the trans-Pacific hop from the American mainland to the Hawaiian Islands. The first American pilot to try this, way back in 1911, was Lt. John Rogers, who, though he did not get very far in this venture, was nevertheless the first United States Naval officer to fly a round trip from Annapolis to Washington and a prominent figure in early United States Naval air service. Over in London, Lord Northcliffe, of the *Daily Mail,* who had offered a prize of 10,000 pounds sterling, in 1913, for the first transatlantic flight, renewed the offer again in 1919. This started a breakneck race between all airmen to take up the gauntlet. Deciding to emulate the *Daily Mail's* prize, William Randolph Hearst offered $50,000 to the first pilot to make the flight across the United States within thirty days of November 10, 1911. Galbraith Rogers tried the stunt, taking 50 days to make the 3,390 miles from New York to Los Angeles in 82 actual flying days, the longest single hop having been 133 miles.

Eugene Ely, a Curtiss test pilot, took off from a sixty-foot wooden platform erected on the bow of the USS *Birmingham,* at Hampton Roads, on November 19, 1910, while on the other side of the world, H. J. L. Hinkler, an expert engineer who had been flying gliders since 1911, flew a light aircraft seven hundred miles nonstop from Queensland, Australia, the longest such flight by a small aircraft up to that time. The stage was now set for an Atlantic crossing, and the first to try were the crews of the United States Navy, who had been preparing on the Q.T. for some time. The NC-1, NC-3, and NC-4 took off from Rockaway Beach on May 8, 1919, with Spain as their ultimate goal. Commander A. C. Read and his men in the NC-4 were the first to cover the 1,380 miles to the Azores, doing it in 15 hours. The others were forced down 200 miles west of these islands.

But the Atlantic had not yet been crossed in a non-stop flight. British fliers had been standing by in Newfoundland, and the British planes that were out to make history were a Martinsyde biplane, manned by Raynham and Morgan, a biplane flown by Harry Walker and Commander Mackenzie Grieve, and a Vickers Remy with Captain John Alcock and Lt. Arthur Brown aboard. Alcock and Brown took off on June 14, intending to cover the 1,900 miles from St. Johns direct to Ireland. They made the grade and landed in a boggy field at Clifden, Ireland, winning the ten-thousand-pounds *Daily Mail* purse, and were knighted by the King. Their plane is on view in the Kensington Museum in London. Sadly enough, Alcock was killed the following December in France, while Brown went back in the RAF, to do his bit for England during the Second World War.

As the British Dominions and Colonies were scattered all over the globe, it is understandable that the British began to think in terms of linking them by air. They realized that the airplane was the ideal vehicle to tie the outposts of their empire.

The Commonwealth of Australia had become so inspired by the Atlantic successes that it offered a ten-thousand pound purse for the first thirty-day hop from Britain to Australia, provided it be accomplished by an Australian. This offer had also tickled the fancy of Britain's air-route visionaries. This eventually led to the great flight by Captain Ross Smith, Sergeants J. M. Bennet and W. H. Shiers, starting out in a Vickers Remy on November 2, 1919. They landed 27 days and 20 hours later at Port Darwin, Australia, where they received a heroes' welcome, winning, of course, the 10,000-pound prize.

These intrepid airmen had crossed some of the most fantastic sections of the world, where civilization had started and been developed, only to disappear again, leaving magnificent ruins as a perpetual monument to its lost splendor. Other areas over which they flew in a few hours had been inhabited centuries ago by countless thousands but now were only trackless deserts. The methods of transportation had remained unchanged in these regions, however, as slow moving camel caravans were trudging along as they must have done thousands of years ago.

Their flight had been made under all sorts of difficulties, ranging from hastily-improvised landing strips to terrific snow storms and torrential tropical rains. Geographic conditions kept contesting with nature to make their flight even more hazardous. As they crossed the equator, their plane suffered a terrific jolt, undoubtedly caused by rapidly moving air currents, often referred to by pilots as "holes in the air."

Their historic flight also had another connotation, as the first Australian Air Transport was inaugurated at this time. Qantas, claiming to be the first, or rather the oldest, airline in the world, commenced its Queensland operation in 1920.

Canada, another great member of the British Empire, enjoyed seeing four of her native sons—Colonel Leckie and a crew of three—make the first trans-Canada crossing from Halifax to Vancouver, on October 14, 1920, in the astounding record time of seven days. Canada was fully convinced that plane travel could solve the problems of her isolated areas in the far north, in the not too distant future. As the time was also ripe for a long distance flight to South Africa two South Africans—Colonel Pierre van Ryneveldt and Captain Quentin Brandt—both wartime fliers, made the first flight from England to Capetown in the dependable Vickers Remy, starting on February 4, 1920, and reaching Capetown on March 20. They successfully charted a route that has been used by the regular airmail service ever since.

Most airmen had their sights fixed on a trip around the globe, and Jules Verne's *Around the World in Eighty Days* was soon to become a commonplace. There were many spots on the map still to be covered before such a flight could be undertaken, however. There was, for instance the 2,700 mile stretch between New York and San Diego. This flight was undertaken by army pilots Lt. John Macready and Lt. Kelly in a big Fokker. Taking off from Mitchel Field with only a thermos bottle of coffee to sustain them, they set down in San Diego 26 hours and 50 minutes later, the first men on record to have made the flight non-stop.

A year or so later, Lt. Russell L. Maugham, of the United States Army, streaking across the country in a Curtiss pursuit plane, landed at Crissy Field, San Francisco in 21 hours and 48 minutes, after some refuelling at Dayton, St. Joseph, and Salduro, Utah. This clipped five hours off the Macready and Kelly non-stop flight.

Still, America had her eyes set on the round-the-world hop and a world record, details of which had been carefully worked out. It was a completely military flight, to be led by Major Frederick L. Martin. The Army had set up a chain of fifteen depots around the world equipped with spare parts, gasoline and replacement engines. Leaving Seattle on April 6, 1924, the four planes first ran into heavy blizzards and fog before reaching Sitka. Three of the four reached Dutch Harbor on April 19, but the fourth plane, piloted by Major Martin, came down in the sea after breaking a crankcase.

Continuing now with Lt. Howell H. Smith in command, they crossed the Aleutians on May 24, and, after touching at Tokyo, resumed their flight to Shanghai. The planes were forced down in French Indo-China, where they were held up because of repairs. Negotiating the long stretches over Burma and India without a mishap, and crossing the Indian desert to the Arabian Sea, they flew via Constantinople, Bucharest, Vienna and Paris to London, where the flyers were wildly acclaimed.

Here their wheels were removed from the planes and pontoons attached for their hops across the Atlantic. Their flight to the Orkneys was merely routine, although two of their planes— the *Chicago* and *Boston*—were forced to turn back. Between the Orkneys and Iceland they ran into a fog. The *New Orleans*, commanded by Eric Nelson, reached Iceland, while the two that had turned back continued their trip. The *Boston* was forced down and badly damaged, and her crew was rescued by the destroyer

Billings. The *Chicago,* her companion ship, joined Nelson in Iceland.

Leaving Iceland on August 21, and skirting Greenland, they continued across the Davis Strait to the shores of North America without a further hitch. When the three planes finally arrived at their destination, their total flying time for the 26,345 miles had been 363 hours.

To add a postscript to this American round-the-world story, it may be of interest to recall that, when one of the aviators on this first global flight—the 66-year-old General Leslie P. Arnold— died at his home on March 21, 1961, the world lost one of the most daring fliers of the old Army Air Service. As a lieutenant in that service, General Arnold was a member of the crew that flew these 27,000 miles around the world, a flight that was hailed by one newspaper as "the greatest air achievement since the Wrights found a way to fly."

In 1921, the General was a member of General William (Billy) Mitchel's group that conducted tests off the Virginia Capes to prove that battleships could be sunk by aerial bombardment. When War II came around, General Arnold organized the 39th Air Freight Wing to become the commander of the Ferry and Transport Services of the Air Services Command in Europe, later ferrying supplies to Normandy during the invasion.

The twenties saw an era of more scientific flying, during which Admiral Byrd, Cobham, Kingsford-Smith, Fonck, Nungesser, Bernt Balchen and Wiley Post, to name but a few, entered the flying arena. No obstacle in those days of long-distance flying proved too great.

Once the Imperial Airways had surveyed the enormous desert area between Cairo and Bagdad, the empire route from Croydon to India was inaugurated. The Qantas pioneers won the concession for an airplane route to Australia. The KLM, Royal Dutch Airlines, blazed the long-distance trail from Amsterdam to the then Dutch East Indies with their 9,554-miles flight on October 21, 1924, four years after that enterprising Company's founding. Taking part and finishing second in the 12,000-mile MacRobertson London-Melbourne race ten years later, this dynamic company added additional luster to its enviable record when it pioneered the aerial path to its Dutch West Indian possession with the epochal Amsterdam-

Surinam-Curacao hop, exactly three hundred years after this colony's founding.

In 1925, the Marchese di Pinedo made the third flight from Europe to Australia in an Italian flying boat. He continued his flight back to Rome, via Manila and Toyko, in the first flying-boat venture since the NC's Atlantic crossing, in 1919.

Nineteen twenty-seven became known as the year for light-plane flights, when Bentley took a tiny Moth (with an 80-horsepower engine) from London to Johannesburg in twenty-five days, while Captain W. N. Lancaster completed the first light-plane hop to Australia, taking along a Mrs. Keith Miller, the first woman to tackle such an undertaking by air.

— 12 —

LADIES OF THE AIR

Not to be outdone by the men, the ladies also began to figure in the flying picture, although it is a fact that Madame Thible was the first to leave this earth in a balloon years before, and her contemporary, a Madame Peltier, is said to have been the first woman to have enjoyed a ride in a plane.

Flying a tiny Avian from Capetown to London in 1928, Lady Heath became the first woman to fly this route solo either way. Another no-less-daring aviatrix, Lady Bailey, used a Moth—or to be more to the point two Moths, crashing the first one in Tanganyika—en route from Croydon to Capetown. She flew back to London by way of the West Coast of Africa, across the Belgian Congo and French Sahara, in the first recorded flight by this western route. This was a great achievement indeed, especially when one considers that if she had crashed or had come down for refueling, the hostile tribesmen of North Africa might have attacked her.

Then there was Jean Batten, a New Zealand lassie, the first one in fact to have crossed the South Atlantic and to have established an absolute record between London and New Zealand and back. Another adventurous lady with a decided liking for aviation was Laura Ingalls, who was the first to fly across the American continent solo and non-stop from New York to Los Angeles in 18 hours, during the summer of 1935.

Making more than 500 balloon ascents and about 200 parachute drops, the first American woman to hold an airplane pilot's license, in 1911, was Harriet Quimby. She was followed by the flying-crazy Moisant sisters, whose brother, the famous pilot John Moisant, crashed to his death in that same year.

As women's interest in aviation grew, Ruth Law won a non-stop 590-mile race in 1911, and later established a 11,200-foot altitude record in 1915. Trying to join the American and French Forces without success, she managed to do her bit nonetheless in recruiting and Liberty Loan drives.

Katharine Stinson, another early bird, not only flew in the interest of the American Red Cross, but together with her sister opened a flying school to train Canadian pilots.

No story about the flying accomplishments of the fair ladies could be said to be complete without recording the unforgettable work done by the late Amelia Earhart (to whom I shall refer in a later chapter) and by the great woman flyer and captain of industry, Jacqueline Cochran. She was awarded the General Billy Mitchel award in 1928 as the American pilot who had made the greatest contribution to aviation.

Jacqueline Cochran has enjoyed a most colorful life, studded with action, adventure, and successful business ventures. When hardly eight years of age, she was already "self-supporting" by pushing a wheeled cart up and down the aisles in a cotton mill delivering spools to the weavers, at a salary of six cents an hour. During later periods in this remarkable lady's career, she was a nurse in a logging camp, worked in a beauty shop, and sold dress patterns and materials throughout the South. She also held a job in a hairdressing parlor, at first in New York and later in Miami.

While attending a party given by Stanton Griffis, U.S. Ambassador to Spain, she met Floyd Odlum, who not only interested her in flying, but later became her husband. After a short stint of instruction at Roosevelt Field's Flying School she obtained her license. She then combined flying and the cosmetic business and became highly successful as a business woman in a company bearing her name, whose cosmetic products have become known all over the world.

Despite her many business activities, Jacqueline Cochran returned once more to her first love as she brought the women's air speed record to the United States with an 842.6 mile an hour jet plane flight on August 24, 1961 (126 miles per hour faster than the 6-year-old 715.92 miles per hour mark held by Mrs. Jacqueline Auriol—wife of the French President). Mrs. Cochrane made the flight in a twin-jet trainer at the desert test center of Edwards Air Force Base.

She also was the first woman flier to pass the sonic barrier, about which feat the equally-famous flyer "Chuck" J. Yeager (the first to crack the sonic barrier) wrote in a foreword to her book: "It is truly remarkable that, with less than six hours flying time and only thirteen take-offs and landings, Jackie set three world records and dived three times past the sonic barrier to beat the speed of sound."

Doing some more digging into the storehouse of women's aerial achievements, we run across Amy Johnson (or Amy Mollison, her married name) whose rise from a typist's chair to flying fame captivated the admiration of every lover of sports and adventure. Almost totally unknown, this girl, who had made a solo flight after but a few weeks of instruction, completed a daring solo from London to Australia, starting on May 5, 1930, and arriving at Darwin nineteen days after she had started, to become flying heroine and collect a purse of 10,000 pounds sterling, donated by the *Daily Mail*.

— 13 —

SAGA OF THE *SOUTHERN CROSS*

The much coveted prize in long distance aviation during the 1920s was a trans-Pacific hop from America to Australia. The flier most likely to do it, and who eventually did, was Kingsford-Smith, or "Smithy" as he was affectionately known to his friends.

Smithy had been an average Australian schoolboy, messing about in his spare time like so many other youngsters with electric gadgets and engines of all kinds. Consequently he was apprenticed by his parents to the electrical engineering trade. But his future was determined one day in 1915—his 18th birthday—when he presented himself at the recruiting office in Sydney's Town Hall to

enlist in the Corps of Signal Engineers. Every patriotic young
fellow was joining up in those hectic war days, and from that
town hall in Australia to France and England was but a short
jump that really meant a most violent change in one's life. After
a short stint of regular training with the 19th Battery, Smithy was
transferred to the Signal Corps, as guns did not appeal to him. He
served at first in Egypt, then in Gallipoli, where he remained until
evacuation.

Then he went from Gallipoli to France where he became attached to a motorcycle outfit. One day in 1916, the opportunity
arose for him to become, if not an airman, at least a trainee for a
commission in the Royal Flying Corps. This was the chance of a
lifetime. It also became the chance of Smithy's flying career.

The story of the war birds over France in those days of 1917
and 1918 has been told over and over again, recording the heroic
feats of such men as Albert Ball, Bishop, Nungesser, Guynemer and
of many others, who had belonged to that famous lot of Knights of
the Air. Smithy came into this world of flying at dawn, and by the
summer of 1918, when hardly 21, he became an instructor. Like
other ex-officers, when the war was over Smithy purchased war
machines to carry on sundry jobs or do some joy riding and taxi
flights. He had made quite a name for himself in the RFC, where
he downed eight German aircraft, was wounded and awarded the
Military Cross.

While in the United States, Smithy first did some stunt flying
for the movies in Hollywood, but finding this too easy, he did a
short stint spraying trees from his aircraft in California. Before
leaving California to go back to Australia, he undertook another
job, that of "Flying Scarecrow" on the rice patrol, a monotonous
task of shooting duck from an airplane over rice crops and spraying from the air. Once back in Australia, he became the first to
cross the Tasman Sea by air, and to make Sydney and Christchurch
the terminals of his pioneering flights. He then received an offer to
join the newly-formed West-Australian Airways as a pilot on the
Perth-Wyndham run. The company, a young and struggling concern, has since grown into one of the finest and most efficient
airways in the world. It was there that Smithy met up with Keith
Anderson, with whom he scraped up enough money to purchase a
couple of old Bristol machines. They flew these crates across Australia to Sydney, each with a passenger. His passenger was a Mrs.

Marshall of Cottesloe, the first woman, in fact, to have flown across Australia. Considering this also very unexciting, he ran into a fellow named C. T. P. Ulm, who was to play an important part in his America-Pacific-Australia venture.

The two men began scouring maps to discover whether there wasn't a spot left that had not yet been covered, and both agreed that the biggest thing left in aviation was the unexplored run from America to Australia. But they had to have money. There they were stone broke in Sydney, but with a terrific fund of flying experience. To attract the public's attention and to impress possible prospective backers, Kingsford-Smith and Ulm bought a de Havilland 1920 plane, equipped with a motor that had already chalked up a million miles. As time was of the essence in an era when records were being made, they flew the 7500 miles around Australia in 10 days and 5 hours, in 1927. This made such an impression on the New South Wales Government and a Sydney newspaper that not only were they promised financial assistance but they jumped at once into prominence and became headline news.

And so, before July had come around and gone, Keith Anderson, Ulm and Smithy, well in the chips, boarded a steamer bound for the States, the goal of their hopes and fears, aspirations and ambition.

Proving himself a terrific organizer, Kingsford-Smith racked his brains about where they could lay their hands on sufficient money to finance their US-Australia venture. The first thing they did was to purchase a three-motored Fokker from the late Sir Hubert Wilkins, another air-minded Australian, who had made his own distinguished mark flying the Polar regions. There was, however, a little catch to the sale—as the plane had no engines, they had to procure three 220 HP Wright Whirlwinds elsewhere. This Wright Whirlwind had quite a reputation, which it fully deserved. On his flight to the North Pole Admiral Byrd had used a Whirlwind, so had Maitland and Hegenberger in the first successful flight to Honolulu, and so had Lindbergh, Chamberlin and Levine.

Since I am mentioning the names of Maitland and Hegenberger, they were the first transocean fliers ever to navigate by radio beam—a system of continuous, directed radio signals making a sort of "path" down which pilots could fly. They had covered the 2,400 miles of open ocean to Wheeler Field, Honolulu, in 25 hours, 50 minutes. This adventure had caused such a stir that people began clamoring for an annual flying event. That event came with the Dole Race, a disastrous contest started on the 16th of August, 1927 and sponsored by the wealthy pineapple grower, Dole with a $25,000 stake. Two aircraft competed, both of which came to grief, while a third coming to the rescue of the other two met a similar fate.

However Smithy did not let this catastrophic junket interfere with his own plans. Good fortune once again was on his side when he met Sidney Meyer, a wealthy Australian business tycoon who, though he was dead set against their dangerous mission, handed him 15,000 pounds sterling as an outright gift.

As the funds needed to purchase the engines had not yet arrived from Australia, Sir Hubert Wilkins came to their rescue by permitting them to pay only half of the purchase price for the plane, making it possible to order the engines. Meanwhile Keith Anderson had left for the Hawaiian Islands to give Wheeler Field and Barking Sands—taking-off places for the second heat of the flight from the Hawaiian Islands to Fiji—the once over.

But once again the three men were strapped for funds, and wondering where they could lay their hands on some money this time, they hit upon the idea of trying to break the world's record for a sustained flight by remaining in the air without refueling for the maximum possible time. Up to that time it had stood at 52 hours and 22 minutes, set in Leipzig by two German airmen in a Junkers J-3 monoplane, in August. They tried their hand at it on January 17, 1928, and after circling around for fifty hours in a plane, christened by them *Southern Cross*, they failed to break that record.

There was, however, some more bad news in store for them. Keith Anderson, yielding to the wishes of the folks back home, had to return to Australia, while the New South Wales Government also instructed them to dispose of the plane and come home. They were absolutely broke, so poor in fact that they even lacked the money to buy themselves a pack of smokes. Driven to all sorts of subterfuges to stave off those to whom they owed money, and even unable to pay their hotel bill, there remained nothing else for them to do but to sell the *Southern Cross*.

And then, as if by magic, the whole picture changed.

Gloomily standing at Rogers Airport, bemoaning their plight, Kingsford-Smith and Ulm were introduced to a Captain G. Allen

Hancock, master mariner, a man keenly interested in long-distance flying. Told about their difficulties and trans-Pacific flight plan, he agreed to buy the plane from them for 3200 pounds, and then let them have it back, so that they would have enough funds to be able to go ahead with their arrangements. Elated at having found a new angel, they first cabled Keith Anderson to return, and then set to work like beavers to get the Fokker ready for their big hop.

The hour for their departure had finally struck. Taking off from Oakland airport on the misty morning of May 31, 1928, as they headed out over the Golden Gate, they experienced a sensation of relaxation and relief. The flight went off smooth as clockwork, in spite of some bad weather, and they landed 27 hours and 23 minutes later at Wheeler Field, Honolulu, setting the Fokker down on the beach because the runway at the airport proved far too short. They started again on June 3, on the longest transocean flight ever attempted up to that time.

After 24 hours in the air, they ran into some heavy black cumulus and nimbus storm clouds, and wild air currents bumped and pitched their vehicle all over the place. The weather got better, however, after a while. Dropping a day out of their reckoning, they crossed the International Date Line and Suva lay ahead, judged by the heavy, sultry tropic air and as their log book recorded. Swooping over the town's white roofs, they set down at Suva's Sports Oval, since there existed no airport in those earlier flying days. They had covered that portion of their flight in 34 hours.

They took off on the morning of June 6, for their last, and also shortest hop to Brisbane. Barely four hours out of Suva, the elements broke loose again with all their fury, and they ran into one of the worst storms encountered on their entire flight. Brisbane, they knew, was only 1,700 miles away, and fortunately for them the engines continued to turn with the same flawless rhythm. However, their earth conductor compass, the most valuable of all the instruments with which they were navigating their course, appeared to be out of commission, so that they had to rely entirely on their magnetic steering compasses for the remainder of their hop.

When they climbed to 4,000 feet for the night, the ocean had not yet done with them. It was getting colder and colder. The moon had disappeared, and visibility, which a short time before had enabled them to see the distant horizon, dwindled first to a mile, then to a mere few yards, until finally complete darkness had closed in on them. As strong gusts tossed their plane about, heavy rains began to drum and rattle the windshield. The wet propellers, reflecting the indirect light from the little bulb on their instrument board, glistened in the lash of the storm. As they climbed more and more to get above it, the weather onslaught bumped and dropped and bucked, while raking gusts jolted the Fokker so that they had great difficulty hanging on to their seats. But the reliable engines drove the *Southern Cross* steadily upward in an attempt to help them escape from this blinding chaos of wind and water. This was real blind flying, which added to their mental discomfort. First came a steady drip on their knees, then a shower, turning into a cascade, so that their overalls were completely sodden. It also turned much colder as they rose, which was far worse than flying through the ordinary darkness of the night.

They were tearing through a black chaos of rain and cloud at 85 knots, and this was a tropical deluge, such as they had never experienced in all their flying years. It was a real electrical storm, whose lightning bolts added fresh terrors to the nights as they ripped holes in the clouds, revealing great masses of black nimbus clouds, shooting across the sky in inspiring jags. Soon a crackle of blue flame played eerily around the plug leads of all three motors. If these became thoroughly wet, they might give out at any moment.

After enduring these terrible conditions for four solid hours from eight until midnight, they began to hope that they might escape the worst of the storm. As they descended to 4000 feet the electrical onslaughts seemed to have abated, although the bumps were, if anything, worse than ever. By seven in the morning, with conditions much improved, they tried to pick up a radio bearing from Brisbane and take a sight, after which they altered their course to 270 degrees which was due west, in the belief they were on Brisbane's parallel.

They figured that their goal now was in sight. The sun warmed the air, and their numbed hands came to life again, but their feet remained chilled. They could see the horizon again like a clear cut line. Grayness seemed to merge with the cobalt blue of the sea, and as they approached it at just over 70 knots it assumed more definite form. And then they sighted land—the Australian coast. Sweeping over Ballina, they knew they were 110 miles off their course, as they had not seen Moreton Island, the airman's land-mark for Brisbane. When they approached Eagle Farm Airdrome, a crowd of some 15,000 had gathered to pay them homage. And if their reception in Queensland's capital was almost overwhelming, the amazing spectacle of the massed crowd of 300,000 as the *Southern Cross* flew over Sydney was even more fantastic. The old but reliable Fokker had done 7,389 miles on this epic flight in ten days, a venture that was called by many airmen the greatest one in all aviation history. The late Anthony Fokker was so elated over the performance of his plane that he called Kingsford-Smith "Australia's outstanding hero" and "the greatest flyer of all time."

For those readers with an interest in statistics, the three engines had revolved with a single hitch 24,000,000 times, had lifted the heaviest burdens, had flown safely through the fiercest storms and blinding rains, and had answered every call. The plane, itself, was a tri-motor Fokker 220 horsepower monoplane, with 71-foot wingspan, with four gas tanks, each holding 96 gallons, in the wings, another tank for 107 gallons placed under the pilot's seat, while the main tank in the fuselage held 807 gallons, in all totalling 1,298 gallons.

Among the many gifts and honors that were showered on the men was the Air Force Cross which his Majesty, the King, conferred on Ulm and Smithy. The Australian Government appointed Smithy honorary squadron leader in the Royal Australian Air Force, and Ulm was made Flight Lieutenant. They received in addition a check for 5,000 pounds sterling. Numerous newspapers and private subscriptions—aggregating 20,000 pounds—were made on their behalf, while they also received the National Geographic Society's Medal, and the Trophy of the Fédération Aéronautique Internationale.

After all the celebrations and speechmaking had run their course, Smithy returned to England. He later flew back to Australia solo, in an Avro, in 9 days, 21 minutes, breaking all previous records.

To illustrate Kingsford-Smith's amazing capacity for organization and clockwise timing, the following may be of added interest. The understanding had been that, when he landed in England, he was to set down in the Thames by the House of Commons at a previously-arranged time. And that is exactly what he did, landing there right on the nose amidst the tumultous cheers of the capacity crowds that had gathered on the embankment and Westminster Bridge. He was subsequently knighted by the King.

After his flight back to Australia, Smithy flew from Melbourne to New Guinea, via Sydney, Cooktown, Thursday Island, the Solomons, Rabaul, and Tulagi, the first exploratory flights to these Pacific islands. But the luck that had been with this intrepid airman throughout his fantastic career finally deserted him when he vanished off the Malayan Coast during a possibly too-hastily-prepared trip from England to Australia, in 1935. He did not live long enough to see the Britain-Australia or Transpacific Airline for which he had so ardently pioneered come to realization.

— 14 —

POLAR FLIGHTS—ADMIRAL BYRD

The inevitable flight across the Atlantic still had to wait for other developments, like the Byrd flight to the Pole. Richard Evelyn Byrd, who had been making scientific flights and Polar expeditions, had made the first North Pole hop on May 9, 1926, and a flight to the South Pole three years later.

Fifteen years old when the Wright Brothers took to the air at Kitty Hawk, and twenty-one when Blériot conquered the English Channel, Byrd was over 25 before having his first airplane ride, and 30 before he qualified as an aviator. But he kept pushing onward until he stood in the front rank of his profession.

Byrd prepared well for his flight to the Pole, although he had to contend with Sir Hubert Wilkins, the brilliant and energetic Australian who was readying his non-stop flight across the Polar Seas, from Point Barrow, Alaska, to Spitsbergen, about that time.

The incomparable team of Amundsen-Ellsworth had purchased the Italian dirigible *Norge,* for a non-stop adventure in the opposite direction. Dr. Hugo Eckener, head of the Zeppelin Works, had announced plans for a specially-designed dirigible with cruising radius that could carry it over the top of the world and the Pole, and down into China.

Edsel Ford provided the springboard for Byrd's de luxe Polar effort with a $20,000 check given without strings attached. Needing more funds, Byrd then approached John D. Rockefeller, Jr. hardly an aviation enthusiast, who wrote a check, nonetheless, equalling the one Ford had given. But Byrd was still far short of the quota he had set as the minimum required to finance the undertaking. Nevertheless, he did get the money in the end, and by the middle of March, less than two months after he and Floyd Bennett had quit their desks in the Bureau of Navigation, the Byrd Expedition had grown from nothing into a highly-organized and smoothly-running undertaking.

Making a long story short, on the afternoon of April 5, to the accompaniment of a shrieking valedictory from the steam whistles of harbor craft, Byrd's vessel, the thoroughly reconditioned *Chantier*, on loan from the U.S. Shipping Board and a relic of the war-time wooden fleet, with 1500 tons of coal in its bunkers, moved out of Brooklyn's Navy Yard and stood out to sea, Spitsbergen bound. In its hold also was the reliable tri-motored Fokker, now christened the *Josephine Ford*, in honor of Edsel Ford's daughter, and a small Curtiss Oriole, christened *Richard the Third*, after Byrd's son.

And thus began the great luxury adventure that would enable Byrd to fly in style to the North Pole. As he jotted down in his log: "I cannot but marvel at the superiority of the airplane. To think that men toiled for years over this ice, a few hard-won miles a day, and we can travel luxuriously, a hundred miles an hour. How motors have changed the burdens of man!"

The first flight to the Pole was made on May 9, 1926, and thus closed one of the most momentous episodes in the history of aviation to that time, and one of the outstanding events in Byrd's distinguished career. Russell Owen, of the New York *Times*, flashed news to the world that Byrd had achieved his goal.

Amundsen, who had been preparing for his own Polar trek at Kings Bay, dashed across the snow to be among the first to greet Byrd, the man who beat him. That night there was a party aboard the *Chantier* attended by the gallant team of Amundsen and Ellsworth, toasting Byrd wholeheartedly for having succeeded.

Two years later the *Italia*, returning from its Polar flight, and commanded by General Nobile, contributed one of the most ghastly tragedies to the history of Polar exploration. Nearly a dozen of the men, who dined with Byrd that night on the *Chantier* to celebrate Byrd's Polar achievement, were to perish.

Then came Byrd's flight to the South Pole, a plan that had germinated during the night of May 10, 1926, a secret he had shared with Amundsen and Lincoln Ellsworth. Byrd had selected the Bay of Whales as the best place to base, because, surrounded by unknown seas, it seemed to offer the likeliest spots for flying. Here were hundreds of thousands of square miles of territory completely unknown to geographers. The flight over the South Pole on November 29, 1929, led to the discovery of five new mountain ranges, five islands, and more than 100,000 square miles of area. Made a Commander of the U.S. Antarctic Services in 1939, the honors that befell Richard Evelyn Byrd subsequently were legend.

At this stage I could not very well leave out the terrific record made by Sir Hubert Wilkins and Carl Eielson from Point Barrow over the top of the world to Spitsbergen, two details of which distinguished this expedition for sheer nerve and phenomenal daring. In the first place, the explorers made a landing in· the arctic wastes en route, spending considerable time in discovery and the collection of scientific observation. Further, they made this daring trip in a single-engined plane with a lone pilot, and entirely without assistance from outside sources. They had not been prepared for their expedition, and had not been in the same position as Admiral Byrd. There had existed no large expedition nearby to lend them aid or to rescue them, nor did they have any radio contact with land bases.

What these two bold men did was simply to hop into a plane without assistance or weather information, and then set out across a trackless waste, haphazardly picking out the most likely spot to land. When their task had been completed, these pioneers took all this in a matter of fact style, having trusted to luck and the help of the Lord. All this displayed an almost unbelievable cocksure courage and iron nerve, so that the foremost aviation authorities and explorers think that Carl Ben Eielson would have been the most outstanding flying explorer of our time, had he not been lost in a crash off the Siberian Coast.

Now let's come back once more to the attempts by airmen to fly the Atlantic. The year 1926 seemed ripe for the flight across, as the $25,000 prize had gone begging for quite a few years. Raymond Orteig, a wealthy Parisian-born hotel man, had staked this amount to the first airman successfully completing a non-stop from New York to Paris. So far there had not been any takers, although several attempts had been made. Taking off from Roosevelt Field in a specially-built Sikorsky on September 21, René Fonck, the French war ace, had come to grief even before he was airborne. Davis and Wooster, both of the United States Navy, also had tried, but their test plane, the *American Legion,* crashed, killing the crew. Millionaire Levine and pilot Clarence Chamberlin had their Columbia monoplane all tuned up for the attempt, and several French pilots were standing by waiting for the right moment to jump into the aerial fray. The French war aces Nungesser and Coli were next in the air, but they vanished in the vast reaches of the Atlantic. The Americans also crashed in their tries, during one of which Floyd Bennett was injured.

The sum of all this was that on this side of the Atlantic there was a score of impatient pilots, jittery as puppies, keeping close check on each other's movements, and on the weather. They had no notion that a tousle-haired lad named Charles Lindbergh, a dark horse, son of a United States Senator, was about to beat them to the hop across.

— 15 —

THE LONE EAGLE

It was May 20, 1927, at Roosevelt Field.

A lean, tanned face grinned at the cheering crowd from a closed airplane cabin. A strong hand flipped good-bye at the earth, and the plane lifted and jerked upward from a spot of earth softened by the rain. And as the small crowd watched, up went the *Spirit of St. Louis,* with a gallant youth at its controls. Charles A. Lindbergh was about to beat the field in a flight that would make him a hero the world over.

Cameras whirred and clicked as the gray bird, outlined against a distant cloud, righted itself in the air and was off.

From his early childhood Charles A. Lindbergh displayed a large measure of determination, self-confidence and skill. Unlike so many boys who developed genius in one particular line, Charles A. was a rather indifferent pupil at school, as it was hard to get him interested in those branches of learning that did not naturally attract him. He liked mathematics, but grammar and English were not his particular dish. Preferring most to be left by himself, with no companion but his dog, he would often spend entire days in the woods or doing some odd jobs at his father's little farm at Little Falls, Minnesota. His father was a man who had nerves of steel, and the source of Charles Lindbergh's greatest happiness was a deep bond of sympathy between himself and his father. When his father died, in 1924, Charles A. scattered his ashes over the family's homestead from his plane.

After a high school education, Charles A. worked his way through a course in mechanical engineering, and because of his innate fondness for mechanics and intense power of concentration, which stood him in good stead later, he tinkered in his spare time with a great many things to find out what made them tick.

Deciding one day in 1921 to become an aviator, Lindbergh applied for tuition at Lincoln's flying school. Possessed of an almost uncanny aptitude for flying, with a rare touch of what airmen call "air sense," he dug in with a vengeance to learn all there was to be known about flying and parachute jumping.

He purchased a Curtiss Jenny, a good, sturdy plane, to which he gave his loving and undivided attention. After months of preparation he joined the Texas Flying School, a preliminary to army training. He subsequently went to work with the Robertson Aircraft Corporation, to become an airmail flier, and clocked 1800 flying hours, the equal of 15 years' experience for the average aviator. He became chief pilot of the air mail route between St. Louis and Chicago in August, 1926. On more than one occasion he spoke to Major William H. Robertson, head of the Aircraft Corporation, about his hopes of a flight to Paris.

Learning his trade the hard way, like other airmen of those days, Lindbergh also had his share of barnstorming and stunt flying in joy-riding crates. These days were among the most colorful and least known of his interesting career.

Then the crazy barnstorming days and his stints in the airmail service were over. Lindbergh began to scout for a suitable plane very early in 1927, with the financial backing of Major Robertson, and with the assistance of Harry H. Knight, a former flier, Major Albert Bond Lambert, for whom the Lambert Flying Field is named, Harold N. Bixter, President of the St. Louis Chamber of Commerce, and F. Lansing Ray, Publisher of the St. Louis *Globe-Democrat*.

Sinking his own $2,000 savings in the enterprise, Lindbergh chose a Ryan monoplane, to be built at San Diego. There, with the assistance of the kindly Benjamin F. Mahoney, plans for the *Spirit of St. Louis* took shape. And for the next sixty days the youthful Lindbergh worked, ate and slept in the Ryan shop until the job was completed. As the plane's engines were, of course, of the utmost importance, work for a 225 horsepower, aircooled, 9 cylinder Whirlwind radial type engine was undertaken at the plant of the Wright Aeronautical Corporation, in Paterson, N. J.

Significantly, up to Lindbergh's actual day of departure, there had not been any outside soul who had an inkling of his New York-Paris plan. Lindbergh had kept his whole business completely hush-hush. The first news to the outside world came when the *Spirit of St. Louis* was wheeled out upon its runway. It headed first for St. Louis, to let the backers give the machine the once over, then on to Curtiss Field, on May 12, 1927.

Lindbergh had discussed the New York-Paris flight casually, as if it were just an ordinary train trip. The courageous and quiet, widowed mother of Charles A., Mrs. Evangeline Land Lindbergh, had journeyed to New York to bid him good luck and then returned to her classroom at Cass Technical High School in Detroit, where she was a chemistry teacher.

Came the gray day of May 19, on Roosevelt Field, near Garden City. Darkness had fallen. Rain was dripping from menacing clouds. Gusts of wind did not seem too inviting.

"Bad weather for flying," said Commander Richard E. Byrd of the U.S. Navy. Byrd was also waiting to make the hop, and his Bellanca was ready in the hangar. At the Garden City Hotel things had been quite lively. Lindbergh had dinner as usual with other fliers, and then took a walk around the hotel grounds. As the weather was still quite soupy, he went to bed at 11:00, leaving a call to awaken him should the wind die down and the clouds lift.

At 3:00 A.M. the president of the Ryan Air Line decided to awaken him, although Lindbergh had had but three hours' sleep. But he was ready in a jiffy. Donning a khaki shirt, riding breeches, army socks and heavy tan shoes, he was off to the hangar in the faithful Mr. Mahoney's car, rubbing his sleepy eyes. Mr. G. M. Sumpf, representative of the St. Louis Chamber of Commerce, ordered the mechanics to fill the fuel tanks with 448 gallons, 145 more than had ever been lifted by a plane before. Although the entrance to the hangar had been roped off, the barrier was removed upon word from Lindbergh and Mahoney, admitting the few VIP's

—Richard Byrd, Bert Acosta, Byrd's pilot Lt. G. O. Noville, booked for the flight of the *America*, Clarence Chamberlin, pilot of the waiting Bellanca, Raymond Orteig, Jr., and Jean Orteig, sons of R. Orteig, the donor of the $25,000 prize for the first successful non-stop flight. Walking in and out of the hangar like a hen hovering over her chicks, Mahoney had brought a supply of sandwiches— two ham, two roast beef, and one of hard-boiled eggs. Stowed away in one nook of the plane was a pocket of U.S. Army emergency rations in tin cans, 56 ounces of dried beef, hard tack, chocolate with dried white of eggs, and flavor of caffeine, enough condensed food to last the pilot seven days. In another cache was a small packet of strong linen fish line and four sturdy fish hooks, for Lindbergh was prepared for catching his food in the Atlantic if forced down. Then he had a heavy-bladed, keen knife in his pocket, a strong seaman's needle and heavy thread, a large ball of heavy twine for use in flying a kite, if need be, and as a last precaution a package of four lifeboat flares.

On the instrument board were a clock, oil and gas gauges, gauges for telling height and speed, and the earth inductor compass, industry's latest invention. As the last provision for sustenance there were also two aluminum canteens filled with water hung beside Lindbergh's wicker seat. And then, of course, there was his fur-lined, one piece flying suit, which he wore with pushed back helmet and flying goggles pulled up high on the forehead.

Lindbergh had felt all along that he would be able to check his flying route along the American and Canadian coast with the aid of maps, while to guide him across the trackless waters he would have his magnetic compass and ground induction compass. This induction compass was so designed that it could tell him at once if he had deviated from his mapped-out course. Added to all this was his almost uncanny bird instinct, that gave him a highly developed sense of direction.

Taking a last look at the clouds as he climbed into the cockpit, Lindberg sat down in the little wicker seat.

Edward J. Mulligan, field engineer for the Wright Aircraft Co. stood beside the plane as it throttled. Mechanics pulled away the blocks from the wheels. Lindbergh flipped his hand at the crowd. "So long," he said again.

It was 7:52 daylight saving time when the wheels of the heavily-loaded plane started down the runway. As Lindbergh gave it the gun and opened the throttle it did not leap forward but made its ponderous way slowly along the strip, so slowly in fact that those watching were breathless. The plane did not seem to be acting in the right way as it loafed along the muddy field, and, refusing to accelerate, hit the bumps in the runway and bounced upwards, only to sink back again in the mud. But further along a stretch of firmer track came under the plane's wheels and the craft began to respond. It passed the safety flag markings along the runway, beyond which it was considered unsafe to proceed if a machine had not attained flying speed.

Then another bump, and this time the plane stayed aloft although it had sprung only a few feet from the ground. In front of Lindbergh loomed telegraph poles and wires, as well as a tractor. But now the plane began to climb clearing the tractor by a bare five feet, just managing to get over the telegraph wires. Then some more trees, and when these had been cleared, the *Spirit of St. Louis* rose gracefully and was on its way to France. And from that moment until he landed at Le Bourget Airport, Lindbergh carried the prayers of the world.

The weather experts meanwhile continued to spread gloom, anticipating storms, fearing the pilot would never be able to weather them. But, ignorant of all this, Lindbergh sped on his way while newspaper offices, radio stations and ships all waited tensely for every word telling of his progress.

Passing over Long Island, Massachusetts, Nova Scotia and finally squaring away from Newfoundland's Cape for his Atlantic hop, it was impossible for him to transmit messages along the seacoast, which also added to the suspense. To every steamship across the Atlantic the message was relayed: "Captain Lindbergh in the *Spirit of St. Louis* hopped off for Paris at 7:52 A.M. summer time, May 20th, following the great circle route. All ships please keep sharp lookout for him. Stay on the lookout for the plane." St. John's, Newfoundland, reported a heavy fog bank drifting in from the Atlantic, adding to Lindbergh's handicap, and if the watchers had known of the sleet storm with which he was battling at that time, their concern surely would have increased.

Then came the first flash of real news and relief. The Canadian Government wireless station at Cape Race, Newfoundland, broadcast this message: "Steamship *Hilvesum* from Rotterdam, Holland, broadcast at 12:10 G.M.T. (8:10 eastern daylight time) Lindbergh sighted 500 miles from Irish Coast. Plane keeps full speed. May be expected 8:00 P.M. New York time in Ireland." Paris and London received messages from the Dutch steamship at the same time. However, some other news had come from East Greenwich, Rhode Island, where women had heard the low, regular hum of a motor, and caught a swift glimpse of a gray shape in the distant glow at 9:05 daylight saving time. Thirty-five minutes later two women in Halifax saw the *Spirit of St. Louis* flying so low that they could catch beneath the grey wings the capital letters NX 211. Some fishermen near Meteghan, Nova Scotia, sighted him as he flew over. Hundreds of others spotted the beautiful gray bird.

The barometer had been steadily dropping. A thick fog continued to roll in from the Atlantic. Little needles of ice appeared on the fuselage. A sleet storm, deadliest of all the dangers in aviation, raged about the plane beyond Cape Race. The experienced Lindbergh knew only too well what this meant. Because a plane in flight is kept aloft by the curvature of its wings, flattening of these surfaces by such a weight as sleet would drop the plane like a bird. Now came Lindbergh's supreme test of skill and courage. Should he turn back, and make a safe landing at St. John's, where he could come down in shallow water near the shore?

But his mind was made up. He would not go back. He would fight on. Flying from beneath the fog bank to escape the sleet, he now tried to reach clear air above it before the weight of the ice should force him down. Lightened by the loss of its many gallons of gas spent, the plane angled sharply upward and up he continued with the sleet storm raging around him. The needle of the altimeter showed he was at a height of more than 5,000 feet above sea level. A mile higher, and still the fog. At 10,000 feet, with the gray wings one broad glare of ice, shafts of pale light came through the fog. He was triumphant at last after a climb of two miles.

Then came the night on the ocean—black night, even though there was the brightness of the myriads of stars. Lindbergh was sleepy, tired. He had slept but three hours before jumping off, and now the biggest battle, his terrible fight against sleep, began . . . a great danger.

Beneath him lay two miles of thick clouds, extending more than 1,000 miles. Luckily it was a short night, for he was flying directly toward the sun at a time of year when daylight lasted until nine in the evening, and dawn came about four in the morning.

His speed of a little more than 100 miles an hour had cut about 130 minutes from the hours of darkness, so that instead of more than six hours of night, he had less than four.

It was not all darkness, however. The moon shone just for a short spell, and the upper surface of the fogbank had a radiance that also became a beacon of hope. Once clear of the fog, he was able to follow that invisible line over the Great Circle, called *straight line flying*. He now had only 500 miles to go, and his goal was in sight. Spotting the green mountains of Ireland, he swooped low over an Irish fishing smack, and yelled "Is this the way to Ireland?" The roar of the motors carried the voice away, but the men in the boat waved frantically. He streaked over Dingle Bay, where he was sighted and reported by the steamer *Collier Nogi*, before he finally vanished over the cliffs of County Kerry on his way toward Cork. Suspense now was at an end as the Lone Eagle sped across Ireland, over England, across the Channel and into France, with beacons lighting him all the way.

As the grand sight of the searchlight of Le Bourget, the most powerful in the world, led him on, Lindbergh had arrived in France at last. The sharp steeple of the Eiffel Tower with its flaring apex, Paris with its boulevards, appeared like a cobweb of light. It was the memorable day of May 21, 1927, indelibly written in the annals of aviation. He descended upon the field with a "dead stick" skillfully, and with infinite care. *"Vive Lindbergh,"* went up from the 100,000 throats of the dense mass of humanity.

After an embrace by Louis Blériot, Lindbergh was borne along on the crest of the wave. An excited Parisian, brandishing a cane to clear a path, struck Lindbergh a whack on the head that raised a lump. His flying helmet, torn from its clasp, disappeared forever. Reckless souvenir hunters with sharp knives hacked away square pieces of the plane's canvas sides. Relating his story to the American Ambassador Herrick later, he said that "the most dangerous thing of all was that landing at Le Bourget, bringing that ship down on a field with all that crowd running. I had more fear at that moment for the welfare of "Our" plane than at any other time in the whole flight." He had taken exactly 33 hours, 39 minutes for the 3,610-mile-long flight. Lindbergh always spoke of *we*, the plane and himself.

"The field in New York was muddy, which made the take-off a little long," he continued, "but *we* got away all right. All the way up the American coast to Newfoundland we had uncommonly good weather, but for the next one thousand miles it could not have been worse for us. After we got away from land, we ran into fog, then into rain, then hail. Sometimes we flew not more than ten feet above the water, and at the highest over 10,000 feet. If we had known that the weather would be as bad over that part of the ocean as it turned out to be, we would not have started, but once we got into it, there wasn't any use in turning back. There wasn't anything else to do but to keep going. Then . . ."

"Pardon me," a voice from the outer ring of listeners called. "Did you do the whole flight by dead reckoning? I am a flier myself, my name is Cobham, and I flew over here from London a few minutes ago to see you to tell you that you have done the greatest thing I have ever heard of."

All heads turned. The voice was that of Sir Alan Cobham, the greatest of British long-distance aviators, the pioneer of the routes to South Africa, India and Australia.

"I had to," Lindbergh replied. "There were no hands for a sextant. I used an earth-induction compass, called a pioneer earth inductor and it brought me to the coast of Ireland within three miles of the great circle indicator."

While Lindbergh was taken to the Ambassador's home, where he soon dropped into a heavy and much needed sleep, the rest of the world saluted Charles A. Lindbergh, whose youth, tremendous courage and achievement fascinated uncounted millions. Decorated by the President of France, he returned home in an American cruiser to meet President Coolidge who pinned a decoration on him for his calculating daring and great perseverance. Recipient of a host of other expressions of recognition, the modest young hero also became a member of the Caterpillar Club. This needs some explanation. Before his flight to Paris, Lindbergh actually was the only living aviator who had saved his life by leaping four times from an airplane to earth by means of a parachute. Thus he became the only fourth degree member of the Caterpillars, an organization in which only those who have thus saved their lives are eligible for membership.

From then on the famous flier made a number of experimental flights over the Arctic and surveyed routes in Central and South America for one of the American airlines. He and his famous wife made a 29,000-mile flight in 1933, visiting 23 nations, with his wife doing much of the piloting while he studied maps and kept busy charting airline routes for the future.

And now, as an epilogue to Lindbergh's flight, let's find out what happened to the other airmen who had been patiently waiting to get across until the Lone Eagle beat them to it.

Chamberlin, and his millionaire passenger Levine, managed to get away in their Bellanca on June 4, flying across to England. But they did not reach Berlin as they had intended, because of a shortage of fuel. Landing 118 miles short of their goal, they had covered the 3,911 miles in 42 hours.

Byrd, Balchen and Acosta took their triple-engined craft on the third flight from the same airfield on June 29. Carefully planned, as befitted the excellent standards of Admiral Byrd, the adventure suffered bad luck from the very start. A heavy fog made them fly blind out of Nova Scotia for almost 19 hours. Once over France they kept searching for a decent landing field, but heavy fog rendered them completely helpless until they risked a landing down in the sea by a beach.

Commemorating the thirty-fourth anniversary of Charles A. Lindbergh's historic Atlantic crossing of May 20, 1927, a needle-nosed, delta-winged United States B-58 jet bomber, piloted by Major William R. Payne, Captain William L. Polhemus, navigator, and Captain Raymond R. Wagener, defense systems operators, made the same flight over the same route, on May 27, 1961, in the record-breaking time of three hours, nineteen minutes, forty-one seconds— or about 1,300 miles an hour, twice the speed of sound, at an altitude above 60,000 feet.

— 16 —

AROUND THE WORLD IN EIGHT DAYS—
THE *WINNIE MAE*

Another success story, and the most daring air adventure around Mother Earth, occurred during the summer of 1931, when American daredevil Wiley Post, ably assisted by Australian-born airman Harold Gatty, streaked around the globe in a plane called the *Winnie Mae*, in eight and a half days. This was the greatest demonstration of pilot endurance and stamina up to that time.

Wiley Post's exploit happened at a time when the public not only had grown stunt weary, but was satiated with barnstorming circuses and air thrills. What the world needed now was something totally different, something original that would stimulate airline passenger travel. This stimulus had already begun in 1927, resulting in nations being crisscrossed by an elaborate airline network. There still remained, however, the bugaboo of flying hazards, so that what the public now needed was more proof of the reliability of the airplane under most conditions.

A cursory examination of the map revealed that a great deal had already been accomplished. The two coasts of the United States had been brought within 12½ hours of each other. Frank Hawks, the famed pilot, had been able to shrink intercity distances almost to the vanishing point. But there still remained the vast ocean stretches.

Flying oceans still seemed hazardous. But the promoters of dirigibles and lighter-than-air machines had challenged the supremacy of the airplane at the 1930 air races in Chicago, and by circumnavigating the globe, the Graf Zeppelin had reduced the time taken by Magellan, the first around-the-world explorer, by more than three years. So what Wiley Post wanted to prove was that a good airplane with average equipment and careful flying could outdo the Zeppelin any time on a flight around the world.

Post was backed by Texas oil man F. C. Hall, whom he had served as a personal pilot. The plane picked for this undertaking consisted of a Standard Lockheed Vega model, high-wing monoplane, the fastest load carrier, with a Pratt & Whitney motor in the nose. Post had just won a purse of $7500 at the National Air Race contest, which came in very handy at a time when the general business depression had put a crimp in the oil drilling business.

Post was born on a farm near Grand Saline, Texas, November 22, 1899 when the main topic of conversation was the discovery of oil in Indian territory, and many farmers picking up stakes, migrated to the reservation. Cities sprang up like mushrooms near the Texas-Oklahoma line, and the Posts moved to Abilene, Texas, too.

Like many boys of his age—Wiley was 13 then—he began earning some money, and saved some, too, to buy himself a bike. Later, knocking around oil wells and garages, he became so adept as an airplane mechanic, that he soon earned the reputation of being

The Fokker F XVIII, used by KLM on the Amsterdam-Batavia (now Jakarta) run, which was once the longest in the world.

Dabry, Mermoz, and Gimie, who made the first commercial flight across the South Atlantic non-stop from France to Brazil, on May 12, 1930, in their *Arc en Ciel.*—AIR FRANCE

Passengers on the first westbound flight of TWA's transcontinental
air passenger service, started in July, 1929. The plane was piloted
into Los Angeles by Charles A. Lindbergh, third from right. Others,
from left to right were Chauncey T. Lamb; D. M. Sheaffer, chief
of Passenger Transportation, Pennsylvania Railroad; Amelia Earhart, who was assistant to the general manager of the airline;
Mrs. G. P. Putnam; Albert A. Garthwaite; Betty Brainerd, a newspaper woman covering the event; Mrs. Anne Morrow Lindbergh;
Colonel Lindbergh; and two crew members.—TWA

Wiley Post after his round-the-world flight in the Winnie Mae in
1926. Cities where the plane touched down
are listed on its side.—TWA

Will Rogers before his last flight with Wiley Post.—TWA

the best in the business. When Oklahoma needed first class trained mechanics, Wiley first got a job as a "roughneck" (general handy man) on an oil drilling rig, then as a tool dresser, until he was promoted to full-fledged oil driller. When a great wave of stunt flying took the country by storm the first year after the war, and parachute jumps fetched one hundred dollars a jump, Wiley decided to get in on this profitable business. He purchased his own plane and built up a nice country business throughout the rough stretches of Southeast Oklahoma, Southern Kansas and Northeast Texas. One of his passengers was a lady named Mae Lane, who later became his wife.

Selling his Canuck plane when business started to fall off, Post went to work for the well-heeled Mr. Hall, who played a vital part in Post's later life and helped to buy him a three-passenger Travelair, the best plane up to that time. Post turned in the Travelair in 1928, and with the help of Mr. Hall purchased a Lockheed B. Vega, a most up-to-date vehicle, christened by him *Winnie Mae.*

The iron-nerved Post, who understood airplanes from A to Z, then picked the 180-pound Australian ex-navy man Harold Gatty as his flying mate. This one also knew all there was to be known about the airplane business. The two then made up their minds to go after the 2,000 pound stake, come what may, for a flight around the world in less than ten days.

Long periods of waiting caused by bad weather wore them thin with impatience and depleted their resources, but they finally took to the air on their 130-mile-an-hour flight, on June 23, 1931. According to their schedule the route would take them by way of England, Germany, Russia, Siberia, Bering Strait, Alaska and Canada.

The first stage of their flight from Harbor Grace was fast and uneventful, but mighty tiring, so that when they set down at Berlin, they were so fatigued that Post dropped fast asleep in the bathtub. Meanwhile they learned that they had broken the Atlantic crossing record, which had been held by the famed Alcock-Brown team for 12 years. After a short day's run of 944 miles to Moscow, the reception accorded them there was nothing to brag about. Taken in tow by the members of the *Ossoaviakhim* (Society for Aviation and Chemical Defense), and the *Voks* (Society for Cultural Relations with Foreign Countries), they refueled and left for Kazan, a 320-mile run from Moscow. Crossing the rest of Russia into desolate Siberia by way of Novosibirsk and Irkutsk, they were unfortunately obliged to make a landing at Blagoveschensk, where their machine became heavily bogged down in the Siberian mire. It took the combined efforts of three horses, a tractor and Russian soldiery to pull the machine out of the mud for their take-off.

The balance of their trip took them via Khabarovsk, Solomon, Fairbanks, and Edmonton, back to New York. Here Walter D. Ward, timer of the National Aeronautic Association, who had also checked them out at Roosevelt Field, computed and established their official time as eight days, 15 hours and 51 minutes, for their record flight around the world.

When the one-eyed Wiley lost his meal ticket with oilman Hall, but was permitted to keep using the *Winnie Mae,* he flew solo this time over the same route, and lowered his time to seven days, eighteen hours, fourteen minutes, on July 15, 1933. He apparently did this to prove his theories about altitude flying. He was furthermore aided by a 40-pound robot pilot, a control which flew the plane once it was airborne, without human hand steering. This weight advantage, the experts contended, reduced about 135 pounds from the *Winnie Mae's* load, and also permitted Post to take much needed snoozes once in a while.

The record established by Wiley Post in 1933 was later smashed by a daredevil flyer, the fabled mystery man and financier Howard Hughes, when he streaked around the world in three days, ten hours and fourteen minutes in a four-engined Lockheed monoplane, in 1938.

— 17 —

WILL ROGERS AND WILEY POST

From the very first day that he rode in a plane, Will Rogers became flying's most ardent booster. He was also the best pal the pilots ever had, and Will Rogers would never take train or car, if a plane would get him there just as well.

When the great drought hit the southwest, it was Will Rogers again who volunteered to help. He decided on a tour that would mean spending at least a week in each of the stricken areas. When he flew to Washington to consult President Hoover and Red Cross

Officials, the United States Navy loaned him a Blue Curtiss Hell Diver piloted by the famed Captain Frank Hawks.

Years later, when Rogers' chum Wiley Post planned to survey an air route between this country and Russia and asked him to come along, it did not take Will long to accept, as he wanted to visit Alaska on the way.

Getting started on July 31, 1935, in a red, silver-striped, Orion Sirius Lockheed, Post first headed for Seattle, where he was joined by Rogers. A stop-over was first made at Juneau, Alaska, and then, after a delay because of foul weather, they headed, via the Taku River, Atlin and White Horse for Dawson, where a large crowd gave them a wild reception. Of course, Rogers did not fail to soak up on yarns of the "Sourdoughs," and to visit the cabin of Robert W. Service, the famous author who, to Will's regret, was living in France at the time. After their plane had been carefully serviced at Fairbanks, their next port of call was Point Barrow, the northern-most tip on Alaska's coast. This stop-over was of particular interest to Rogers, as he was anxious to visit with the 73-year-old operator of a trading post and whaling station, Charles Brower, who had resided there more than 51 years and was known in the States and Alaska as the "King of the Arctic."

About the time that they were ready to take off a dense fog rolled in, so that the careful Wiley Post decided to postpone their departure until the fog bank had cleared and the weather reports were better. Once shafts of pale light had penetrated the fog they roared northward, in spite of oncoming darker clouds.

It was hardly seven hours later when Sergeant Stanley R. Morgan, United States Signal Corps operator stationed at Point Barrow, was distracted by excited voices coming from the beach and rushed out to investigate. He found an excited mob crowding around an Eskimo who, in broken English, kept saying, "red plane, she blew up." Questioning the fellow, Morgan soon learned that the Eskimo had witnessed an airplane crash near his sealing camp, 15 miles south of Point Barrow. The plane, he said, had been fly-ing low, and had made a landing in a small river, whereupon two men had climbed out, "one wearing a rag on a sore eye, the other big man with boots."

As that description fitted Wiley Post and Will Rogers, Morgan hastily got a crew of 14 Eskimos together, notified the Bureau of Indian Affairs, and then, guided by the Eskimo, left Point Barrow in an open whaleboat powered by a small motor and arrived at the scene of the crash six hours later. Meanwhile, natives had been able to cut into the cabin and take out the body of Will Rogers, who apparently had been in the rear of the plane when she struck, whereas the body of Post was pinned tight so that the rescuers had a hard time extricating his body from beneath the heavy motor.

Placing the bodies in a tight skin boat and eiderdown sleeping bags, the party took them to Point Barrow, where Dr. Henry W. Greist, a Presbyterian missionary, washed the bodies, sewed the cuts and laid them out. Then Morgan broadcasted the tragic story to a stunned world.

While it was never possible to pinpoint the cause of the crash, what probably may have happened according to the stories told by Eskimos was that Post, sighting the sailcloth tents in which the Eskimos lived during the summer, may have stopped his plane to ask the natives the way to Point Barrow. Then, after receiving their directions, he and Rogers set off again. After they had taxied the plane to the far side of the river, the Eskimos heard a terrific roar. What they probably heard was the spluttering and coughing of the motor as the plane tried to break through the fog.

It is also possible that the motor stalled during the take-off, and there might not have been sufficient room in which to right the plane. This may have caused the plane to drop into the water, smashing her right wing, and toppling her over on her back.

Thus the lives of two great Americans were snuffed out, adding another two names to the honor annals of the history of aviation.

— 18 —

THE CHALLENGE OF THE PACIFIC

A flight across the Pacific offered an even greater challenge to daring airmen than one across the Atlantic. Distances in the Pacific were greater, and the navigational problems in making landings, especially on the Hawaiian Islands, were extremely hazardous.

The first man to try the trip in a flying boat was U.S. Navy Commander John Rogers, on August 31, 1925, but he failed 150 miles out of Honolulu, and though he was rescued by the submarine R-4, he was killed in a crash later. Two years later, Lt.

Lester Maitland and Albert F. Hagenberger tried it, with better luck. Taking off from Oakland's Crissy Field in a Fokker monoplane, on June 28, 1927, and landing in Honolulu, 25 hours and 50 minutes later, they established a record for the longest over water flight bringing new laurels to the USA and the Army. Bearing their substantial victory with grace and great modesty, and congratulated by President Coolidge's cable, they even refused a $10,000 stake offered by an American newspaper. They claimed to have done this stint neither for glory nor financial gain but in the ordinary course of army routine.

They could have competed otherwise in the flight from the United States to the Hawaiian Islands, for which the pineapple tycoon, James D. Dole, had posted $25,000, in which 15 planes were entered, eight of which started and two of which got lost at sea. The winners: A. C. Goebel and William F. Davis, in a single-engined Bellanca, made the hop in 26 hours, 17 minutes, an adventure which, apart from costing many lives, proved aviation-wise little else.

Modern man's desire to see how fast he could go had also captivated the interest of two other Americans, Hugh Herndon, Jr. and Clyde E. Pangborn. They made an attempt to better the record of Post and Gatty but were forced down in the wilds of Siberia where they abandoned the project. In the hope of getting a steamer back to the States, they decided to fly to Tokyo, where they were held for some weeks by Japanese authorities because it was claimed they had taken some photographs of fortifications. Meanwhile, a Japanese newspaper syndicate had posted a $25,000 prize for the first airman to accomplish a non-stop Tokyo to New York flight. This was just up their alley, so Herndon and Pangborn decided to fly to New York immediately after their release rather than go by ship. But just as they were readying their plane for the hop, the Japanese government put a stop on further flights from Japan.

Disregarding this edict, they took to the air on October 4 and disappeared as fast as they could into the blue yonder, making sure that they stayed clear of the Kurile Islands and volcanic mountain ranges. Except for the drone of a motor heard by radio men at the Unimak-Aleutian island group who were unable to identify the plane in the heavy fog, little else was heard from them until they set their plane down in Wenatchee, Washington, on October 5, 1931, having covered the 4,500 miles in 41 hours, 13 minutes, and winning thereby the $25,000 prize.

— 19 —

EDDIE MUSICK AND THE CHINA CLIPPERS

No story of the fantastic Air Clippers would be complete without reciting some of the facts in the life of one of its most famous pilots: Eddie Musick.

A headliner from the very day that he began taking an interest in aviation, Eddie Musick busied himself from his early boyhood with carburetors and ignition systems, while daydreaming about airplanes. However, it took the 1910 Los Angeles Air Show, where such pioneers as Paulhan, Curtiss, Moisant, Walter Brookings and others thrilled the mob with their crazy antics, to egg young Musick on to make his own bamboo and baling wire crate.

After this contraption had cracked up, he was told that a fellow named Glenn Martin had opened a small airplane factory in Los Angeles. He applied for a job there and got it. As time passed Musick, like so many other flying bugs before him, became a stunt flier and such a showman to boot that it did not take long for him to become known as "Daredevil Musick."

Sent to an officers' training camp during World War I, and attached to the staff as a civilian instructor, he learned from a friend, who was stationed at Rockaway Beach, that the Marine Corps needed pilots for overseas duty. Mustered out of the Marine Corps in 1919, he began to devote himself to the development of aeronautics in real earnest. This led to his meeting famed Anthony Fokker, and the ambitious Juan Trippe, who had organized a company known as American Airways. Musick agreed to fly for the Company, and he subsequently made the 90-mile flight from Key West to Havana, Cuba, in one hour and 20 minutes, in a wood-and-fabric, three-engined Fokker. Trippe had seen in the Fokker a future for air travel far beyond the hop-skip-and-jump flights of the days of the kites. He had visions of whisking passengers across the seas to South American cities and all around the globe. The Caribbean was to be the testing ground for this early achievement. Meanwhile Musick, agreeing to go the whole route with the company, moved to Key West with his wife Cleo, whom he had married in 1924.

Later, when it was planned to throw an airline across the Pacific to China, it became Musick's turn again to break the trail, connecting Honolulu, Midway Islands, Wake and Guam, with Manila, thence crossing the China Sea to Hongkong, and skirting the China Coast to Shanghai.

Following a flight test of a new luxury-high-altitude-4-motored-Sikorsky, carrying an automatic pilot—the first installed on a transport vehicle—and with Charles A. Lindbergh as co-pilot, a trial trip was made to Buenos Aires in June, 1934, during which the giant Clipper clocked a speed of 192 miles an hour. A year later on April 16, 1935, Eddie Musick took the giant ship Honolulu-bound with Tom Noonan, who was to make history later with Amelia Earhart as pilot.

Musick was a national hero by now, so that newspapers even expressed the view that the mantle of Charles Lindbergh had fallen on his shoulders. After receiving the Harmon Trophy for his pioneering activities, he was named the world's outstanding aviator for 1935. Two others, Lindbergh and Wiley Post, had been so honored.

Then came the China Clipper's first scheduled passenger flight via Manila, Wake Island and Guam on October 21, 1936, with Musick, of course, in command. This was followed by the hook-up with New Zealand. The first leg was begun on St. Patrick's Day, 1937, and Musick set his Clipper down at Samoa, and then 1800 miles southwest at Auckland, New Zealand, where the arrival of the first air transport Clipper from the States had the populace in a tizzy of excitement and became an event of national importance. On a later flight Musick took the China Clipper to Manila, giving the Sikorsky a first look at China—taking Macao and Hongkong in its stride.

On January 9, 1938, came Eddie Musick's third trip to New Zealand in the Samoan Clipper. His second progress report: "Oil Leak in number four engine. Am returning to Pago Pago. Musick" almost threw the radio operator receiving it for a loop. The radio operator telephoned the station manager, who immediately ran up the hill.

Musick then reported from Apia Harbor, located 70 miles from Pago Pago, at 7:59, that he had to shut down his radio and had to dump some more gas because he wanted to lighten the ship before making a landing in the harbor. Then an ominous silence followed, as all waited anxiously for Musick's signal, which, however, never came. Hours passed, and fears increased that Musick must have suffered a major disaster, as nothing else could have put the radio out of commission.

A search party was organized, and along the north coast, 12 miles from Pago Pago they questioned a native woman who had been fishing off the reefs nearby, and who had claimed that she had witnessed the Clipper's destruction. The Clipper had passed directly over her canoe, she said, and she had followed it with her eyes as it went out to sea, spouting liquid from the wings. Then, a flash of fire and a loud report, and the Clipper trailing black smoke had plunged into the sea.

The following morning a naval vessel was despatched from Pago Pago to make a thorough search of the region concentrating especially on the spot pinpointed by the native woman. Finally they came upon a large oil slick, and boats were lowered to scan the surface thoroughly. Bits of wreckage were picked up, an arm rest from the pilot's seat, several of the navigation books, and papers. Even pieces of plywood flooring. The sad news was radioed back to Alameda.

The City and County of Los Angeles held memorial services on January 24, 1938, in the rotunda of the City Hall for the officers of the Samoa Clipper. Mayor Rossi paid tribute to the great courage of Captain Eddie Musick and his crew, who, far out in the South Pacific, slept under many fathoms of water. And then a lone bugle sounded taps. Thus Captain Eddie Musick, the Clipper pioneer, came to the end of his illustrious career, a career that few aviation trail blazers could have matched.

— 20 —

AMELIA EARHART, HEROINE OF THE SKY

It is now over 25 years ago that the blonde, tousle-haired Amelia Earhart, international flying celebrity at the peak of her colorful and illustrious career, flew to her doom on a 2,556-mile flight from Lae, New Guinea, to Howland Island, a tiny speck in the Pacific. What happened to this great woman on that ill-fated last trip remains as much a mystery today as it was then.

She was not quite forty when she vanished. Born at Atchinson, Kansas, on July 24, 1897, of sound and sturdy American stock, Amelia showed a definite flair for being a natural leader and trail blazer and had few interests that could be termed womanlike. The appelation "tomboy" might have suited her better.

Her father was a railroad attorney and due to his particular calling was given to do considerable traveling. Hardly ten years old, Amelia became greatly fascinated by what she saw at the Iowa State Fair in Des Moines. The sight of an airplane attracted her the most.

Employed as a nurse's aid in Toronto's Military Hospital during the last year of the first World War. Amelia used to visit the nearby flying field during her spare hours to watch the taking off of planes, and the training of officers. Planes simply intrigued her. Men did not. After entering Columbia University to work toward a medical degree, she finally returned to Los Angeles, where she ran into a young aviator named Frank Hawks—a name meaning little then, but to become famous later.

She told Hawks she wanted to go for a ride, and, liking her first flight immensely, she signed up for flying lessons. To pay for them she took a job in the Telephone Company's office. That did not prevent her from spending most of her spare time at the airfield, where her instructor was Neta Snook, the first woman to graduate from the Curtiss School of Aviation. When Amelia obtained her pilot's license in 1923, she bought a second-hand plane with the help of her mother, and enrolled for a photography course at the University of California. Being a rather restless soul she headed east again and enrolled at Harvard for a course in physics and affiliated subjects, while applying for a position as a social worker at the same time at Denison House in one of the poorer sections of Boston. Devoting herself to settlement work with great vigor from 1926 to 1928, Amelia at no time lost her interest in aviation, evidenced by the fact that she joined a chapter of the National Aeronautic Association and became its vice-president.

One day, while attending class, she was called on the phone by a Captain Railey, who asked her whether she would be interested in doing something constructive for aviation and invited her to come to his office that evening. Calling at his office later that day, she asked him what he had in mind, and he asked her point blank, "How would you like to fly the Atlantic?"

"Alone?" she asked.

"No, you will have an expert pilot." Asked why he had picked her of all people to do such a job, he replied "I am merely acting for some one else." That someone else proved to be Mrs. Frederick Guest of London, a former resident of Pittsburgh who had bought a tri-motored Fokker from Admiral Byrd. Mrs. Guest first had planned to fly the Atlantic herself, but when her family objected, she decided to find another woman who could be just as enthusiastic as she about aviation, a woman who was a good aviatrix and represented the finest example of womanhood. A later conference was attended not only by Mrs. Guest, but also by Admiral Byrd and George Palmer Putnam, world traveler and publisher. Amelia passed muster, of course. She was told that there would be a mechanic, Lou Gordon, and a pilot, Bill Stultz, on the trip with her. When she suggested that she would like to do some piloting herself there was no objection.

She was invited subsequently to inspect the plane, which was equipped with pontoons (in case there had to be a landing on water), with powerful Wright Whirlwind motors, and with an orange-colored fuselage that could be easily spotted if there was a forced landing.

With the whole plan still shrouded in secrecy, and after the terms had been arranged, the orange-colored Fokker—since christened *Friendship*—took off for Newfoundland on June 5, 1928. The refuelling took place at Trepassy, a small fishing hamlet. Thus started Amelia's earliest aerial adventure, which gave her the first nerve-wracking moments of her young life.

There were heavy fogs and rainstorms, during which the flying was done by instruments, the sort of blind flying with which she was not familiar. After blind flying practically the rest of the way, they finally set down in a channel, skimming low over fields, hedges and houses, at a place that turned out to be Burry Fort, in Wales.

Having covered the 2,246-mile stretch at an average speed of 113 miles per hour, Amelia Earhart became the first woman to have flown the Atlantic. The proud citizens of Burry Fort were so delighted with the feat of Amelia and her flying companions that they erected an 18-foot monument bearing the inscription: "Erected in commemoration of Miss Amelia Earhart of Boston, U.S.A., the first woman to fly over the Atlantic Ocean. Also of her companions, Wilmer Stultz and Louis Gordon. Flew from Trepassy, NFL, to Burry

Fort, in 20 hours and 40 minutes, in the seaplane *Friendship,* on June 18, 1928."

When the *Roosevelt* steamed into New York harbor bearing Amelia on her return to the States, a tremendous crowd was waiting to honor her. Among the hundreds of faces she soon spotted George Palmer Putnam, who introduced her to the Mayor of New York, who said, "You are a celebrity now. You will ride in a colorful Broadway procession. You are the most famous lady in the whole world."

Then there was to be, of course, a book of her exploits, titled *Twenty Hours Forty Minutes,* which became a success and as confessed by her later: "Writing the book was really much harder work than the flight itself." While in England, Amelia had bought Lady Mary Heath's neat little sports plane, which had come back with her on the ship, and once the book was out of the way she climbed into the cockpit and headed for the Pacific Coast. Amelia's activities ranged far and wide, from taking a couple of diving lessons with the famed oceanographer William Beebe, to joining the staff of Cosmopolitan Magazine as its aviation editor. During this time she was awarded the Air Transport license, held only by three other women fliers—Lady Mary Heath, Ruth Nichols and Phoebe Omlie. Next she took part, with a dilapidated Lockheed Vega, in what since has become known as the Powder Puff Derby (a name coined by comedian Will Rogers) from Santa Monica to Cleveland, on August 18, 1929. When Wiley Post saw the plane she had used, and called it "a pile of junk," the Lockheed people most graciously traded her a new Vega for it.

Joining the staff of the Transcontinental Air Transport Company—one of the first commercial air passenger lines—her duties consisted mainly of selling the idea of flying to American women. In 1931 she had married George Palmer Putnam, who in 1932 published her book *The Fun of It* (random jottings of her own experiences and those of other flying women).

When the first autogiro appeared on the flying scene, Amelia Earhart not only became the first woman to fly solo in an autogiro, but, endowed as she was with a crackerjack business head, was sponsored by and advertised the products of the Beechnut Packing Company.

When she had clocked over 1,000 hours in the air—quite a sizeable number for any aviator or aviatrix—she confided to her husband that she had decided to fly the Atlantic again, but solo this time. And she did, beating the then existing transatlantic record by covering the 2,026.5 miles in 14 hours and 56 minutes.

The honors by now came fast and furious. A motion picture company sent a plane to pick her up. The American ambassador met her at the airport in London, and invited her to stay at the Embassy. Her husband came across on the *Olympic* to meet her. Among the many honors she received, the one she cherished most was the honorary membership in the British Guild of Air Pilots and Navigators. She spoke before the French Senate and was awarded the French Cross of Knight of the Legion of Honor. She was received by Mussolini and by the King and Queen of the Belgians, who awarded her the flying medal of the Cross of the Order of Leopold. Once back in the States, she addressed the National Geographic Society, which presented her with a special Gold Medal at Constitution Hall in Washington. Finally, President and Mrs. Hoover invited her to a very "sedate" dinner at the White House.

A symbol of the new youth, and chosen by many young girls as their ideal, Amelia, like Charles Lindbergh, exerted a decided influence on her own young generation, who patterned their lives after hers by clean thinking, clean living, and doing worthwhile things.

In 1934 she was asked by Dr. Edward C. Elliott, president of Purdue University, to join its staff (Purdue then had an enrollment of 6000 pupils, 1000 of whom were girls.) Becoming a visiting faculty member, Amelia gave the girls some idea of her own philosophy of life and advised them about careers and aeronautics.

This made such an impression on the University's trustees and directors that they set up the Amelia Earhart Fund for Aeronautic Research. And in order for her to carry out this research properly they made sufficient funds available for her to purchase a twin-motored, ten-passenger, all metal monoplane Lockheed electric transport. It was fully equipped, including a Sperry-Gyro pilot, an automatic flying device. It was the last word in airplane construction, and she often referred to it as her Flying Laboratory.

The time then drew near for the one thing she had always dreamed about—a round-the-world flight for which she had been preparing for a long time. Her plan was to fly from east to west, from Oakland to Honolulu, thence to New Guinea, Darwin, Australia—about 27,000 miles—and then to return via the South Pacific to Brazil.

Meanwhile in 1935, she flew the Pacific alone in her Lockheed Vega. Her flying time from Honolulu to Oakland was 18 hours, 16 minutes. She did this, she said, "for the fun of it," also to prove that a woman could fly over difficult routes as well as a man. She astonished the world when she landed, tired and bedraggled but still retaining her great enthusiasm for flying. She was already recognized by then as the world's greatest woman flier, a position she retained until she vanished on her last flight across the Pacific.

On March 17, 1937, she was ready for the big hop. The Lockheed, christened *Electra*, started from Oakland, Honolulu-bound. The carefully-picked crew consisted of aerial navigator Fred Noonan, who had agreed to go along as far as Howland Island, expert flier Paul Hantz, who would ride to Honolulu, and finally the experienced navigator Paul Manning, who would leave her in Australia so that Amelia would fly solo the rest of the voyage.

They suffered an accident after take-off from Honolulu, and it became necessary to return the plane to Burbank for repairs. After a closer study of the flight plan, they decided to commence the big hop from the east, rather than from the west, so the Burbank-Miami trip could serve as a test flight. Manning then returned to his command, and Fred Noonan replaced him as the plane's navigator.

The *Electra* was to take off two months later from Miami, where arrangements had been made in the meantime for the Coast Guard Cutter *Itasca* to leave San Diego and cruise off Howland Island to guide the *Electra* on its further route.

It appeared that the *Electra* had one drawback, however. The plane was equipped with a high frequency radio to operate a telephonic and direction-finding apparatus, but the device had a very weak carrying power over long distances, which would make the taking of bearings from ships extremely difficult. If the *Electra* had had the proper radio equipment, it may be that the flight might have turned out differently.

The ill-fated flight began in an early morning haze on June 1, 1937, from Miami. It followed a route that took Amelia over Puerto Rico, Venezuela and Brazil, where the plane hopped across the South Atlantic to Senegal, West Africa. Then via the Sudan, Eritrea to Karachi, India, where she received a long distance call from her husband in New York, 8,274 miles away. She then skimmed over terrifying mountain ranges, past long stretches of desert lands—the monsoon had already set in, so that airfields were flooded—over endless rice fields and, to avoid the even steeper mountains, she took the plane up to a height of 8,000 feet. Then followed a stretch of blind flying through torrential downpours, until they reached Calcutta and subsequently Bangkok, where the monsoon again delayed them. Thence Amelia continued the arduous trek, through Malaya, across the Gulf of Siam, and Singapore, until she reached Bandoeng, in the beautiful Preanger Highlands of Java, on June 21, 1937, where engine trouble developed. And, as she wrote in her logbook, she greatly enjoyed her stopovers in what was then still the Netherlands East Indies. The Dutch colonial people not only were most efficient and extremely hospitable, but the plane was serviced with the proverbial know-how by expert Dutch mechanics. Amelia had made arrangements with her husband before her departure that she would jot down everything that transpired on her trip, and then send the notes back on each landing. These notes were to be included in her next book, called *World Flight*. It was at Soerabaya, Java, that she again talked to her husband, for the last time. Setting down on the Dutch-Portuguese island of Timor on the 27th, they continued the following day to Port Darwin, landing at Lae, New Guinea, on the 30th and taking off again on July 1 for Howland Island. By this time she had already covered 22,000 miles, with only 7,000 miles to go. It was from Lae—exactly 2,556 miles from Howland Island— that Amelia sent off her last batch of notes to her husband.

She acquainted him in those notes with the fact that they were now making straight for Howland Island, a mere pinpoint in the middle Pacific. An item appeared in the New York *Herald Tribune,* dated July 2, that, "Amelia Earhart departed for Howland Island at 10 today, beginning the 2,557-mile flight across the Pacific by a route never traveled by an airplane before."

Then the real trouble must have begun. The *Itasca* had also sent a despatch on July 2, via the Associated Press, that "United States sailors and coast guardsmen set watch tonight along one of the loneliest stretches of the earth's surface to guide Earhart on the longest, most hazardous flight of her career. The *Itasca* and the cutter *Ontario* awaited word of her take-off from Lae for Howland Island, an almost microscopic bit of land representing America's frontier in the South Pacific."

Twice before the take-off of the Electra from New Guinea, Commander W. K. Thompson of the *Itasca* had sent warning messages to Washington reporting unsatisfactory radio contact with the plane.

At 4:53 A.M. an unintelligible message was received from Amelia, and at 6:14 she radioed, "Please give me bearings on 3,105 kilocycles. I am about 200 miles out. I will whistle into mike." The whistle and message were heard by three radio operators. The radio operators sent out desperate messages begging her to come in on the 500 fequency, as they could not understand why she continued to use the 3,105.

At 6:20 Amelia asked once more, "Please take bearing on us and report in half an hour. I will whistle into mike, about 100 miles out." The signal then was clear, but too brief for the *Itasca* to take bearings on the plane.

Then a message: "MHAQQ (Amelia's call signal) calling *Itasca*. We received your signals but failed to get minimum indication of direction. Please take bearings on us and answer in 3,105 with voice."

At 8:00 A.M. the signals indicated that the plane flew close to the reef then away again. Time and again the Coast Guard cutter tried to get a response from Amelia. Finally her voice came through: "KHAQQ calling *Itasca*. We must be on you but cannot see you. Gas is running low. Have been unable to reach you by radio. Flying at 1,000 feet." The crew anxiously scanned the sky, but no plane was in sight.

At 8:04 Amelia's voice, still calm, came over the air. "KHAQQ calling. We are circling but cannot land. Go ahead with signals."

At 8:44 Amelia's voice was heard again, this time a cryptic message undeniably frightened, "We are on the line position 157-337. We are now running north and south." The last words sounded broken and her voice seemed choked. This was the last contact with the courageous woman. Although the following words came calmly, they rang a hollow note from out of the sky to the ears of the world. "Gas is running low; we are circling, but cannot see island." Then an ominous silence . . .

The *Itasca* signalled frenziedly, but the wide ocean gave back no answer.

As soon as word was received that the Earhart plane was lost, one of the greatest searches in aviation and maritime history was begun. Secretary of the Navy Swanson ordered a diligent search. A number of ships combed the water for weeks in the broiling sun. Carrier-based planes skimmed over 100,000 square miles of ocean. All of the islands where the fliers might have landed were searched.

No trace of the intrepid Amelia and Lt. Commander Fred Noonan was ever found.

— 21 —

AIRCRAFT DEVELOPMENT—WORLD WAR II

The Golden Age of Aviation may well have occurred between 1927 and 1940. This was the era in which Lindbergh spanned the Atlantic, Amundsen and Ellsworth explored the Poles, General Jimmy Doolittle established world speed records, and in which such famed aviation pioneers as Spaatz, Eaker, Quesada did their plane-to-plane refueling stunts. It was also the period in which Igor Sikorsky built his Copters and Clippers, and Jacqueline Cochran was awarded the General Billy Mitchell award as the American aviatrix to have made the greatest contribution to aviation.

The public's interest in aviation during that era had been steadily growing. Planes, too, had undergone one improvement after another. The antiquated grasshoppers, crates and Jennys, with their bamboo, bailing wire, metal tubing, welded fuselage frames and open cockpits had made way for the more advanced types of high- and low-wing planes. Then, when the powerful Wright J-5 Whirlwind, 220 HP, aircooled engine appeared on the scene, the aeronautical picture changed completely.

Cockpit instruments also underwent vital changes. Elmer Sperry adapted the gyroscope into an ideal flight instrument to guide the airman through darkness, sleet, snow or rain. The Sperry, Kollsman and Pioneer instrument companies introduced such novel devices as the artificial horizon, the gyro direction indicator, and earth indicator compass, which operated without the influence of customary vibrations and effects of the earth. These instruments played an important role, for instance, in Lindbergh's Atlantic hop. It was Sperry who invented the automatic pilot in 1932, and created the variable pitch propeller-gear shift, Kollsman produced the finest and most accurate altimeter ever constructed. It not only let the airman know within a few feet the plane's position off the ground, but also when the wheels would touch the landing strip.

Actually becoming the proving ground for what is known as aerodynamics, the air races also did their bit in advancing airplane travel. It was at these races that the frames, engines and endurance of the planes were tested. Other contests determined whether heavier- or lighter-than-air vehicles would rise to greater altitudes. For a time the airplane was ahead, when Major Schroeder, of the U.S. Army, held the record. Then the coveted honor went to France, until the German Willi Neuenhofer established an altitude record of 41,794 feet. This record did not stay overseas long, as Lt. Soucek, of the U. S. Navy, brought the prize back to the United States in 1930, attaining an altitude of 43,166 feet.

Then the old standby, the balloon, had to get into the act, when the famous Jean Felix Piccard gunned for stratosphere supremacy, first with a record climb of 52,000 feet, and subsequently establishing a height record of 59,000 feet, or more than 10 miles up, in 1932. Three years later, Captains Albert W. Stevens and Orvil A. Anderson, both United States Army Officers, rose 72,395 feet or nearly 14 miles in a balloon of the National Geographic Society, establishing a new world record.

In speed competition, Jimmy Doolittle established a world speed record of 294 miles an hour in 1929, on a Gee Bee Racer at the National Air Races in Cleveland. Not to be outdone, Britain's Super-marine S-6B racing seaplane hit a speed record of about 407 miles an hour at the Schneider Cup Trophy Races, in 1931.

During this period of plane innovations, lighter-than-air and large transport planes also underwent great improvements. The Dornier DO-X, a giant plane with 12 engines, on a trial cruise to the United States in 1931, was able to lift 169 passengers. Toward the end of this era of plane construction, prior to the beginning of World War II, came the pressurized cabins. This led to the first four-engined pressurized Stratoliner, designed and constructed by the Boeing Company.

Flying boats large enough to span the oceans also began to appear, and a four-engined craft was designed and created by Igor Sikorsky, who also built the S-38, for Colonel Lindbergh, with which the main service between the United States and Panama was inaugurated. Before World War II, Germany prided herself on the Messerschmidt ME-109, armed with cannon, and attaining a speed of 350 miles an hour. The British had a handful of Hawker Hurricanes and Spitfire fighters, but the United States had only some Curtis P-36s and Seversky P-35 fighters to show.

But once the United States was drawn into the world conflict against Japan, on December 7, 1941, and against Germany and Italy three days later, the wheels of the American aviation industry began to hum. President Franklin Delano Roosevelt called for 50,000 planes. In 1944, production of Lockheed P-38 fighters and B-17 Flying Fortresses, equipped with ten machine guns, had soared to 96,315 planes. In those frantic war years, the Navy Grumman F-4F, Wildcat, Hellcat, Vought F-40, Corsair, Thunderbolt, King of the Skies, and Mustang of the Army did yeoman duty to put an end to Japanese supremacy in the air, while in Europe, thousands of lend-lease planes, together with those of the fighting allies, worked to cripple the air might of the Nazis. Meanwhile the Nazis sprung a surprise with a small, bat-wing, jet plane equipped with four thirty-millimeter cannons and reaching a speed of 560 miles an hour. But the Allies had not been caught napping. Their Gloster E 28/39 jet plane made its presence felt in May, 1941. It was equipped with the famous Whittle engine (named after its inventor, Squadron Leader Frank Whittle of the RAF) and proved itself even faster than the famous Spitfire. This was followed by the Meteor, a fighter powered by two Whittle jets, and the Rolls-Royce Derwent jet engines. This spectacular Whittle engine subsequently found its way to America, where it was the basis for the no-less-renowned Bell XP-59A Airacomet, a midwing plane without benefit of a propeller which created quite a sensation in aviation circles.

Thus began the era of super speed, and of planes faster than the speed of sound.

This period also gave rise to our very newest bombing planes, powered by 2,500 horsepower Wright engines, one of which nick-named *Enola Gay* dropped an atom bomb on Hiroshima, on August 6, 1945, and another on Nagasaki, a few days later.

When World War II finally ended, and war plane production had come to a standstill, demand from the public for air transportation began to skyrocket. The lend-lease planes returned to airlines proved hardly adequate to meet the pent-up demand. It was in this post-war era that such planes as the Lockheed Constellation, and the Boeing Strato Cruiser—planes having a 50-70 passenger capacity—were run off the assembly lines.

Turning attention now to jet propulsion, and research in sonic speed possibilities, the first United States speed aircraft, powered by four rocket engines—the Bell X S-I—was created in 1947. In this plane Captain Charles (Chuck) Yeager of the United States Air

Force cracked the speed of sound or sound barrier. (The speed of sound is 1,100 feet per second, or approximately 762 miles per hour.)

The very light plane had outlived its usefulness, and commercial or civil aviation swung over to fast jets at the close of 1952.

— 22 —

GENERAL JIMMY DOOLITTLE

During the early days of this century a magazine that was eagerly read by American boys was Popular Mechanics, not only because it told them how to make things, but because it gave them the latest dope about planes and gliders. When later issues carried an account of Bleriot's flight across the Channel, this achievement filled the readers with deepest admiration. One of these boys was James Harold Doolittle, a student at the Manual Arts High School.

Jimmy was the son of an itinerant carpenter of Alameda, California, and was taken along to Dawson City and Nome, where his father had come under the spell of the magic word Gold. But his practical mother thought it a great deal more sensible to take Jimmy back to Los Angeles, leaving Doolittle senior to chase the elusive yellow metal.

After completing grammar and high school with honors, Jimmy liked most to swing his hands as a boxer. He did this so well that he became the undisputed bantom-weight boxing champ of the west coast in time. Anxious as he was to make boxing his career, he finally turned his hand to the construction of a glider—without much success, however, as it failed to soar. After taking a two-year course in engineering at Los Angeles Junior Collége, he then entered the University of California, where he majored in mining engineering, and became the middle-weight boxing champ of the University. During the summer months he took a job at the Comstock Mines in Virginia City, Nevada, but seeing so many of his class mates joining the army during World War I, Jimmy also decided to jump in the fray, and he joined the Reserve Signal Corps. He had, however, only two major thoughts on his mind: mining engineering and courting a girl named Jo Daniels.

Unable to tell when he would be called up for active duty, he took a temporary job at the Jones Quicksilver Mine in Napa County,

California, until he was ordered to report to the Aviation Ground School at the University of California. Here he received his basic military pre-flight training and was taught military science. Returning home for a short spell during the Christmas holidays, he married Jo Daniels. Then, after receiving thorough flight training, and being commissioned a second lieutenant in the aviation section, on March 11, 1918, he was ordered to Camp Dick, Texas, instead of being sent overseas.

When the war was over, Doolittle was first transferred to the control on the Mexican Border, and subsequently assigned to the Air Service Mechanics School at Kelly Field, and finally to Langley Field in 1921, to take part in experiments conducted by the controversial General Billy Mitchel.

It was about this time that he competed in a cross-country flight with one of the DH-4 biplanes. He streaked across the land in 21 hours, 19 minutes, at a record speed of 101 miles an hour. When the Air Corps Engineering School was established at McCook Field to engage in a study of the many still unknown phases of aviation, Jimmy was picked to do research, so he could become acquainted with every angle.

After he had spent a year at McCook, the University of California conferred the Bachelor of Arts degree upon him in recognition of his Florida to California flight and his studies at the Air Corps Engineering School. Subsequently sent to the Massachusetts Institute of Technology for special post-graduate studies (where his wife, Jo, and his two young sons, Jimmy and Johnnie, joined him) and with a Master's degree in his pocket, the brilliant and energetic Jimmy now decided to go after a doctor's degree in aeronautical engineering. He selected as his thesis the wind velocity gradient, and its effect on flying characteristics.

Jimmy left M.I.T. in June, 1925, by which time he was already recognized as a first-rate aeronautical engineer, and one of the finest pursuit and acrobatic pilots in the country. Competing in the Pulitzer Race, the Mitchel Field Air Show, and the Schneider Cup Race of seaplane racing, and winning the events against the world's outstanding airmen, Jimmy was made chief of the Flight Section at Wright Field, and awarded the much coveted Mackay Trophy, given to the most outstanding flier annually.

But this dynamic man had only just begun to show his mettle. He was given the opportunity to display his great knowledge in another field, when the Curtiss Export and Curtiss Wright Companies, anxious to expand their foreign airplane business, appealed to the Army authorities to "loan" them Jimmy Doolittle for a time, so he could undertake some flights to South America in the interest of their aviation business. They gave Jimmy a leave of absence to demonstrate the Curtiss fighter plane over there. Having discharged himself of this stint, he was once more "loaned," at a later date, to demonstrate an observation plane Curtiss had created. He acquitted himself of this task in a similar manner, during which time he also crisscrossed the Brazilian Matto Grosso jungle.

Then in 1928, when Harry Guggenheim, President of the Guggenheim Fund for the promotion of aeronautics, established the Full Flight Laboratories, to make planes available for testing out devices and schemes, Jimmy Doolittle was considered the best qualified to head this phase of work. Once again Jimmy got a leave of absence from the Army, and he, Jo, and the kids took up their new residence at Mitchel Field. Blind flying and blind landings now engaged his attention.

A reliable altimeter and fathometer had been developed. This latter instrument used the sonic principle to give the depth of the sea by sound waves, which were sent from a ship to the bottom of the sea and then were bounced back. With sound traveling 4,000 feet per second in water, the fathometer measured the length of the round trip, so that the ship's skipper could tell at once how much water there was beneath him. Jimmy Doolittle therefore figured, if there were a similar gadget in a plane, the pilot would be able to figure out precisely how high above the ground the plane was flying. Next he was after an instrument that would give the exact direction, as the only instrument that was available to pilots at the time was the magnetic compass, which was totally useless under certain conditions. He therefore believed that the solution lay in a very light and compact gyroscopic compass. The scientist to figure this out was Dr. Elmer Ambrose Sperry, whose instruments are standard equipment on all commercial and military aircraft.

Jimmy Doolittle then tried landing blind at night, also with great success.

When his work at Mitchel Field had been completed, he contacted the Shell Oil people in St. Louis, who hired him to organize their aviation department and to head the development section of all Shell's aviation products. While he was still in Shell's employ, the

Curtiss Wright Export people again approached Jimmy to have him demonstrate their planes in the European market. He obtained a four months' leave of absence, during which he covered many European cities. When this demonstration trip was ended, he returned again to the Shell.

Still, the incredible, restless Jimmy Doolittle, the guy with the infectious grin and twinkle in his eye, could not stay put long. He decided to enter the Bendix Trophy Race from Los Angeles to Cleveland with a new plane, the Lair. This race, together with the Thompson Trophy, constituted one of the two greatest racing events. Establishing new records, Jimmy Doolittle publicized the products of Shell at the same time.

The people at Shell were vitally interested in developing a powerful aviation fuel that could be produced eventually at a lower cost, and Doolittle lent his hand and genius in 'the creation of the sulfuric acid alkalation process. This resulted in the production of octane improvements without hydrogenation, and of what is now known as 100-octane. This high-octane virtually became the lifeblood of World War II bombers and fighters. By using the 100-octane fuel the speed of the fighters was increased about 50 miles per hour, and the bomb load of each bomber increased by about one ton. This improvement meant the difference between success and failure in combat.

In 1940 Doolittle was made President of the Institute of Aeronautical Science. He was only 44 then, and he already had a tremendous bag of accomplishments to his credit, having won almost every honor in civil aviation, besides the Mackay and Harmon Trophies, the Spirit of St. Louis Medal, and many others. The Army had awarded him the DSC for his experimental work at McCook, and added an Oak Cluster to this decoration.

Meanwhile war clouds had again gathered and, bidding the enterprising people at Shell goodbye, restless Jimmy got his old uniform out of mothballs and reported to famed Hap Arnold, as Major James Doolittle.

Making history once more as America's first hero of the war, Jimmy Doolittle wreaked destruction on Tokyo, Yokohama, Osaka, Kobe and Nagoya, with 16 planes, a raid that made him a general and earned him the Medal of Honor, on April 18, 1942.

After a stint at Bolling Field to organize the 4th Medium

Bomber Wing, Jimmy was summoned to organize a branch of the 12th Air Force, and to take part in the European fighting. A week later found him in London, where he met General Eisenhower, who could not get warmed up to the idea of entrusting the air command "to a former stunt flier, who had been engaged, after all, during a dozen or so years in a job publicizing and selling gasoline for Shell."

Yet in spite of the fact that General Eisenhower would rather have appointed a Spaatz or an Eaker, Jimmy Doolittle was selected nonetheless, and was asked to organize the 12th Air Force. And what a splendid choice it proved to be, evidenced by the following heartening message later sent to him by General Eisenhower.

> Dear Jimmy:
> When you joined me in London you had much of what it takes to exercise high command. I am not exaggerating when I tell you that in my opinion you have shown during the past year the greatest degree of improvement of any of the senior United States officers serving in my command. You are every day rendering services of inestimable value to our country.
>
> Eisenhower

Doolittle was fully aware of the tough assignment. But he buckled right down. He had arrived in England on January 4th, 1944, and on January 5th, he dispatched the first operation against Kiel, Elberfeld, Tours, and Bordeaux, with 600 fighters and 500 heavy bombers, the largest single raid Doolittle had ever directed up to that time.

And then, when the war was over and Jimmy Doolittle had performed all these herculean duties as only a man with his terrific qualifications could have done, he returned to Shell Oil, where he was elected a director, in 1946. The immortal newspaper man Ernie Pyle, who often accompanied Jimmy on stints around the bases, had said, "Jimmy has more gifts than any one man has a right to be blessed with."

Shortly after 1946 he was made a member of Shell's Executive Committee, a post from which he resigned a few years ago to take an active part in Space Technology, with which he is now completely taken up.

— 23 —

IGOR SIKORSKY AND HIS CHICKEN HOUSE

There once lived in Kiev, the ancient and romantic capital of Russia, a lad named Igor Ivanovitch Sikorsky, whose mother had showed him a drawing of da Vinci's helicopter. This set Igor dreaming about building helicopters one day. Most adept with his hands, he carved wooden toys with wheels that moved, and finally constructed a model of a helicopter, propelled by rubber bands.

Nineteen hundred and three proved a momentous year for young Igor. Not only did he enter the Naval Academy of St. Petersburg, but something world-shaking had taken place in America that was to change his whole life. It was the year in which the Wright brothers had made their historic flight. He left Naval Academy three years later, and, after a short spell in Paris, he entered the Polytechnic Institute in Kiev, where he constructed a motorcycle propelled by steam. Then, in the summer of 1908, the very year that Zeppelin flew his fourth airship, Igor started on another project. His mind was still set on creating a better machine than the Wrights', firmly convinced that the helicopter was more practical.

Continually haunted by the passion to construct one, and anxious to discover the secret, Igor realized that this would require lots of money—and his relatives were hard working people, and poor. His sister Olga was deeply interested in his work, and, having faith in her brother, volunteered to stake him so that he could purchase a suitable motor for the job.

Journeying once more to Paris to talk to aviators and mechanics and visit airfields, he happened to run into Captain Ferber, a French aviation pioneer, who had built airplanes and gliders. When Igor told him that his mind was made up to build a helicopter, Ferber shook his head and uttered one sentence Igor never forgot, "To invent a flying machine is nothing, to build a flying machine is little, but to make a flying machine fly is everything."

Igor then enrolled in an aeronautical school Captain Ferber had started. Buying a motor from the Anzani people, identical to the one Blériot had used for his airplane, after four months in

Paris Igor returned to Kiev to start assembling his brainchild. He completed the machine in 1909, but it failed to become airborne. He then built another one—the S-2—which also crashed to earth. But the third one, for which he had purchased another motor in Paris, took to the air after several short hops, and rose forty feet. The 13th successful flight came on December 13 when he took it up 100 feet. He was forced to make a landing, and his plane turned over. Undaunted, he persevered, so that after experimenting three weeks more, the S-5 rose 800 feet and stayed in the air for four minutes.

Once he secured his pilot's license, Sikorsky received an invitation to the army air maneuvers near Kiev, where he was presented to Tsar Nicholas II. He subsequently received the highest award at the Moscow Aircraft Exhibition with his S-6A, and the Russian Baltic Railroad not only bought the rights to this plane, but offered him a job as designer and chief engineer of an airplane plant they were building.

Then, on May 13, 1913, Igor built the largest monoplane, which took to the air without a single mishap. He followed this with the construction of another, this time a four-engined monster equipped with a pontoon. Named the Ilia Mourometz, in honor of one of Kiev's tenth-century heroes, this craft established a record as the largest seaplane in the world. It carried ten persons, and was capable of landing on water and land.

Russia was also buzzing with the talk of war in those days, so that Igor was asked to build more planes for the army. Having pioneered the multi-engined aeroplane and constructed a large four-engined cabin biplane, he is said to have made over seventy multi-engined bombers for the Russian government during World War I. While he was supervising work on five monstrous bombers that the French government was building according to his specifications, the armistice was signed, and the work in France came to a halt.

Unable to return to Russia, and fearing a threatened slump in aviation, Igor's thoughts turned to America—happy hunting ground for all kinds of pioneers, trail blazers, and . . . crackpots.

And that is how Igor Sikorsky, setting out for the proverbial land of opportunity, landed at New York, on March 30, 1919, speaking hardly a word of English and with but a few dollars in his jeans. Realizing full well that it would take him some time to land a job, as he did not speak the language, and watching the few dollars vanish like snow in the sun, he became a steady visitor to the marvelous New York Public Library, where he began sketching plans for his next helicopter and studying English.

Running into some countrymen from Mother Russia, he formed a small company to construct a helicopter, but the enterprise soon folded for lack of money. He then trekked to Washington, in the hope of interesting some aviation bigwigs. As this led to nowhere, he boarded a bus for Dayton, Ohio, where he secured a job with the Engineering Division of the Army Air Service, which had a large three-motor bomber in the blueprint stage. But this job did not last long. The work was suddenly discontinued, and the despondent Igor returned to New York. Now tasting real defeat, Igor had a tough time existing until he ran into a group of Russian workmen. This became the turning point in his career. Evincing more than ordinary interest in his work, they offered him enough money to start anew. A cooperative was formed in 1923, in which these good people not only invested, but agreed to assist him, with the actual work. As one of his compatriots owned a small tract of land in Long Island, he permitted Igor to use it for his operations, including the use of a very large chicken coop which was turned into a drafting room, office and workshop.

And here in this chicken coop Igor's S-29 was built, which took to the air in May 1924. It made a crash landing, however, cracking both radiators and breaking the propeller, and what was left was badly bent and shaken up. With defeat again staring him in the face, Igor still did not want to give up. He told them that he knew where he could lay his hands on two overhauled Liberty motors, provided he had another $2,500. These loyal friends came to his rescue again.

The result of all this was that the new S-29—the first twin-motor ship built in the United States, and capable of flying on one motor—was rolled out on Roosevelt Field, with Igor at the controls. After circling about the field for ten minutes, and rising to about one thousand feet, it finally made an excellent landing. Victory had come to Igor Sikorsky at last.

Things began to hum now, and the first commercial job they got was to fly two grand pianos from Roosevelt Field to Washington, which gave the brand new company some excellent publicity and put it on the map. Next came an order from the French ace, Captain Fonck, for a plane he wanted to use to cross the Atlantic. This machine crashed. Then came orders for the S-37, which made short trips across the South American Andes, and for the S-38, used by Colonel Lindbergh to inaugurate the mail service between the United States and Panama. As the Navy liked what they saw, Sikorsky received an order for two more. The partners now were completely out of the woods and getting more business than they could handle, so Sikorsky was obliged to enlarge his plant. The Sikorsky Aviation Company was founded, which became a subsidiary of the United Aircraft Corporation later.

Igor's reputation as an airplane and helicopter builder now was well established, and orders came pouring in, including one from the late Martin and Osa Johnson for two zebra-striped amphibians. They took the planes with them to Africa, for use on their 60,000-mile safaris. When Lindbergh and Sikorsky drew up plans for a flying ship some time later, a ship that would combine comfort, lifting capacity, greater range and speed, it led to the creation in 1934 of the S-42, the first successful long-range Clipper.

It is safe to say that no one in modern aeronautics has done more than Igor Ivanovitch Sikorsky for having turned the helicopter into the practical vehicle that it has remained to this very day.

— 24 —

INTERNATIONAL AIRLINES—AIR FRANCE AND KLM

Of all the international airlines on whose planes I have had the pleasure of traveling, the KLM-Royal Dutch Airlines and Air France may well be the most outstanding. So, although I should add that there are many others, such as BOAC, SAS, SWISSAIR, SABENA on which I have also been aboard, that have their own particular accomplishments, in the next few pages I would like to trace the historical significance and spectacular development of these two carriers, and explain why they were bound to attain the pinnacle of honest-to-goodness airline service.

AIR FRANCE

Undeniably the world's largest airline net, Air France has been a spearhead of world air activity.

Its history can be said to go back to 1919, when Lignes Farman, a parent company of Air France, made the first international passenger flight in aviation history. Eleven travelers made the two and a half hour flight from London to Paris, on February 8, 1919, in a Farman Goliath aircraft of the French airline. The flight was piloted by Lucien Bossoutrot, who became one of the pilots for what eventually became known as Air France.

Flying in those days was a great deal different, of course, from what air transportation is today. The passengers in those earlier days were seated in wicker chairs, and were not served the luxurious repasts and vintages with which the super starliners and jet aircraft entice passengers today. They were "treated" to some sandwiches and cookies instead, and were mighty glad to get that.

The record of Air France—flying over hundreds-of-thousands of unduplicated air routes covering more than 201,043 miles, and serving some 71 countries all over the globe—rings with such names as Blériot, Farman, Nungesser, Coli, Mermoz, St. Exupéry, Roig, Daurat, Bossoutrot to name but a few.

Prior to the day in 1932 when the name of Air France came into being, and the world-renowned Air France insignia became widely known, one of Air France's predecessors was the Ligne Aeriennes Latécoere, which made a survey of a route to be flown from Toulouse to Barcelona, in October, 1918. Since then a number of French airline companies have pushed steadily ahead, and have added to the world-wide chain. In order, therefore, to better understand what makes the Air France business tick, let's trace the spectacular developments that have taken place from the very first day that the foundation of this Goliath in airlines was laid. So we had better start with a Monsieur Pierre Latécoere, a Toulouse industrialist, who had received from the French Government some orders to manufacture war planes in 1917. He had visions of an airline that would ultimately link Paris with South America, a dream that would come to fruition some years later. Meanwhile, he surrounded himself with men who had flown airplanes before and who knew the airplane business.

Being the type of man who always wanted to know where he

was going, and who never wanted others to do what he could not do himself, he flew a plane piloted by Cornemont from Toulouse to Barcelona, crossing the Pyrenées, on Christmas day, 1918. Subsequently he extended the line to Alicante, Spain. A plane piloted by Lemaitre then flew to Rabat, on March 19, 1919, where they delivered a bouquet of French-grown violets and the March 18 Paris edition of *Le Temps* to Marshal Lyautey, the then Governor of French Morocco.

After that the Latécoere line grew by leaps and bounds, with the cooperation of the French Government. Flying for this line were the most able pilots and aviators, whose names—Massini, Vanier, Dalrieu, Dombrey, Morraglia, Daurata, Mermoz, St. Exupéry—have become famous bywords in the history of France and of that historic line.

In 1923, three planes of the Breguet make, commanded and piloted by Captain Roig, completed the flight from Casablanca, Morocco, to Dakar, on the West Africa Coast. This led to the opening of the first French postal service between these points in June, 1925. In spite of the extreme hostility of savage Moors and Berbers, and extreme heat, the Line succeeded in delivering the mails on time.

Proof that all was not milk and honey for these indomitable airmen in the very beginning was the case of the young military pilot Jean Mermoz who, tortured by thirst after a crash landing in the desert, on May 22, 1926, had to drink the rancid water from his plane's radiator. He then fell into the hands of hostile tribesmen, who, transporting him in a gunny sack on camel's back, liberated him fourteen days later, after a ransom of 1,000 pesetas to the bandits had been paid.

In that same year, another group of French pilots, comprised of Gourp, Erable and Pintado, was attacked by a band of marauding Berber tribesmen after their plane had crashed. The Berbers killed Erable and Pintado on the spot, and then caried off the severely wounded Gourp, to release him for a stiff ransom later.

Another French flier who, with characteristic modesty, always made light of the enormous difficulties encountered by him on his flights, and whose name is still being spoken of with great reverence by the people of France, is the late St. Exupéry, a well-known novelist. Like Mermoz, he began his apprenticeship as a mechanic with Air France.

As Latécoere had not abandoned his long-cherished hope of establishing an airline that would link France with South America, an aerial mission was sent which culminated in the dispatch of three pilots— Roig, Vachet and Hamm—who completed the distance from Rio de Janeiro to Buenos Aires in three stop-overs. This led to the signing of an aerial agreement between the Argentine Government and the Compagnie Latécoere, whose name meanwhile had been changed to Compagnie Aeropostale. The French companies pushed steadily ahead, gradually consolidating each technical gain by adding to their world-wide system, spanning the South Atlantic, laying the foundation for a vast international service which was to grow out of this patient pioneering.

A Portuguese crew had made a South Atlantic crossing in 1922, with stop-overs at Cape Verde and Sao Paulo. The Spanish also had done it, followed by the Italians and Portuguese again in 1927, and a French team with Coste and Le Brix had succeeded in completing the first non-stop flight from Dakar to Natal in the same year. The French Aéropostale Company was not yet satisfied, however, for their ultimate goal of a regular non-stop flight linking Paris and Buenos Aires over the treacherous South Atlantic Ocean had not been achieved.

This dangerous mission, which was to shed additional lustre for Air France, was left to the French idol, pilot Jean Mermoz, navigator Dabry (who is still technical advisor to Air France) and radio operator Gimié, in a plane, christened *Arc en Ciel.* They succeeded in crossing the Atlantic on May 12, 1930, and established a regular postal service between South America and France.

On May 2, 1958, when Air France completed its 1,000th direct crossing of the South Atlantic, a monument was unveiled to the memory of Jean Mermoz and his comrades in the center of Buenos Aires. Other Frenchmen had also contributed their share to French aerial pioneering before this date. Roland Garros, for example, had already made a non-stop flight from Saint Raphael to Bizerte on September 13, 1913. Captain Vuillemin had conquered the Sahara on March 31, 1920, and Maurice Nogues had opened up the airlane from France to Saigon, French Indo China, on March 9, 1930, leading to the establishment of a regular airline to that point a year later.

To complete this section dealing with Air France, here follow a few outstanding characteristics of this company whose record of

A Sikorsky S-58 helicopter used by Sabena Belgian World Airlines. The ship carries 12 passengers and serves an 810-mile network between 12 cities in four European countries.—SABENA

The Air France Paris-Tokyo inaugural flight sets down at Anchorage, Alaska.—MAC's

Dr. Albert Plesman, founder and later President and Director of KLM, Royal Dutch Airlines.—KLM

The Flying Dutchman: a Douglas DC-7C airliner at Schiphol-Amsterdam Airport.—KLM

A sunny day on the terrace of Schiphol Airport.—KLM

A tax-free shop where international passengers can save up to 60 per cent on articles purchased at Schiphol.—KLM

traffic performance vividly illustrates the great development of aviation.

In 1938, Air France carried about 110,000 passengers; in 1948, the figure rose to 573,000, and by 1958 the number of passengers carried by Air France totaled more than 2,517,000 travelers, helped along by greater speeds, increased comfort, and added seat capacity.

The General Manager of Air France in New York, Henri J. Lesieur, a former pilot, planned and actually pioneered many Air France routes and services. When World War II ended, and Air France resumed flights on the North Atlantic route, he was assigned to establish and develop the North, Central American, and Caribbean Division. In 1952 an air agreement was signed between Mexico City and Paris, followed in 1953 by the Paris, Fort de France, Caracas, Bogota route.

In 1960, after a new bilaterial agreement was signed between the U.S.A. and France, a new Air France jet route was opened between Los Angeles and Paris, via Montreal.

When Anchorage became a new gateway to Europe, the first jet flights over the North Pole in Air France's Paris-Tokyo route via Anchorage were started, bringing the people from Alaska rapid service to Hamburg and Paris. Nineteen hundred and sixty also saw a service being conducted by Air France, as general agent for the Transports Aeriens Intercontinentaux, serving Tahiti, and the South Pacific from Los Angeles.

And so, from a modest beginning, Air France in North America has developed into a highly integrated organization as a major trans-Atlantic carrier under the dynamic direction of Henri J. Lesieur. In 1961 Air France carried 3,593,317 passengers from 71 countries of the world and from all walks of life.

At latest figures available, the Air France line has some 2,387 pilots, flight engineers and navigators, and all pilots on the North Atlantic have flown at least 5,000 hours or about a million and a half miles. Forty Air France captains have logged between 15,000 and 20,000 hours of flight. Eight veterans have passed the 20,000 hour mark, which means they have flown well over 6,000,000 miles. This extensive flight experience accumulated by Air France crews is the equivalent of five and a half centuries of flight. Every two and a half minutes an Air France plane somewhere in the world takes off or lands.

The quality of Air France crews is assured from the outset by meticulous selection and rigorous training. Captains or First Officers are chosen from among co-pilots who have three or more years of service and have completed a minimum of 4,000 hours of flight.

Also the choice of Air France hostesses and stewards is highly selective. A hostess must be single, between 21 and 30, have studied for a baccalaureate degree, have fluency in French, English and a third language, be in excellent health, and have an attractive appearance. Of 200 hostess applicants considered for training, usually ten per cent or less are accepted. When accepted, these candidates then begin a seven-week training course. For example, too, during training period future hostesses take turns serving one another meals in a model jetliner cabin. During the first 100 hours of service on regular passenger flights, new hostesses are paired with experienced hostesses and then subsequently assigned to one of the five sectors of the Air France network.

Well-balanced gourmet menus are selected from hundreds of superb French specialties. They are particularly suited to preparation and serving while in flight. Veteran Air France Chef des Cuisines, André Chemery, and his staff of 200 assistants, tested and re-tested scores of recipes at the Company's central commissary at Orly Airport in Paris. The dishes were grouped according to seven distinct gastronomic regions of France. Today, the Air France passenger can enjoy a choice of authentic meals from Ile de France, Champagne, Flandres, Artois, Picardie, Orleanais, and Touraine.

Air France passengers spend one-third of the 3,612-mile transAtlantic jet flight enjoying an eight-course French repast served in Paris-designed interiors.

The Air France cargo service is a lifeline of international commerce. Freight and commodities carried by Air France range from artichoke to Zebra. A 420-lb. baby elephant named Zimbo, loaded at Fort Lamy in Chad, Africa, was delivered not so many years ago to Dwight D. Eisenhower, as a gift from the French community. And this very important passenger disrupted every rule of Air France protocol "by carrying his own *trunk* aboard."

THE INIMITABLE KLM - Royal Dutch Airlines

On August 1, 1919, the foundation of this enterprising and unexcelled world airline was laid. Because on that date an energetic young Hollander succeeded in promoting the first large Air Show in Amsterdam, firm in the belief that a new era in air transportation was close at hand. The name of this young man was Albert Plesman, through whose almost prophetic foresight and great genius the first stone was laid of a commercial enterprise of such magnitude that it became one of the largest and most indefatigable airlines in a few years.

Two months later, on October 7, 1919, the KLM or Royal Dutch Airlines began operations. Less than a year later, on May 17, 1920, Lt. Albert Plesman of the Netherlands Army, accompanied by Captain H. Shaw, flew across the English Channel aboard the first *Flying Dutchman*, a single-engined de Havilland open cockpit biplane which had been used in World War I. Three hours later they set down in a cow pasture near Amsterdam which in time was to become the world-renowned Schiphol Airport.

This initial and modest beginning inaugurated the first officially-recognized air route between London and Amsterdam. A few months later the first passenger airplanes—four passenger, single engined Fokker F-2 monoplanes—were placed in service, and the first ticket office was opened in Amsterdam, on May 9, 1921. It did not take the young company long to improve its airport from the meadow and few shacks it had originally started with. Then three years later, in 1924, plans of this company came to fruition for a flight from Amsterdam to its colonies in the Netherlands East Indies, where exactly 329 years before an agent of the East India Company had dropped anchor with a small squadron of armed ships to start colonization.

After thorough preparation, Holland was again to make history when a KLM master pilot, named van der Hoop, flew the 9,554 miles from Amsterdam to Batavia, in a Fokker VII plane on October 1, 1924, arriving at his destination November 24. And so another dream of Plesman had begun to bear fruit. A second flight was made on June 14, 1927, when a much improved Fokker of the KLM headed once more for Batavia. This flight made the KLM the first line in the world to open an intercontinental air service. A weekly service was established in 1930. It was no surprise, therefore, when a Dutch journalist referred to The Hague as a cool suburb of Batavia.

As the first to introduce the American-built Douglas DC-3 planes in the Netherlands, the KLM was able to step up the Holland to Java frequency to three flights a week by June, 1937. The

KLM plane *Pelikaan,* piloted by Ivan Smirnoff, had made the flight
from Amsterdam to Batavia in four days, four hours, and 40 minutes.
Nineteen hundred and thirty-four proved a good year for the KLM,
when, as a participant in the Melbourne Race, the KLM entered
the MacRobertson race with the Uiver, a regular KLM transport
vehicle, carrying 421 pounds of mail and three passengers, and
won first prize in the handicap feature.

But there were other records to be made. Exactly 300 years
after the founding of Curacao, the route between Holland and the
Netherlands West Indies was opened in 1934. The plane making
the transatlantic flight was the *Snip,* a Fokker F-18, Holland-built
machine, piloted by Commander J. J. Hondong on this 17-hour hop.
And when the *Snip* swooped down on Curacao's Hato field on that
day, it landed on the identical spot where, 300 years before, Governor Peter Stuyvesant had hobbled along on his wooden leg.

A few years later the fast-growing KLM, in cooperation with
the Royal East Indies Airways, extended its route to Sydney,
Australia.

Then came the fateful years of World War II, when tiny Holland was ruthlessly invaded by the Nazis, and Schiphol Airport,
undeniably Holland's pride, became the first objective of Hitler's
paratroopers and Luftwaffe, who attacked it with all their fury. In
spite of the valiant efforts of the Dutch, who had been marshaled
in their country's defense to a man, every plane of the KLM (there
were then 35) was destroyed, except these few that were fortunate
enough to escape the Nazi wrath. To make matters even worse,
KLM's genial and indomitable guiding spirit, the late Dr. Albert
Plesman, was taken prisoner and incarcerated first at Scheveningen,
Holland's seaside resort, then exiled to Twente, the eastern province
of the Netherlands near the German border.

When the destructive war finally came to an end, and Holland
had been liberated by the Allied armies, first attention was paid
to the restoration of KLM's Schiphol Airport, which had been
completely destroyed. Connections with the rest of the continent
and the world were most essential for the speedy recovery of the
ravaged land. As the airline had to be completely rebuilt, the resourceful Dr. Plesman lost no time in taking a trip to the United
States in the summer of 1945. And after some down-to-earth discus-
sions with President Truman and General Hap Arnold, he returned
to his homeland a few weeks later with 14 Douglas Skymasters

(DC-4 Transports) and with more to follow. On November 28, 1945, only six months after the armistice, KLM was already in position to reopen the first of its intercontinental services—the Amsterdam-Batavia Line—with one of the new fleet of surplus Douglas Skymasters. Resumption of the services to many points in Europe followed and the transocean flights to Curacao, Rio de Janeiro and Johannesburg, South Africa, were resumed in 1946.

The dynamic line made another record in May, 1946, when it became the first European line to begin postwar service between Europe and the United States. By that time the KLM's airfleet was being continually enlarged and Schiphol turned into a most up-to-date, efficiently-run, and fully-staffed airport.

Another milestone in KLM's airline history was reached when KLM won the handicap section of the London-Christchurch (New Zealand) air race in 1953, with a DC-6A Liftmaster, carrying a load of 59 passengers and crew of 11.

It was, therefore, considered most regrettable that the line's founder, Dr. Albert Plesman, was denied the joy of witnessing his line assume the leadership in commercial aviation again, as he passed away on New Year's Day, 1953, at the age of 63, after a lengthy illness. He was laid to rest in the capital city of The Hague, a short distance away from the very seat of the company he had founded. No story about the KLM, Royal Dutch Airlines could be complete without some additional facts about this remarkable man.

Wise and astute, strong-willed, and enterprising, this heavy-set, gray-haired, red-cheeked, blue-eyed, rugged individualist knew the aviation business from A to Z. And though his start was not too auspicious he was fortunate enough to have lived at precisely the right time. Interested in planes and aviation from the very outset of his career, he had tinkered with and piloted planes since 1919, using them as stepping stones in the building of his empire of aviation. True, it had not been always easy sailing, as he suffered financial and economic setbacks that could have undermined the morale of many another, less strong character.

Albert Plesman was the seventh child of Jan Plesman, a Dutch baker, and of Jan's wife, Heintje van Wessel. After attending the elementary and high schools, where he liked sports and arithmetic best, he attended the Military School at Breda, where he not only had to compete with the scions of Holland's upper crust, but where many of his farsighted ideas of an aviation empire germinated.

His was the guiding spirit of Holland's Air Show and of the First International Aviation Exhibition in Amsterdam, conceived in order for his countrymen to become better acquainted with aviation, where one and all could gape at stunt pilots and parachutists. Here, too, portly Dutch housewives went up for their first spin, and Queen Wilhelmina (who later expressed great interest in all of KLM's many enterprises) honored the show with her royal presence. It took some doing to make Holland's staid and ultra-conservative people airminded. As Plesman explained, "We've been seafaring people for centuries. We should now go in for airfaring, before others beat us to the draw."

Prominent merchant princes, notably slow in decision but thorough, endorsed Plesman's greater plan. Their support led to the birth of Plesman's brainchild, with Plesman acting as its administrator. He rose first to director, then president and finally to become the great company's *Baas*, or chief.

However, KLM's world-wide business, and particularly that over the longest aerial route in the world, was not secured without much harassment, and he often had to haggle about landing and other rights with Indian princes and other potentates. Yet he most often won. Plesman also had his setbacks and sorrow in private life, because, when a virtual prisoner of the Nazis, he received the sad news at Christmas time, 1944, that his son John, a pilot with the RAF, had been shot down over France. And later his first-born, Hans, crashed piloting a plane in 1949.

After the war, under Plesman's guidance and with the help of $26 million allotted by the United States Economic Administration and the Marshall Plan, the creditworthy KLM was enabled to revamp and develop its network until it far exceeded its pre-war size.

As the author of *World Aviation Means World Peace*, Plesman also presented a plan for international cooperation at a London Conference on World Government, in September, 1951, which called for the establishment by the 18 countries cooperating through the Marshall Plan of a 30-year institute to further international understanding and teamwork.

Receiving the honorary degree of Doctor of Technical Science on January 8, 1947, in the beautiful old Westerkerk at Delft, Plesman left his mark wherever his work took him, giving meaning and dimension to aviation. Although he lived simply and without undue ostentation, and sought no acclaim or honors, he was generously honored, nonetheless, and was the recipient of several Dutch and foreign decorations.

At home or abroad, at his office or wherever he might be, Plesman was a born leader, whose name personified KLM, and whose deep sense of duty and devotion served as an example for all who knew him. An outstanding character trait of his was his immense interest in practically everything that came in his path. Showing an unusual capacity for appreciating and understanding methods and viewpoints even contrary to his own, Plesman was never a fanatic but always fair in his appraisals, and he was rather too ready to give a man credit for what was good in his work. Ideas would often absorb him. He would always look for new fields to conquer.

It should therefore cause no surprise that the Dutch people have given this great leader complete credit for making their little "big" country one of the world's leaders in civil aviation, and for having made their LINE the KLM, the world's oldest airline, the best managed, the best operated, the envy of many, but surpassed by few.

The people of Holland considered him a national hero whose popularity was exceeded only by that of their Queen.

— 25 —

FEEDING THE AIRLINE PASSENGERS

Feeding airline passengers entails a great deal more than serving breakfast, luncheon or a filet mignon dinner on a plane. Food and the serving thereof on short or long hauls are very important to a line, because leaving a passenger hungry or serving badly prepared food is the worst kind of publicity.

All airlines—whether Air France, BOAC, Swissair or SAS—have solved the catering problem in their own way to satisfy the culinary requirements of even the most exacting traveler, and no story about them would be complete unless something is said about their kitchens. And I have picked the kitchens of the KLM, as these, together with those of Air France at Orly, appealed to me the most.

Let's start by saying that KLM's Schiphol Airport, situated 13 feet below sea level, is built on a strip of land that, like a great deal of the Netherlands, was once under water. On this very spot a battle was fought against the Spaniards in 1573, and to this very day ships use a canal that borders the airfield though its surface is 13 feet higher.

The real showplace of KLM's Schiphol Airport is called the *Aviorama,* a sky-room restaurant, from which an excellent view is obtained of airstrips and fields where planes of many nations are setting down or taking off.

There are, of course, many other and even larger airports in the world, including the many in our own American cities. Many foreign airports are set near tropical jungles, others are in some Arctic tundra or dreary place, while there are a great many that are ultramodern and exciting. And those of you who may have traveled, or may travel some day soon, will not be able to forget Tokyo's International Airport, or the one at Bangkok, Thailand, which forms a junction for airline routes connecting the west with Saigon, Singapore or Hong Kong. The Europe-bound traveler will never forget the pleasant and hospitable Shannon airport—Irish refueling station for incoming and outgoing vehicles—or the incomparable Orly airport of Paris. Turning now to our neighboring lands to the south, the Ezeiza airport at Buenos Aires is not to be scorned, a gleaming place set in glass, chrome and marble, complete with restaurants, casinos, and swimming pool.

However, let's come back to Holland's Schiphol, which appeals to us greatly because it has every type of comfort the often weary traveler would look for. Its terminal, 240 feet long and two stories high, is one of the largest and most streamlined air terminals in the world. Aside from the unparalleled restaurant, it also sports a snack bar to serve the KLM personnel, a separate restaurant for technicians, and a canteen for the catering staff. The food, which can be said to satisfy every size of purse, is on par with the sort of food one expects only in the most luxurious dining places in the world.

The catering division is located on the ground floor, a section that serves many thousands of foreign and Dutch planes. The hot kitchen prides itself on an 18-foot-long range, a soup kettle with a capacity of 22 gallons, a super frying pan which prepares some 80 beefsteaks—succulent and tender—simultaneously.

Food intended for the deep freeze is ladled from the stove into small aluminum trays, which are then placed in grease-proof bags. Each type of menu intended for short or long flights is provided with an identifying number. The complete meals then are placed in deep freeze units, where the food is kept for many hours.

When it is time for the food to be placed on the planes, the food is packed in metal deep-freeze containers, which are then filled with solidified carbon dioxide or dry ice and flat boxes of deep frozen refrigerant.

When the time has arrived for feeding the passengers during the flight, the plane's stewards thaw the meals in electric ovens, making doubly sure that they are at the right temperature when served.

Then there is the cold kitchen, where salads and all sorts of sandwiches are prepared, or should one say created, because many of these tasty sandwiches are creations in themselves. It is in this section, too, that the appetizers and hors d' oeuvres are readied. Another section comprises the pastry division and pastry bakery, where rolls as well as all types of cakes and deserts are baked, while next is the coffee kitchen, which produces at one time 1,500 gallons of tea and coffee.

As there are many passengers of Jewish or Moslem faiths, there is also a kosher kitchen, and other sections where meals for orthodox Jewish passengers and for those of other beliefs are prepared.

A short walk brings one to the butcher shop and cold-storage section with 15 refrigerators, store rooms for raw supplies for the kitchens. Renowned for its proverbial Dutch cleanliness, the scullery is also a most interesting section, equipped as it is with the most modern dish washing machines, each of which, we learned, could wash and dry some 20,000 items per hour.

The catering division provided me with statistics which should give some idea as to the vast activity of this Dutch airline. I was told, for instance, that the Catering Division uses for its world-wide activities 150,000 knives, forks and spoons, 100,000 plates and plastic dishes, 60,000 drinking glasses, while its linen requirements reached the phenomenal figure of 150,000 napkins, 10,000 pillow cases, mats and rugs.

The laundering division would appeal to many a traveling housewife. All the items that incoming planes discharge have to be laundered. This takes place in the section adjacent to the kitchens, where two large washing machines with a combined capacity of 220 pounds are flanked by two centrifugal machines, in which most of the water is removed from the items. After this operation is finished, the laundry is stowed into hot-air dryers, to be finally relayed to ten-foot-long steam mangles for pressing.

Some years back, on one of my former trips, I was given the statistics of the Catering Division's annual output, which recorded at the time 450,000 deep-frozen meals, 550,000 other type meals, 30,000 sponge cakes, and 200,000 other cake and pastry items. That time's annual consumption aggregated 400,000 eggs, 44,000 pounds of creamery butter, 26,500 pounds of all types of cheese, 800,000 pieces of fruit, 4,000,000 packages of sugar, 2,000,000 packages of mints not forgetting the omnipresent chewing gum. Thirsty palates were not overlooked either, as some 18,000 bottles of red and white wine and 12,000 bottles of champagne were dispensed.

In connection with Schiphol Airport, of added interest to most if not to all travelers is the tax-free shopping center where such items, as liquors, cigarettes, perfumes, Dutch candies and cocoa and knick-knacks can be purchased at greatly reduced prices.

Finally, I should not overlook KLM's personnel training pantries consisting of a mock aircraft cabin complete with galley. Here future stewards and stewardesses are being trained in the highly specialized art of working efficiently and quickly in the interior of an airliner. Here, too, the cabin stewards and attendants are being given cooking lessons by an expert chef from the KLM's main kitchen.

— 26 —

ANIMAL CARGO

The airlines' cargo traffic has become an important part of the general airline business of all foreign and domestic carriers. In order to facilitate the packing, repacking and transportation of air cargo at Schiphol Airport, KLM engineers have designed plastic containers for airborne fish, coat hangers that carry three coats each, bag-enclosed dress hangers for fifteen garments, horse stalls, and many other innovations to facilitate cargo shipments and minimize time loss.

Now not wanting at this time to go into a lengthy discussion of this large and lucrative business, and how this has affected to a great extent international air traffic, I would like to discuss a phase of this traffice that has a sort of romantic overtone. I have in mind the traffic in animals. Thus we find at Schiphol Airport a so-called Animal Hotel, where a large collection of various bird species, tropical fish, monkeys, reptiles, elephants and many other animals are kept until they are readied to be shipped to points beyond. The traffic in monkeys has been found very rewarding, what with the demand from zoos and from those scientific quarters interested in research for the medical profession and space age. Many plane loads of these simians are flown in from Africa, India and further in the Far East. These airline "passengers" ranging from elephants to ants, from snakes to rhinoceros to tiger and aardvark, tropical fish and lions, have given KLM the nickname of Flying Noah's Ark.

Animals had been shipped by air for many years. The Montgolfier brothers transported a duck, a sheep and a rooster in one of their historic balloons, in 1783. About 140 years later, a valuable bull was transported in Holland in a small, single-engined Fokker, much to the surprise of many Dutch farmers, who had come from all parts of the tiny kingdom to witness the flight of the first "flying Bull."

Now a variegated lot of animals of all sorts, ranging from lap dogs to carrier pigeons, chickens and tropical birds are flown in from countries of origin. As all these animals require attention, special animal keepers—animal stewards—many trained at zoos, go along for duty on board to watch over and attend to them. They keep close tab on temperature control, feeding and accommodations and carefully observe the condition of the animals when they are checked in for air transportation. They see to it that the cages are strong and well constructed, and that the animals are fed the proper food. Speed of the plane is also an important factor, because animals are exceedingly sensitive to temperature changes and many cannot tolerate too long voyages.

Veterinarians from the faculty of one of the oldest universities have therefore been consulted, and two members of the scientific staff have even taken a number of voyages to accompany and study the livestock. Their reports have formed the basis for the special services given these travelers. The nature and behavior pattern of each animal type has also been taken into account. For instance, a cage in which a tiger is housed during the flight is never placed close to the one in which monkeys are kept. Electric eels from

South America have had to be cased in specially insulated containers, because they are able to generate a current of from 300-350 volts. In connection with the shipment of horses, KLM has done some special research and useful pioneering. Hence owners of valuable horses have availed themselves of KLM's special services, as did the late Aga Khan, who airshipped 18 horses by KLM.

In 1954, the famous horse Halla, who won the world jumping championship, was shipped by KLM, as well as the motion picture favorite Trigger and many others. The KLM tells a story of how two Argentine queen ants, accompanied by twenty consorts, all closely packed in a tin container which was packed again in a wooden box, were transported many years ago by the KLM animal cargo service. On another flight four queen bees, escorted by a detachment of sixty worker bees, were shipped to Colombia in special boxes made with honeycomb cells so that the insects would not lay any eggs on route, but would restrain their activities until a new bee colony had been set up on their arrival in South America. Even the bird kingdom has not been overlooked, and countless valuable species have been shipped by air, like the five swallows that had missed their annual migration across the Swiss Alps. These swallows were turned over to KLM at Stuttgart's airport, with instructions to release them on their arrival at Rome.

The KLM tells about one of their largest flying menageries when the shipment via the KLM Douglas Skymasters *Limburg* and *Flying Dutchman* from Bangkok to Amsterdam consisted of three elephants, one royal tiger, two tapirs, four pandas, 425 monkeys, and 10,000 birds. Later, on another flight, an American girl animal buyer known as Jungle Jenny accompanied a shipment of 2,000 wild animals across the Pacific.

Some interesting studies have been made by veterinarians who accompanied these shipments, such as the case of the transport of live fish, which used to be carried in tins. What puzzled these veterinarians and scientists was whether the assorted species of fish really got "sea" or rather "air" sick. This question was solved in due time, when a decision was made that these fish should be transported in plastic bags, three fourths filled with water, and then suspended in the cargo section. It has been reported by all concerned with great satisfaction and relief, that there have not been any airsick fish since then.

But there exists one specimen of the animal kingdom that

M. Chemery, first chef of Air France at the Orly kitchens, samples
Champagne served on the flights.—AIR FRANCE

KLM chefs at work in the pastry kitchens at Schiphol.—KLM

Qantas stewardess Maria Hendriks entertains a kangaroo passenger before his flight from Australia to the United States.—QANTAS

Two animal passengers amuse themselves after a flight from dark-
est Africa to Orly airfield outside Paris.—AIR FRANCE

KLM's Flying Noah's Ark has not been able to take along. This specimen happens to be the long-necked giraffe. Maybe something will be devised by the imaginative and ingenious Hollanders, that will permit the giraffe to "stick his neck out" through the plane. Reports so far have indicated that there has not been any change in the situation. Until then the giraffes will have to be content to be shipped by steamer, and I don't think the giraffes will care.

— 27 —

JETS AND HOW THEY OPERATE

As we have noted, all air vehicles are divided into two distinct classes according to the principle of suspension: the lighter-than-air ones, such as balloons, airships or dirigibles, which are supported by gases lighter than the atmosphere, and the heavier-than-air variety, of which the airplane is the most common example, which depends for its support upon the dynamic reaction of the atmosphere *under* the moving surface of the plane.

The chapter that dealt with the Montgolfier era explained what made a balloon ascend. Elaborating upon this a bit more, let's immerse a piece of wood in water and then release it. It will rise immediately to the surface and will float partially immersed. Similarly everyone knows that when air is heated it has the tendency to rise, because the atmosphere becomes less dense as the distance above the surface of the earth increases. Coming back now to the piece of wood, the weight of the water displaced by the immersed portion of the wood equalizes the total weight of the piece of wood.

A light gas, such as hydrogen or helium, will, therefore, continue to rise until it reaches an altitude where the rarefied air is equal in weight to an equivalent volume of the light gas. To make use of this principle for aerial navigation it is only necessary to confine the light gas in an envelope, bag or container to prevent its escape into the atmosphere. Thus we know why balloons ascend, and that all gases, including the air we breathe, have weight. The actual weight is not constant, but varies with the temperature, humidity, and barometric pressure. For example, the average weight of 1,000 cubic feet of air at normal temperature is about 75 pounds, whereas an equal volume of hydrogen weighs only a little over five pounds. The difference, therefore, between the two actual weights, or 70 pounds, represents the rising force available for raising a useful load, such as a kite, balloon, or plane.

The question now of why an airplane is supported by the atmosphere, or how an airplane of several tons can be raised against the force of gravity and sustained in the air, first requires an appreciation of the fact that the atmosphere has considerable weight without which the aircraft could not ascend. What we feel as the force of a strong wind is the actual impact of a definite weight of air against the plane's body. When therefore 75 pounds of air is thrown against the underside of the wing surface, the wing will move upward and backward. Part of the force of impact, effective in an upward direction, is called *lift,* while the remaining force continuing in the direction of the impact is called *resistance* or *drag.*

There are actually four forces that act on an airplane in level flight: they are *thrust, drag, lift,* and *gravity.* When these four are in complete harmony or balance, the plane will be in level flight. Some 80 to 90 per cent of the *lift* occurs along the upper surface of the wings during the level flight. *Thrust* has a bearing on the action of the propellers, and when the plane propeller turns through the air, a thrust or forward motion is created. *Drag* refers to the resistance to the forward motion of the plane, and finally, with regard to *gravity,* the weight of the plane has the tendency to pull it toward the earth.

And now let's find out what all this has to do with the creation of jet propulsion, which involves many intricate mechanical problems. The forward motion of a plane is based on Sir Isaac Newton's Third Law, which is that every action produces a reaction, equal in force and opposite in direction. The action in a jet plane is the acceleration of gas leaving the nozzle, whereas the reaction is the thrust. It is, therefore, not the gases pushing against the air behind the engine, which gives the plane its thrust. For example: Let's take a toy balloon and blow it up. Good. Then, when it is held tightly by the nozzle, there is no action. But once the nozzle is released, it sails forth because the escaping air creates an unbalanced pressure inside the balloon, and the pressure against the bottom side where the nozzle is has become stronger than the pressure created against the opposite side. Hence, the balloon is pushed upward, or rises. In other words, the action of the released air produces the reaction, which sends the balloon in the opposite direction.

This proves that there is power in compressed air. By adding fuel to and burning the compressed air, the power is increased. By generating the pressure with a compressor driven by a turbine, we get what is called a Jet Engine. Something is needed, of course, to drive the turbine, which, in turn, is to drive the compresser again. This is done with a burner. This process of heating the air not only expands the air, but expels it at a higher velocity than that at which it has entered the engine. And that is what makes a jet engine tick. Complicated? Not at all. This engine power control in a jet takes only a single lever to send a signal to an automatic device called fuel control. This latter device, which is sensitive to constantly changing conditions of operation, regulates the fuel flow. This mode of operation is vastly different, of course, from that employed in the old type piston engines, which are controlled by the many levers and switches found on the dashboard of the pilot's cockpit.

Jet engines thrive on speed, and jet speeds are almost double those of present-day piston planes. Altitude, payload, fuel load and many other factors have an important bearing on the speed of the jet in the air.

Servicing and fueling the jets presents quite a problem. The jets have healthy appetites, and also do a great deal of work, and therefore consume more fuel than ordinary planes. By having their fuel tanks in their wings, the largest jets are capable of storing more than 21,000 gallons, and they have been so designed that they can be fueled at the rate of 2,000 gallons per minute from hoses through underwing pressure fueling points. This makes up a big portion of the jet's total gross weight. When loaded with a full payload, a jet will carry as much as 40 per cent of its weight in fuel, compared to 30 per cent for the piston planes still flying today.

Vibration, be it from a piston plane or jet, constitutes a prime source of fatigue, not only to the plane traveler but also to the plane's metal. However, travelers will have a much more relaxing and less fatiguing ride on a jet, as there is a great deal less vibration. Noise has also been a nuisance on ordinary planes, so that a solution had to be found to overcome the greater noise that was to be expected from the jets. Because the reputation of jet aircraft as noise generators had been so well established in the minds of the public, airlines have worked night and day to make these jets acceptable to the communities located near airports. Many airplane makers have developed noise suppressors which now have become integral parts of the powerplants of their jet planes.

The training of jet plane personnel is also a most important factor in the scheme of operation of every airline flying jets. It is this thorough and never-ending training that is largely responsible for the excellent safety record achieved by practically all scheduled airlines, especially if one compares it with the great number of accidents suffered in automobile traffic. Jet teaching ground schools have been initiated not only at our international airports—LaGuardia, Idlewild and Peconic Airport on eastern Long Island—but many international airlines have also started their own jet training schools abroad.

Basically, the jet is steered up and down, right and left, on the same principles as those used by conventional planes. But a jet, which flies nearly twice as fast as a piston plane, has to have additional control devices, too, such as the ailerons on the trailing or rear edge of the wings, plus the rudder on the tail to control turns. Then there are the spoilers, of which there are two on top of each wing, which assist in the making of turns. When a spoiler is raised, like a trapdoor opening up, it reduces the lift on that wing. The spoilers also enable the jet to descend from high altitudes rapidly and with great comfort. There are in addition the leading edge flaps on the wings, to improve the control characteristics during a low-speed flight, and the adjustable horizontal stabilizer, to keep the plane level at high speeds.

To give an idea as to how a jet "sits down," the captain first reduces the lifting power of the wings by raising the spoilers, which causes the plane to "settle" down. Next, he lowers the landing flaps—the curved appendages situated on the trailing edge of the wings. By that time you hear a "roar" to let you know that the wheels are being lowered; this roar is caused by the rushing of air into the wheel way in the belly of the plane. Once the wheels are down the supports lock, which will cause a bang. Incidentally, there are usually ten wheels, eight in the main landing gear and two in the nose of the jet.

While all this is going on and the wheels touch down, the jet is still making a speed of 150 miles an hour, but the moment the jet "kisses" the runway, the pilot or captain turns to the brakes or thrust reversers. The brakes are also interesting from the standpoint of ultra safety, as each has an automatic anti-skid device, keeping its finger, so to speak, on the pulse of the wheel. Should the wheel begin to skid, the wheel's brake is automatically released until it feels that the skid stops, whereupon the brake is reapplied.

To navigate the jet and plot the course, the navigator and pilot have several technical devices at their disposal. First they have the "Loran," automatic long-range position, and automatic direction finder; two gyro compasses; one magnetic compass; two radio compasses; radio contact with ground stations, and other modern radio aids. There still remains, of course, the galaxy—the mariners' old friends the stars—from which an exact "fix" can always be had through the periscope sextant. The pilot also has the weather radar to fall back on. This radar enables the captain to be on the lookout for thunderheads way in advance, and to circumvent them, so that he can pick the best route through any overcast that may be hovering around.

Thus modern man's instinct to see how fast he can go has now received greater impetus with the advent of the jet. Jets have done to commercial aviation what the steamboat once did for passenger shipping. It actually made our world some 40 per cent smaller. In fine, the jets have brought greater challenges, benefits and opportunities and a new dynamic to our economy.

— 28 —

TODAY'S TEST PILOTS—THE X-15 ROCKET PLANE

On March 30, 1961, test pilot Joseph Walker scored a new world altitude record of 165,000 feet with the X-15 rocket plane, in spite of momentary engine failure immediately after launching from Edwards Air Force Base. Flying the stub-winged experimental plane 31.25 miles above the earth, the courageous test pilot said he could see "all the California Coast, as well as part of Oregon and Baja California, Mexico."

On October 17, the X-15 rocket ship set a speed record of 3920 miles an hour for controlled aircraft, with Walker, a National

Aeronautics Space Administration pilot, at the helm, flying at nearly six times the speed of sound. And yet, he described the flight as "completely uneventful."

This flight, during which the temperature reached 1,110 degrees Fahrenheit on parts of the X-15, bettered the record made a few days previous (of 3,647 m.p.h.) by Air Force Major Robert M. White, who went so fast that he shot to a record altitude of 217,000 feet. Six days before, Major White had flown the X-15 rocket plane more than 40 miles above the earth—actually to the threshold of space. As he described his flight, he was "essentially outside the atmosphere" and he "could definitely feel the increasing pull of gravity, as I pulled back." During part of the gruelling flight the major's heartbeat and respiration rate rose to twice the normal readings. Whereas the normal pulse rate is 70 to 80 beats a minute, Major White's rate that day may have been 170 during critical portions of the test, flight surgeons said. His respiration, normally 18 to 20 breaths a minute, also doubled. He said he experienced no trouble during the two minutes of weightlessness.

The Major furthermore said that "he had to be very accurate in his operation of the X-15 rocket, as the ship would have burned up as a result of friction, if his 15 degree angle on re-entering the atmosphere had been in error."

This rocket-propelled aircraft, with its strange wedge-shape, vertical tail and stubby wings, housed in heat-treated nickel alloy to beat the 1,200 degrees Fahrenheit at highest speed, was designed to go to the edge of space. Thus speed, and more speed, has become the order of the day.

Fifteen years ago, Captain Charles (Chuck) Yeager cracked the speed of sound in the Bell XS-I, a speed that reached 1,100 feet per second, at sea level approximately 762 miles per hour. Closeted into the cockpit of his orange-painted vehicle as he fell away from the underbelly of the four-engined bomber, Yeager a few minutes later had his name written with glory in aviation's annals. He had broken the sonic barrier on the morning of October 14, 1947.

It is unfortunate that these famous test pilots—the pace makers and real heroes of the sky, who set the mark for all others to follow —often pay a terrific price.

Chuck Yeager, the torch bearer for those pilots from the U.S. Air Force going into supersonic flights, a married fellow blessed with four kids, was once completely blown out of the sky on his ninth combat mission during World War II. Eluding his German aerial pursuers, he escaped into Spain, where the Spanish authorities threw him into jail. He managed to escape, and, flying across to England, he then flew an additional 55 missions. Some years later, after copping one record after another, the breaking of the sound barrier meant nothing to this daredevil test pilot. He joined with Major Arthur Murray on June 4, 1954, in an X-IA silver plane, and extended the space frontier once more by making a new record, during which a 90,000 feet altitude was reached.

Of course many other test pilots had their sight fixed on attaining altitude and the border of space, so that it should be recorded here that the actual flight into the border of space occurred on November 11, 1935, when Major General Orvil Anderson of the United States Air Force and Captain A. W. Stevens rose to an altitude of nearly 14 miles in the balloon *Explorer II*. Since then many test pilots have gone higher, like Captain Iven C. Kincheloe, Jr. of the United States Air Force, who took the rocket-powered X-2 up to nearly 24 miles, or 120,200 feet, on September 7, 1956. Almost a year later Major David G. Simons, also of the United States Air Force, went up in a sealed capsule, beneath a balloon (in Project Man High) to 102,000 feet for a new manned-balloon record. It was then generally believed that the advantage of the balloon over a research rocket plane was its capability of staying aloft longer. Sadly, Captain Kincheloe flew his last flight when he failed to eject from a crippled F-104 Starfighter and crashed to earth before he could open his parachute and separate from his seat.

Going back a few years, NACA'S (the National Advisory Committee for Aeronautics) Herbert Hoover became the second test pilot to pass the sonic wall in an XS-I, on March 4, 1948. The Douglas test pilot Bill Bridgeman achieved a new record of 1,238 miles per hour on August 7, 1951, with his little plane, the *Sky-rocket*, clocking a height of 79,494 feet, the highest ever attained by man at that time.

A few weeks after Kincheloe'se X-2 flight, Captain Milburn Apt made a new record of 2,170 miles per hour, attaining an altitude of 70,000 feet. He, too, came to a terrible end when the capsule in which he rode smashed to the ground, killing him instantly. He was the 13th test pilot to lose his life at Edwards Air Force Base.

Of course, more and more records are being made in the X-15, although things move so fast now that, by the time that the ink is dry on these papers, the last records may already be obsolete.

While the preceding pages have attempted to interpret the parts played by these courageous and capable test pilots, it may be of added interest to return to test pilot Walker's most recent flights. Having achieved complete control of the stub-winged X-15, Walker's aim was to explore the perils of heat created by air friction. This friction occurs when the plane enters the thicker atmosphere from the nearly airless fringe of space. Hence the heating characteristics of the X-15 during the exit and re-entry into the atmosphere was closely measured. The unusual temperature in the cockpit did indicate the air friction was heating his plane to an extremely high temperature, but Walker managed to increase the flow of nitrogen coolant through his pressure suit so that he was never really uncomfortable. Heat sensing devices on the X-15's skin have recorded temperatures as high as 700 degrees on previous occasions. The 50-foot-long X-15, specially designed to obtain knowledge of flight conditions at extremely high altitudes, also carried some pressure sensing devices, in addition to special equipment to measure structural and aerodynamic loads and pilot reaction. One of the most interesting features of the X-15 is its two sets of controls: the aerodynamic surfaces providing control while the vehicle is flying within the mantle of the earth's atmosphere, and the monopropellant rocket thrust units using hydrogen peroxide gas, enabling the pilot to maintain proper flight attitudes in the vacuum conditions outside the sensible atmosphere.

An official of the NASA called test pilot Walker the first "hypersonic aircraft pilot." He was the first, too, to fly a winged vehicle five times the speed of sound. During Walker's 12-minute flight, he not only controlled the plane's speed, but altitude, attitude and the plane's safe landing, as well.

In connection with this X-15 and the marvelous exploits of the test pilots, President Kennedy awarded the Harmon International Trophy for Aviators to the then three pilots who had flown the record-breaking experimental rocket plane. The pilots cited on November 28, 1961, for "outstanding and extraordinary feats of individual piloting" were A. Scott Crossfield, Joseph A. Walker, and Air Force Major Robert H. White. Major White recently flew the X-15 at a record speed of 4,095 miles an hour, and set the altitude record of 217,000 feet, or about 41 miles. Mr. Walker is chief en-

These Pratt & Whitney jet engines are similar to most that power today's jetliners. An over-all view of the JT4 engine.

A cutaway drawing of the JT-3C-6 engine showing its interior construction.—PRATT & WHITNEY

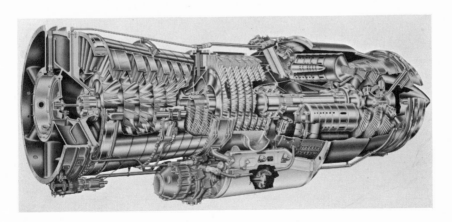

The Convair B-58 jet used by the U.S. Air Force is one of the world's most advanced jet planes.

—GENERAL DYNAMICS

The X-15 rocket plane drops from the mother ship at the start of a mission.—NASA

Diagram of a typical X-15 mission.

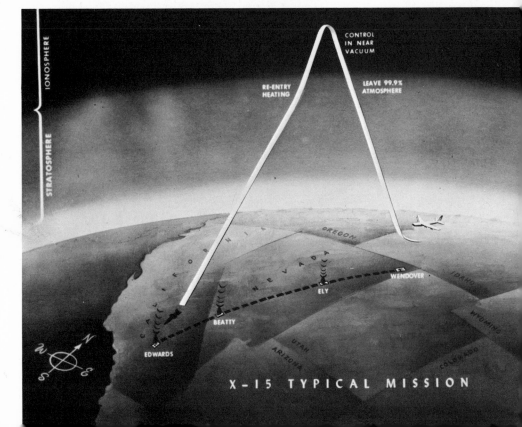

X-15 TYPICAL MISSION

Test pilot Joe Walker grins from the cockpit of the X-15 rocket plane.—NASA

gineering test pilot and a physicist with the NASA, and Mr. Crossfield, a former Navy pilot, is developing engineer and research test pilot of the North American Aviation, Inc.

— 29 —

AN AIRPLANE OF THE FUTURE

While we are embarking on the most ambitious undertaking in history, carrying man into space as far as the moon and subsequently beyond into the solar system, we are also heavily engaged in blueprinting the airplane of the future—a supersonic transport which it is hoped will be in operation some time before 1970. As a result of this project—now in the drawing board and blueprint stage at the Lockheed Aircraft Corporation—it is predicted that hurried man will be able to fly from New York to Los Angeles in one hour and sixteen minutes. In other words, the plane will be traveling three-and-a-half times the speed of sound, at an altitude of 14.5 miles or 75,000 feet. Interestingly enough, the traveler will arrive in Los Angeles (Los Angeles time, of course) one hour and forty minutes before he left New York, because of the time differential.

This, then, was the project outlined by Najeeb Halaby of the Federal Aviation Agency Administration, the successor to General "Pete" Quesada, at a meeting of the Society of Automotive Engineers. He explained that the plane's surface would be heated to 500 degrees, a temperature at which all but special paints would be burned off. Development of this plane could teach engineers much about materials, and how they would stand up in near-space environment at fantastic speeds.

These supersonic airlines, Halaby predicted, would have to be flown at least one year or more in cargo operations, before they could be considered safe for passenger traffic. He also made it plain that he had "no preconceived notion on whether the United States should go right ahead to the Mach 3 [2,000 miles an hour] or make a start with an interim Mach 2 [1300 miles an hour]." This amazing airplane, now on the drawing board, would probably carry 100 passangers, be 200 feet from nose to tail, be 3 stories high, of stainless steel and titanium, and have a fuselage that would be straight and cylindrical like a stove pipe. The information jointly issued by the

Federal Aviation Agency, the NASA, and the Defense Department, indicated that a 2,000-mile-an-hour speed was considered feasible, that it could be developed by 1971 for about $500 million, and that each production line model would cost from $12-25 million.

This study, made with White House approval, was based on information gathered from industry and government sources. As private industry could not do the job alone, the government would have to render considerable assistance.

An estimate of the potential market varied from 75 to 540 planes. Such a plane, Mr. Halaby said, in matters of national security could move soldiers from New York to Berlin in two hours. It would help the national economy and would also maintain national prestige. However, there are many problems that have to be solved before a plane gets off the ground. Electronic instruments to control the plane's stability will have to be developed. New standards of safety will have to be met. Computers will have to be devised to guide the flight from take-off to touch down. Pilots will become monitors of the equipment, as opposed to navigators and communication officers. And all traffic control facilities will have to be revised drastically. So much will have to be done before this "monster" will be airborne. Maybe by 1970 something else, even bigger, will have been devised. Who knows?

— 30 —

NAVIGATION AND WEATHER

A study of history reveals that stars were one of the first means of navigation. And the exploration of space actually means nothing new, because man was exploring the heavens with eye and mind many thousands of years before he began setting foot on the road to the stars.

As early as the 13th century, the people from Polynesia went far afield and crisscrossed the vast stretches of the Pacific solely by aid of the stars. They used for that purpose a rattan chart concocted from sea shells and bamboo sticks. Thus they were able to read and comprehend the language of the stars that guided them safely wherever they desired to go. As man's knowledge grew, one of the first instruments used in more modern celestial navigation was the sextant, first as a shipboard aid and later as an aircraft instrument. Today, the stars aid the exploration of interplanetary space even further.

Weather has been the most common topic of conversation from time immemorial, and it affects aviation and space conquest in general. To quote Harry Wexler, Director of Research of the United States Weather Bureau, "as man leaves Planet Earth for space, a backward glance reveals a globe covered by a lively and ever-changing pattern of brightness, clearly visible against the darker background of oceans and continents. These bright areas are clouds, which cover about 50 per cent of the earth's surface, and are the visible manifestations of storms and other processes in the atmosphere.

"It is in this cloud cover of the earth that our weather is born. Because of the space age developments, we are now able to study the mysterious cloud formations and movements, viewing them in pictures taken from many miles above, a point of view impossible without space satellites."

Aviators, scientists, meterologists and space men have a more than average understanding of the weather. Knowing the idiosyncrasies of the weather along the routes by which the aviators and spacemen travel often means the difference between accident and safety. Together with foreign weather bureaus and weather stations, the U.S. Weather Bureau provides us with the status of and predictions about weather conditions on sea and land.

Consisting of a network of weather stations, a valuable section of the U.S. Department of Commerce predicts conditions close at hand and, together with pilot balloon stations, releases weather balloons every six hours to determine the direction of the wind and the velocity at lower and higher strata. Together with their multiple radio Sonde stations, they release their radio devices or radio Sondes as they are called, every 12 hours to altitudes of 50,000 feet. These Radio Sondes consist of small radio transmitters that report humidity, barometric pressure and temperature. As these balloons rise, it is that sort of information that is sent forth, providing records on all levels to all concerned.

After the information is received, these data, together with all else that is gathered by radio, telephone, telegraph, is minutely set down at least four times daily on what are known as the United States and Foreign Weather Maps. These maps are of inestimable value not only to our many friends manning the planes, but to all having an interest in weather all over the globe.

These countless reams of weather data, collected from hundreds of points all over the world, are made available to pilots, scientists, business organizations, and all those having to do with the conquest of space.

The winds in low pressure areas, where the air over land or water is surrounded by cooler air, flow in a counter clockwise pattern, whereas in high pressure areas they move in a clockwise direction. Taking full advantage of these winds, aviators on long treks are immeasurably helped by what have become known as tail winds. All this information is of immense importance to airmen, and without it no one is safe to set out on his route. The question now is, how is the airman able to navigate his course along invisible upper-air currents? This is facilitated by an upper-air group known as the Wind Analysis Unit, a meteorological command post that has access to weather data ranging, say, from Hawaii in the west to Rome in the east, a radius of some 11,000 miles. This Wind Analysis Unit may be located for example in the operations area of an airline's hangar at New York International Airport. And since New York is about halfway between the Hawaii and Rome terminals of the area covered this location facilitates the receipt of necessary weather data. Information relating to wind directions and speeds, temperatures, pressure, and other data pour into the center on eight clacking and humming machines. These readings have been gathered by civil and military weather stations on two continents and numerous islands, by weather ships posted at strategic points in the Pacific, and Atlantic, also by crews of hundreds of planes flying an intricate pattern of air lanes and routes throughout the vast Hawaii to Rome region.

To make a long story short, a meteorologist at the Wind Analysis Unit sets to work on a special upper-air chart which has been prepared to portray the movement of the air 24 hours in advance. Taking Los Angeles as the starting point, he marks off along certain headings in the general direction of London the distance a plane would fly in its first hour if there were no winds. He then draws an arc through these points. He then corrects this arc to account for the upper-air wind forecast for various points on the arc at a time when a plane would pass each point. He finally plots the shortest flight course from arc to arc, until finally the Minimum

Time Route has been worked out. The upper-air unit in New York now works out a flight's Minimum Time Route eight hours before take-off time. Then conferees at various points discuss the proposed route in the light of general weather forecasts. As a result of this conference a recommended route is decided upon. This route, with expected weather and other operational phases of the pre-flight planning, is presented to the captain for his consideration. The captain then makes his final decision as to the route over which the flight will operate.

At the same time operations officers in Europe are preparing similar material from maps prepared and provided by European weather services. Forecasts of flying weather are always made many hours ahead, together with a forecast of the range of the cloud formation, to predict visibility within so many miles. Hence the definition at which part of the sky is covered by clouds and the height of the cloud masses have become known as the ceiling, actually meaning the greatest distance at which many objects can be seen clearly to establish their position and identity.

Icing is also of vital importance, because of the danger caused to planes and their performance while in flight. Icing on the plane's wings is bound to change the airflow, the plane's lifting capacity, and also affects the power to sustain flight. Taken into account, too, is the phenomenon known as jetstream, the unexpected wind flows and seasonal variations, often exceeding 200 miles per hour. They may aid the pilot when the winds are with him, and dangerously upset the cruising range when flying against the jetstream.

— 31 —

OUR ATMOSPHERE AND OUTER SPACE

Let me begin by saying that we are living at the bottom of the atmosphere, which is composed of about four-fifths nitrogen, one-fifth oxygen, and a small amount of other gases and water. The total weight of the terrestrial atmosphere is 5,000 million tons, which amounts to an atmospheric pressure of about 15 pounds per square inch of the earth's surface.

When we consider that the air is a very molecular structure compared to the nothingness of space, such air not only possesses nature's suitable source of life-sustaining oxygen, but being solid and heavy enough has the barometric pressure necessary to hold the human body together. It is to this atmospheric pressure that man has been accustomed from the beginning of time.

What we have come to know, then, as atmosphere, extending from the earth's surface to a height of approximately 100 miles, grows thinner and thinner as we are going up. The atmosphere at sea level presses upon each square inch of every object or creature with a force of 14.7 lbs per square inch, and if we multiply this by square inches of skin area of an average person, we discover that each person actually withstands about 60,000 pounds of atmospheric pressure. Physically we are not aware of this pressure. Nature has made it possible to brace our bodies so as to resist this compression. But once such pressure is removed, the decompression of atmospheric pressure becomes one of the greatest hazards of extreme altitudes.

The dense atmosphere near the earth contains a heavy concentration of life-sustaining oxygen, and about 21 per cent of the atmosphere at sea level is composed of oxygen molecules.

Nature has made and adjusted the breathing apparatus of man in such a way as to function well when man inhales atmosphere at 21 per cent oxygen. Because of this he is able to breathe concentrations of up to 100 per cent oxygen for quite some time without feeling ill effects. If, however, the oxygen content is reduced too much, or kept low for too long a time, man will get into trouble. This is the reason why mountain climbers suffer the effect of short windedness when they reach a height of 6,000 feet and more. On the other hand, we may recall that Tenzing Norkay, the famous Mount Everest guide, was able to climb to heights over 25,000 feet, without having recourse to bottled oxygen. The Indians of the Peruvian Andes are said to be able to live and work in altitudes of 18,000 feet, the highest known community in the world, seemingly suffering no ill effects.

But the United States Air Force and the United States Navy won't permit fliers to go above a certain altitude unless they are thoroughly equipped, know how to handle oxygen, and have undergone test flights in pressure chambers. It is true that some people need more oxygen than others. A variation in the atmosphere's pressure has a bearing on the pilot as well as on the passengers, plane and engine. Pressurized cabins have overcome all this, so that pressure is maintained comfortably in all airliners. On the other hand, decreased pressure affects landings and take-offs at high altitudes, when lack of oxygen affects all.

As the atmosphere contains moisture in some form or other, this also plays a deciding role. When the air has a large amount of moisture, and the vapor condenses, it turns into dew or fog in the lower and into clouds in the higher strata. Both temperature and what is known as dew point are, therefore, of great significance to the airmen. If these two happen to meet, airmen may expect poor visibility and precipitation. When this dew point and temperature meet on the ground fog and low clouds may result.

Recognizing the fact that the atmosphere of the earth consists of a rather thin belt of encircling gases, held down to the earth by the pull of gravity, the next thing to discuss is the height of the sky. Scientists have divided the earth's sky atmosphere into four main layers: 1: the Troposphere, the realm of all air-supported life known by us, reaching from sea level to an altitude of about 35,000 feet (about 7 miles). This atmospheric layer has most of the earth's necessary atmospheric moisture, including its array of storms and clouds. The lower region of this layer or sphere possesses sufficient oxygen to support plant and animal life. 2: the Stratosphere—second main layer—extending from approximately 40,000 feet to 50 miles, containing about one-fourth of the air's weight and oxygen content, in which the temperature varies from 67 degrees below zero Fahrenheit in the lower regions to a scorching 170 degrees above zero near the top (the heat in the upper stratosphere is caused by a narrow belt of ozone). 3: The Ionosphere—deep layer of very thin air—in which less than 1/1000th of the atmosphere's total weight is contained in an area of several hundreds of miles of depth, extending from an altitude of 50 miles to about 400 miles above the earth, with a temperature of 400 degrees caused by violent electric activity. 4: The Exosphere—often called part of the earth's atmosphere, although really it isn't—from 400 miles above the earth to an approximate 1,000 miles altitude. It is here that space begins, where the air is so thin that it no longer causes what has been termed drag upon a missile or rocket.

I ought now to say something about the physical data of our solar system, before going into the subjects of gravity and heat, all of which do affect our space men.

All of the nine planets move around the sun in the same direction on near-circular orbits. The mean distance from the earth to the sun is 92,900,000 miles, whereas the diameter of the solar system, across the orbit of its remotest member, or Pluto, is about 7,300 million miles. The nearest distances from Venus to the earth is 25 million miles, from Mars to the earth 35 million miles, from Saturn to the earth 744 million miles, and from Jupiter to the earth 367 million miles. It is but a *mere* 50 million miles distance from Mercury, the closest planet to the sun, to our earth.

The four inner Planets—Mercury, Venus, Earth and Mars—all relatively small, dense bodies, are known as the terrestrial planets. The next four in distance from the sun—Jupiter, Saturn, Uranus and Neptune—sometimes also called the major or giant planets, are all relatively large bodies primarily composed of gases with solid ice and rock at unknown depths below the visible surfaces of their atmosphere. Little is known of Pluto.

— 32 —

GRAVITY, HEAT, AND SOUND

We are able to keep our feet on the ground because gravity keeps them there. It has been established that the normal gravitational force of the earth is the force accountable for our own weight, and for the weight of all material bodies. In connection, therefore, with spacemen and spaceships, with each increase in speed of the most up-to-date aircraft, man has come closer to a velocity that will cancel out the pull of terrestrial gravity. The horizontal speed necessary to counterbalance gravity has been established at approximately 17,500 miles per hour. At this speed the human passenger, as well as the spaceship and everything in it, is weightless, a condition produced by the orbiting action in which the earth's gravitational pull is in fact balanced by the internal forces created by the spaceship's speed.

With respect to satellites, they are weightless because the gravity pull exerted by the earth is balanced by the satellites' tremendous speed, known as orbital velocity.

Whereas our first astronauts—Shepard and Grissom—experienced a small measure, or about five minutes of weightlessness, the Russian cosmonauts, Gagarin and Titov, experienced 85 minutes and 25 hours of weightlessness respectively, demonstrating for the first time that, from a physical and psychological standpoint, man could withstand prolonged weightlessness seemingly well. The Russian dog, Laika, which orbited the earth for more than a week in November, 1957, had already proved the point, having adjusted itself from a physical standpoint to an environment in which the law of gravity did not exercise its force in the same manner as it would do on this earth.

A great deal of research has been and will be done in matters affecting gravity. One of the world's most powerful and largest devices created to manufacture artificial gravity is the one at the Naval Air Development Center, in Johnsville, Pennsylvania. This device, called a centrifuge and weighing 250,000 pounds, has a 50-foot steel arm with an enclosed pod or capsule suspended from the outer end. Whirling at high speed with the aid of a gigantic electric motor, the machine is able to generate a centrifugal force equalling many times that of the earth's natural gravity. Here, too, the space men are being gravity-trained.

As already stated, heat is generated by atmospheric friction at high velocities, and the heat at velocities even as high as 500-600 miles per hour is so terrific that a plane's cockpit and cabin have to be refrigerated as the crew and passengers would otherwise be roasted alive.

As long as planes stick to the confines of the earth's atmosphere, and as long as speeds increase, friction heat will be a problem. The only way to escape this friction heat entirely is to soar higher out of the atmosphere into space. This is an airless vacuum with no molecules to drag and no heat to be generated by the aircraft's speed. Above the atmosphere, there is another heat source called solar radiation caused by the beating down of unfiltered sun rays upon the object. Beyond the atmosphere, too, rays are stronger and extremely dangerous, and above 100,000 feet these become very hazardous. Altitude is a partial solution to the problem of aerodynamic heating. As the altitude increases, the air becomes cooler and thinner, and the outside temperature, between the altitudes of about 30,000 and 100,000 feet, remains constant at 67 degrees below zero Fahrenheit. Flying at moderate speed in this frigid area, refrigeration is no longer needed, but in fact the airman must have heat to keep from freezing. (Incidentally, the air's density at the 100,000-foot level is only one hundredth of the air's density at sea level.)

Understandably, because of friction and compression, metals lose strength at high temperatures. Aluminum, for example, loses 40 per cent of its strength at a temperature of only 250 degrees Fahrenheit. Metals have also been found to stretch or flow at extreme temperatures, which has given rise to the term "creep," the tendency to go through such performance. Each particular vehicle has to be gauged for such a danger. One metal of great importance to the aeronautical industry, especially in the creation of rockets and guided missiles, is Nobium, because this metal has been proved to withstand much higher temperatures than other metals used. Those alloys making use of Nobium have been able to perform at temperatures up to 2,200 degrees.

The next phenomenon that I would like to discuss is sound, which is actually a definite form of energy expressed in terms of vibration. Sound waves travel at approximately 760 miles an hour at normal sea-level conditions. They decelerate in thinner or colder air higher up at around 35,000 feet, and travel at approximately 650 miles an hour.

To understand fully what this sound vibration means, we may even have to go back to earliest times—to the Bible even—which, as all of us undoubtedly know, referred to the sound of trumpets in one passage as having caused the walls of Jericho to tumble. In more modern times, the story is told of how Caruso was able to shatter a wine glass with the sound waves of his tremendous voice. Swiss avalanches have often been caused by the sound of gun shots, and ultrasonics are said to produce sound waves of such high frequencies that, though inaudible to the human ear, they can cause similar disturbances nonetheless.

Sound generated by the warming up of a jet can attain such a volume and intensity that the ear drum structure of a man standing close by may often be impaired. Likewise, ultrasonic energy can cut through metals and drill teeth painlessly.

Who has not heard the familiar sound of jet planes in operation, when what seem to be loud claps of thunder come from a cloudless sky? This sound is the familiar sonic boom. No better illustration could be given than that of a speeding aircraft, and other high-speed vehicles, producing sound ripples in the sky, not unlike those caused by a speed boat in a calm stretch of water. When an airplane's speed equals the speed of sound, all it does is to catch up with its own sonic waves. Instead then of remaining spread out ahead of the plane in ripples, these sonic waves become tightly compressed against the nose of the plane and the edges of wings and tail, forming what have become known as shock waves.

— 33 —

THE LORE OF SPACE TRAVEL

The conquest of space and of that mysterious world of stars has been in the minds of men from time immemorial. Tales of space ship voyagers and imaginary accounts of men traveling to the moon were apparently first circulated by Greek and Babylonian astronomers. They were not only intrigued by the movements in the sky, but believed the heavens a vast area in which gods, demons and mortals were used to travel.

Lucian was the author of the first accounts of voyages through space in the second century. In one of these accounts he told of a ship, swept up in a whirlwind and carried for seven days to a great country, which appeared like a shining island. He undoubtedly referred to the moon, which, he said, was inhabited by gigantic, three-headed birds, huge spiders and human beings who, when they died, would dissolve into vapor and smoke. Another, no less fantastic, tale by Lucian dealt with the adventures of a man named Icaromenippus, who flew to the moon, and from there into the highest heaven, with the wings of an eagle. He said: "I know not how, and I much desired to learn what matter the sun was made of, but the greatest marvel to me was the moon." Known to a certain extent from earliest times, Jupiter, Venus, Mars, Mercury and Saturn to the average man were but wandering stars or planets (the name planet actually meaning wanderer).

Followers of Pythagoras imagined that the earth was one of these planets. Many of the Greek philosophers also believed that the moon was a globe, and they made almost accurate estimates of its size and distance from the earth. No wonder that a whole crop of stories evolved about the moon, and journeys to those mysterious worlds.

After the fantastic tales of Lucian and others, there came a lull of about 1,500 years until a new era began and the earth was no longer believed to be the center of the universe. Stories attesting to the seriousness of a contemplated journey to the moon appeared within a generation of Galileo's invention of the crude telescope and the revelation of new secrets when the authors of heavenly journeys attempted to make their accounts seem more practical and less supernatural.

Galileo not only observed the mountains and valleys of the moon, but he proved that it was a solid world, and that the planets, unlike the stars, presented visible discs. He claimed that four tiny points revolved around Jupiter, that the moon went around the earth, and that Jupiter—a world with satellites—seemed small only because of its tremendous distance from the earth. Galileo gave man the first direct revelation of the real scale of the universe, and man secured an instrument in the telescope enabling him to pierce the vast reaches of space.

When an Englishman wrote his *Discovery of a New World in the Moon,* the earliest serious account of a voyage to the moon made its appearance within a generation of Galileo's invention. Then Johannes Kepler, the greatest astronomer of his time, made a discovery of the true laws governing the movements of the planets, the very same laws that govern the movements of space ships.

Kepler's work, titled *Somnium,* published in 1634, actually was written years before, but he was afraid to publish it during his lifetime. Man still believed in magic in those days, and Kepler's mother had been charged with witchcraft. Hence, astronomers like Copernicus, Kepler and Galileo really took a chance, as the Church accused everyone who believed that the earth was not the center of the universe of being a heretic. Kepler wrote to a friend in 1629: "If they chase us from the earth, my book will be useful as a guidebook for emigrants and pilgrims to the moon." Convinced that there was no air between the earth and moon, Kepler was also the first to suggest that there existed great problems of gravity, of weightlessness in space, and of cold and lack of air. It was this sort of information that greatly influenced all future writers of fact and fiction, including H. G. Wells, two and a half centuries later. At a time when adventurous men were quite busy drawing maps of the moon, the first English account of a moon trip made its appearance in 1638, when Bishop Francis Godwin wrote his *Man in the Moone —A Discourse of a Voyage Thither by Domingo Gonzales—the Speedy Messenger.* It gave a vivid description of how his hero traveled to the moon in a flimsy craft drawn by trained swans.

Moon-trip stories became the fashion in those days, and another English Bishop, named Wilkins, published a rather interesting volume, *Discourse Concerning a New World,* in 1640, which gave a most scientific and physical description of the moon, and the suggestion even that the moon might have inhabitants. He predicted that ingenious man would create a "flying chariot" some day, and he even went so far as to suggest that colonies of human beings from the earth might settle there.

As these volumes about space flight—some scientific, others fantastic—grew more plentiful, Cyrano de Bergerac's travel fiction story, *Voyage to the Moon,* appeared in 1656. Having had a real "nose" for things fantastic, Cyrano, a French satirist and philosopher, referred to a theory in one of his parodies of a possible moon voyage that, as the sun soaked up dew, the hero attached vials of this dew to his toes, body and head, and thus was drawn up into the sky. To him should also go the credit for having popularized the use of rocket propulsion, for having anticipated the ram jet, and for having created a flying machine consisting of a light box closed on all sides, except for a nozzle at either end, and a mirror to focus the sunlight on its interior. The air thus being heated would escape through one nozzle and be replenished through the other.

Fontenelle wrote a very popular book on astronomy, in 1686, while Voltaire became the author of *Man and His Planet,* in which he had a fellow named Micromegas and an inhabitant of the solar system of Sirius pay a visit to the earth accompanied by a crony from Saturn.

A hundred or so years later, people began to pay more attention to ballooning and travel within the atmosphere than to the moon and planets. By the second half of the nineteenth century—the fantastic era of Jules Verne—space travel stories not only became more scientific, but due to the engineering achievements of the Victorian Age gave rise to newer ideas. Bridging of space and flights into the cosmos were no longer considered fantastic and out of reason. Travel fiction stories began to see the light in greater numbers, and the belief that other beings lived on other planets became generally accepted in the popular mind. Jules Verne's *Five Weeks in a Balloon, From the Earth to the Moon,* and *Trip Around the Moon* (the first half published in 1865, and the other in 1870) greatly appealed to scientifically minded people.

Jules Verne's spaceship was but a huge hollow shell, a monstrous round bullet, shot out of a gigantic cannon at the moon. Verne's description of the use of rockets that would slow this vehicle down as it reached the moon may well be considered the ancestor of all modern space-travel stories. His *From the Earth to the Moon* was really based on sound scientific principles, and he believed that if a body could be projected away from the earth with sufficient speed it was bound to reach the moon.

H. G. Wells, a man less scientific but more adventure-minded, wrote one of the very few interplanetary romances for the space-minded world. In order to get his people to the moon, Wells created some kind of concoction, named Cavorite, which was said to act as a gravity insulator. Once his space traveling people were coated with this, they could easily leave the earth.

Another writer and mathematician named Schiaparelli disclosed that he had observed grooves (*canali*) on the surface of Mars, which the general public interpreted as man-made canals. After a great deal of research, the German mathematics professor Kurt Laswitz was of the opinion that Mars not only was much older than our planet, but that Martian people really existed and were a great deal more advanced.

So much for the earlier background which brings us now to the matter of rockets.

— 34 —

EARLY ROCKET DEVELOPMENTS—
GODDARD AND OBERTH

The rocket is one of the oldest, perhaps, of man-made devices. To quote the historian and sophist Lucian, it was probably invented by the Chinese. These ancient Chinese people employed a so-called rocket during the Siege of Kaifeng against the Mongolian invaders around the year 1232. They called this rocket affair "Arrow of Flying Fire." It was made up of charcoal, sulphur and saltpeter (later referred to as gunpowder) and emitted so much gas that it often exploded the container. They packed this mixture into round balls or shells, whereas the actual arrow of flying fire was but an ordinary arrow to which a tube, well packed with the mixture, was attached. After this mixture was ignited the arrow would dart out of the tube and spread the fire. The Chinese were not the only ones, however, who had invented such a mixture.

Roger Bacon, an English monk, completely unaware of the fact that the Chinese had already used it, invented a similar mixture of charcoal, sulphur and saltpeter. In the days of Bacon a very simple gun was used, consisting of a muzzle or metal tube, packed with this so-called gunpowder, while a ball of stone or metal was packed with some wadding atop the powder. When the powder was ignited the force of the explosion sent the ball on its way. It was, however, a most unreliable weapon.

In the earlier decades of the 19th century, solid-propellant rockets designed by Sir William Congreve were extensively used in the Napoleonic Wars and the War of 1812. Congreve had been a close student of Sir Isaac Newton's theories. In point of fact, Sir Isaac not only had analyzed the nature of the power that permitted the rocket to soar into the air or space, but also the force that guided and controlled the flight and made it descend. These theories, now universally referred to as The Third Law of Motion and The Law of Gravitation or Gravity, are of great import to present-day rocket and missile makers.

Although I have referred to this law before, Newton's Law of Gravitation specifically theorizes that every object in the universe has the power to attract unto itself other objects, a power that increases with the mass of the object and decreases with its distance. To cite an example: A peach falls to earth the moment it is detached from the branch because the earth pulls it down by attraction. By the same token, our earth is attracted by the greater gravitational pull of the sun. It is this pull that makes the earth travel in a steady orbit around the sun. As for the action of the moon, the same two counter-balancing forces cause the moon to circle our globe in its orbit.

Working out this law, Sir Isaac Newton had been aware already in 1687 that an earth satellite could be launched if it had enough velocity. He even drew pictures to show how it could be fired, and he was way ahead of scientists of those days.

Returning to Sir William Congreve, he envisaged a weapon with enough gravity-defying force to leave the earth and shoot to an opposing position as it was drawn back to earth, in other words, the Newtonian idea of reaction, and part and parcel of the three Laws of Motion, which says that there is an equal and opposite reaction for every action.

In Congreve's days toy makers used to be the natural source of supply of rockets that were not unlike the skyrockets in use today. Consisting of a cylindrical case of very tightly rolled paper, these rockets were equipped with a nozzle, while the combustible payload or rocket charge was stuffed into the cylinder's front end. Launched into the air by combustible gases, and guided or balanced by a stick attached to the rocket's cylinder, ignition would continue to take place after the rocket was in flight. The rocket was set in motion by gas forced out of the cylinder by a pressure that had built up inside the rocket, because of the burnt rocket powder. Heat transformed the powder into a great many gas particles doing their very best to escape through the open end whence they dispersed into all directions.

Sir William Congreve had been devoting long hours of research to create a rocket that not only could travel great distances, but could also destroy a target. So aided, by the people at the Woolwich Royal Arsenal, he built a rocket cylinder that could stow larger quantities of powder. Used most actively by him in 1805, this rocket was able to shoot a six-pound ball for a distance of 2,000 yards. These rockets were used against Napoleon's Armada of ships and barges massed at French ports, which were to be used against Britain. Lord Nelson used some of these rockets against the French forces in the port of Cadiz, and they also did formidable duty at the battle of Leipzig against Napoleon. They were likewise used in Britain's American colonies. Our national Anthem refers to the "rockets' red glare" for the British also used this type of rocket after the White House burning and their Washington victory, on September 13, 1814, when the British fleet bombarded Fort McHenry and finally, these rockets inspired Francis Scott Key, as he observed the "bombs bursting in air" against the night sky, and won him undying fame.

Still, these rockets proved impractical and inefficient in the end and had to give way to guns with rifled bore, as the gun's projectiles would go straight to their targets because of their rotary movement.

At the turn of the century another rocket scientist appeared on the scene, the Russian school teacher, Konstantin Edwardovitch Ziolkovsky, called the Father of Space Flight. Evolving some of the first theories of rocket-jet propulsion and multi-stage missiles, he outlined his ideas in *Science Survey,* in 1903. These theories could have created quite a stir in the science world, had people abroad been able to read Russian. Another series of articles on rockets and space travel—based on Ziolkovsky's innate knowledge of physics, chemistry and mathematics—appeared in the Russian magazine *Aviation Reports,* in 1911. It was the consensus of many scientists that this Russian was 'way ahead of his time. Long after his death in 1935, rocketry was no longer reserved for mathematicians and physicists, but was well on the way to becoming a science in its own right.

During the first World War, a man who had devoted considerable thought to the Russian's theories was the great American scientist, Doctor Robert Hutchings Goddard (1882-1945). Goddard almost single-handed worked out his own practical and technical details of rockets, without, however, getting the recognition in this country he so rightly deserved. He was, however, honored posthumously for the great work he had done. Financing Goddard's work the Smithsonian Institution published his first monograph on rockets in 1919, entitled *A Method of Reaching Extreme Altitudes,* a booklet that greatly helped to further the modern era of rocket research.

Goddard's theory was based on the premise that it should be possible to build rockets powerful enough to leave the world's gravitational field and get to the moon. Actually making and firing rockets, often at great cost and after patient research, Goddard patented a design for a nozzle and a combustion chamber in 1914. He also designed a step rocket, which could soar into space. He received a grant from the Smithsonian Institution and a Robert Hutchings Goddard professorship had also been created in his honor by the Daniel and Florence Guggenheim Foundation.

At the end of World War II the Smithsonian announced that this great rocket pioneer had invented and tested a new type of multiple-charge, high efficiency rocket of an entirely new concept and design for the exploration of the unknown regions of space. When this rocket and missile pioneer died in 1945, posterity was not only left the richer by his many patents and papers relating to rockets and airplanes, but many scientists were stimulated in their own efforts through his great influence. One of these scientists was the spaceship designer and Rumanian professor of mathematics,

Hermann Oberth, who published *The Way to Space Travel,* a veritable bible of astronautics. He gave details of the kind of spaceship in which passengers might be able to survive. He also referred to a moon rocket with enough powder to make a flash against the moon's surface. He was absolutely convinced that liquid fuel would drive a rocket as far as the moon. Oberth did not leave a thing to the imagination. He explained, for instance, why a rocket could move at a velocity exceeding that of its exhaust jet, and why it continued to rise even after its fuel had been exhausted. He also gave details of the kind of space vehicle to use and of the research instruments to take into the upper atmosphere. He emphasized that the vehicle could be used for weather studies and as a refueling station for rockets traveling farther out into space.

Significantly, he gave details of the kind of suits space men would need, of the use of a hammock instead of a seat, and a kind of shoe provided with hooks that would make it possible for space men to move about in the space ship once outside the sphere of gravity. To summarize, Oberth elaborated the principle of the step rocket, and like Goddard, proposed the idea of a space station traveling in an orbit around the earth. He also studied the possibility of a rocket-propelled plane, with its requirements and drawbacks.

While space does not permit me to go much further into his activities and those of the other hard-working pioneers of the American Rocket Society—which was started in 1934 as the outgrowth of the American Interplanetary Society—suffice to say that the really first productive organization of rocketeers, founded in America in 1927, counted among its members such men as Johannes Winkler, editor of the first issue of *Rocket, Journal of the Society for Space Travel,* Dr. Walther Hohmann and Willy Ley, whose comprehensive volume, entitled *Rockets, Missiles, and Space Travel* was published over here and who, after breaking away from the Nazis, eventually came to the United States.

In the United States a rocket program (such as that maintained by the German Rocket Society—or *Verein Fur Raum Schiffart*) led to the founding of the American Rocket Society, with which the late Sir Hubert Wilkins, G. Edward Pendray, Dr. Goddard, and David Lasser (editor of the fiction magazine, *Wonder Stories*) were actively associated in addition to those already mentioned.

With the advent of World War II, when many active members

of the Society were drawn into the conflict and the war put a crimp in the efforts of the pioneering rocketeers, their projects were taken over by military authorities. This inaugurated mass research and investigations by government bodies, and led to the production of a large number of rocket weapons and missiles, in addition to such high-altitude rockets as the Viking and Aerobee (also known as the WAC Corporal).

Still, some civil pioneering in rockets continued by such men as Wyld (known for Wyld's motor, which greatly interested the U.S. Navy) Shesta, Pierce, and the electronic engineer Lovell Lawrence. In another part of the United States a small rocket society became part of what was then known as the Jet Propulsion Experimental Unit, operating at the California Institute of Technology and Guggenheim Aeronautical Laboratory. Here the famous Dr. Theodore von Karman had been at work on high altitude rockets since 1936.

In Germany, practical work on rocket engineering from 1926 was largely inspired by the researches and findings of Oberth and the German War Department, which financed the infamous V-2, and many other rocket weapons later, and with which the next chapter shall deal somewhat more in detail. They were developed between 1936 and 1945, as their scientists proved conclusively that the theories of the American Goddard and the German Oberth were basically correct.

— 35 —
THE V-2 AND THE PEENEMÜNDE GROUP

Let's trace the spectacular development of the V-2 rocket and Peenemünde where they were first made. The V-2 actually was foreshadowed when Germany was made to sign the Versailles Treaty at the end of World War I. Ironically enough, one of the clauses in the Treaty stated that Germany was to be prevented from rearming and starting another war, and from manufacturing war material, cannon and machine guns. But it failed to mention rockets. Whether this was deliberately overlooked or not, the fact remains that due to the existence of this loophole, the German Weapons Department devoted its attention to rockets in 1929. That task was assigned to

Walter Dornberger, whose book, called *V-2,* and published in the United States in 1954, gives a most illuminating account of what transpired during the years after the First World War.

The practical work on the creation of rockets from 1926 was, however, largely inspired by Oberth. Dornberger tells how an experimental unit was set up at the Weapons Department's proving ground at Kummersdorf, south of Berlin, and he refers to his association with a fellow named Rudolph Nebel, once the assistant of Oberth and later engaged in producing the Repulsors with VFR (German Rocket Society). Another one of his associates was the very young VFR member, Baron Werner von Braun, now in the U.S.A. and actively engaged in the production of missiles and rockets, a Director of the American Rocket Society, a Director of the National Aeronautics and Space Administration at Huntsville, Ala., and in charge of the development of the Saturn rocket, which is to be the free world's most powerful space tool.

Dr. von Braun considered himself most fortunate in having such experts as Oberth and Dornberger as his teachers. There were a great many problems that had troubled the rocket builders at the *Raketenflugplatz* (Rocket Flying Field), such as the inaccuracy that had characterized the black-powder rocket weapon of Congreve's days. They endeavored to improve the control of the heavy, high speed rocket. Another problem was the test stand for testing large rockets and motors. After a series of experiments, one of the improved rocket specimens constructed by them in 1934 rose to an altitude of 1.4 miles.

And so it came to pass that the largest rocket-research station in the world was erected at a spot selected by von Braun not far from the fishing hamlet of Peenemünde on Usedom island, where their work could come to fruition. It was here that work was started on the A-4, better known as the V-2, which was to become such a dangerous projectile during World War II and which they hoped would blast the daylight out of the Allies and Great Britain in particular. This aluminum-nosed rocket, with a thrust of one and a half tons and exhaust velocity aggregating 6,000 feet per second, just before the beginning of the Nazi holocaust reached a height of five miles. This gave Dornberger and the rest the success for which they had schemed, tested, and sweated. It had taken them about seven years to construct a liquid-propellant rocket and with success apparently within their grasp, Hitler suddenly ordered the research project stopped. However Dornberger was not at all discouraged, for his mind was set on producing proper launching pads from which to shoot this deadly cargo against England. Hence he persisted, and together with von Braun and his associates completed the job. Meanwhile, Hitler's German Air Force, on order of the Fuhrer, had worked on a rival rocket in its own research department, and ultimately produced the V-I (its name signifying Vengeance) a winged rocket that looked like a small plane and operated on the theory of jet propulsion by using fuel oil and securing its oxygen from the air through opening and closing valves. Stacking all their hopes on the V-1 and V-2, Hitler and his henchmen cherished the wish that these rockets would save the Fatherland from defeat.

The Nazis had also developed and operated, although on a smaller scale, a four-step rocket, known as Rheinbote, propelled by solid fuels and with a range of 100 miles.

After the end of World War II, the United States manufactured two-step rockets by using the V-2 (of which at least 200 were brought over from Germany) for the lower stage, and a smaller American rocket—the WAC Corporal—for its upper section.

The British had not been sitting still either. They unloaded more than 1,500 tons of high explosives on the Peenemünde Rocket Nest in August, 1943, crippling the project and holding up work there for at least a month.

It was not until 1944 that the first buzz bombs and V-2s were sent across the English Channel, dropping on London and other places from a height of sixty miles and more. However, the damage the Germans had hoped to inflict was not as bad as they had anticipated, although psychologically speaking their damaging effect was greater.

The end of the German rocket story which came with the Nazis' defeat also meant that Dornberger and von Braun had outlived their usefulness to the German cause. After spending the last days of the war hiding in the mountains, von Braun, together with many other first rate scientists, was rounded up and "invited" to come to America, to continue his rocket research here. This undertaking, or rounding up, went by the curious name of Operation Paper Clip. While the Germans were employed by the Guided Missile Development Division of the United States Army, the famous scientist Dornberger became the consultant on missile design for the Bell Aircraft Corporation.

But, as asserted by Major Alexander P. de Seversky, the Russians not only grabbed most of what was left behind by the conquered Nazis, but also managed to bring to Russia many of the German guiding spirits with scientific know-how about rocket making, so that the Russians were way ahead of the U.S. at once.

— 36 —

THE U.S. MISSILE PROGRAM—CAPE CANAVERAL

Our own guided missile program got under way with a vengeance shortly after the end of World War II. Added impetus was given to this program when the German V-2s were brought over here for study. However, long before the work had started at the Cape's launching pads, Dr. Robert H. Goddard, America's great pioneer of space research, had fired the first liquid-fueled rocket (forerunner of Yuri Gagarin's vehicle) on March 16, 1926, a rocket that rose 184 feet into the air.

Man's road into space was further paved by America's two-stage, liquid-fueled missile Project Bumper, on February 24, 1949, fired from a flat desert valley in White Sands Proving Grounds, N.M. This hybrid German-American rocket blasted 250 miles up, to a point where the atmosphere was so thin that one molecule of air had to travel five miles to collide with its nearest neighbor. This rocket, the first to be fired successfully, was a combination of one of the captured German V-2s brought back to the United States, and a 700-pound WAC Corporal, a World War II research vehicle.

As the missile research program began to assume greater prominence, it soon became apparent that it would be necessary to establish an efficient testing area for long range missiles, with the result that the Defense Department authorized the Air Force to have a test base set up at the Cape for the launching of missiles for all the Armed Services.

The first missile was sent on its way from Cape Canaveral—Patrick Air Force Base in 1950. However, as it became obvious that for the good of the services the management and operation of the base be stabilized by personnel in order to provide continuity of service, it was decided to have all these functions performed by a civilization organization. Hence the announcement on April 30,

1953, that Pan American World Airways and the Radio Corporation of America had been chosen respectively as range contractor and sub-contractor. Pan American's Guided Missile Range Division started operation as prime contractor to the United States Air Force, for the management, operation and maintenance of the 5,000-mile missile test range in October, 1957. This Range has since become known as the Atlantic Missile Range of Cape Canaveral.

Starting at the wedge-shaped bit of islands jutting out into the Gulf Stream the Range embraces some 13 islands of various sizes, from cays to larger bits, and even stretches to the coast of Africa, bridging a 3,000-mile gap between St. Lucia and Ascencion Island.

As new rockets, missiles and satellites were developed, demand for greater and newer facilities grew. The operations required bigger staffs, more high voltage and high pressure lines to the pads, hangars and machine shops, for volatile fuels. They also demanded wells, waterplants, power stations, additions to the complex control points besides camera towers, mobile tracking sites at launching areas along the beaches and down the Florida Coast.

Besides all these, complex tracking and recording equipment became necessary, in addition to larger sewage disposal, bottled gas plants, laundries, garages, supply stores, barracks, administration and general control buildings. In short, it turned into a project of such complexity that the whole Canaveral area began to look like a small city in itself, with all the problems that such places entail. Since the space project has assumed such proportions, Nasa recently announced that the Cape Canaveral Rocket Center would be enlarged to more than five times its present size, in order to be well-prepared for manned flights to the moon and comparable missions.

The Guided Missiles Range Division or GMRD in itself does not build or fire missiles, but rather operates and oversees every function of missile ground support. The Air Force or other Command Force furnishes each missile builder with hangar space and launching pad, while the GMRD assigns electrical operating crews and engineering facilities to each contractor to insure smooth operation. The GMRD fuel trucks also load rockets and missiles with the required propellants.

Astronomical and aerological observations are conducted at weather stations all along the range and relayed at once to the Cape. When a missile is finally sent on its way from the pad, tracking begins from the many designated strategic points until the missile is recovered if such is to be the case. This becomes the task of ships who have to grapple for the capsule or missile, a task to which each tracking ship (or plane) is assigned.

In final analysis, though, Cape Canaveral Control Central is the heart, brain and nerve center of the whole launching operation. While each of the island bases along the 5,000-mile Atlantic Missile Range renders its reports, the Cape Range Clearance plots ships and aircraft in the area that is being fired. Then, when all is clear, the Air Force range safety officer determines in the final seconds of the countdown that all the danger areas are clear. The pad safety officer does likewise and affirms that launching conditions on the launching pad are secure, while finally the Panam super of range operations does his bit to make sure that all the details that insure support of the range are equally taken care of. Then, when all this has been done, each of the parties closes one switch in the firing circuit, and only when all the switches are closed is the test conductor's firing button connected to the missile.

Here follows a resume of the reports as they flow in from the missile test chief or conductor at the Cape's blockhouse:

"Propulsion, OK. Guidance Check, OK. Destruct Check, OK. Missile Telemetry, OK." These are followed by readiness reports from the Range Instrumentation and Cape optics leader: "Optics, Go. Range Telemetry Reports Telemetry, Go." Next, the Cape radar chief calls: "Radar, Go." And after each one of the island bases over the long range has made its report, the familiar follows: "Three, Two, One, Zero . . ." after which the test conductor presses the firing button, and the missile or rocket slowly rises and shoots into space, while the anxiety among missilemen, workers, newsmen and the rest grows. The missile's flight is then followed not only on the complicated consoles and vertical plotting boards all the way down the Range and along the Florida Cape but also on the ocean vessels bobbing at anchor. And all that time those in all sections of the operation are bending and crouching over their instruments, while thousands of miles away, maybe only a few minutes after countdown, divers tracking vessels, far out in the Atlantic, are seeking to pick up the nose cone that may hold the answers to so many important questions.

After this the real job starts of studying and evaluating the data that have been sent back to the Cape, where plans for the future and for subsequent missile firings are being laid.

A Thor Agena B rocket launches *Discoverer XXI* from Vandenberg Air Force Base.—DOUGLAS AIRCRAFT

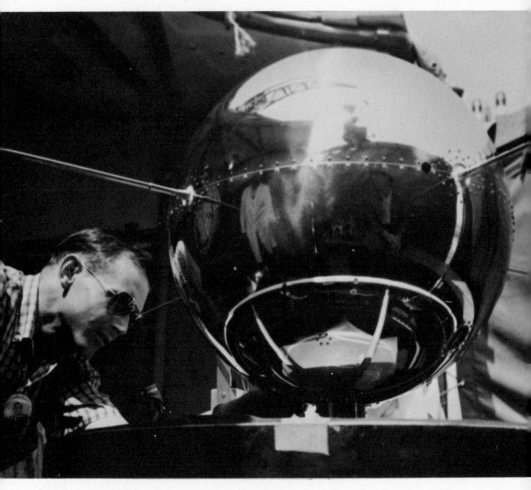

A Vanguard satellite is checked out at Patrick Air Force Base prior
to launching.—U.S. AIR FORCE

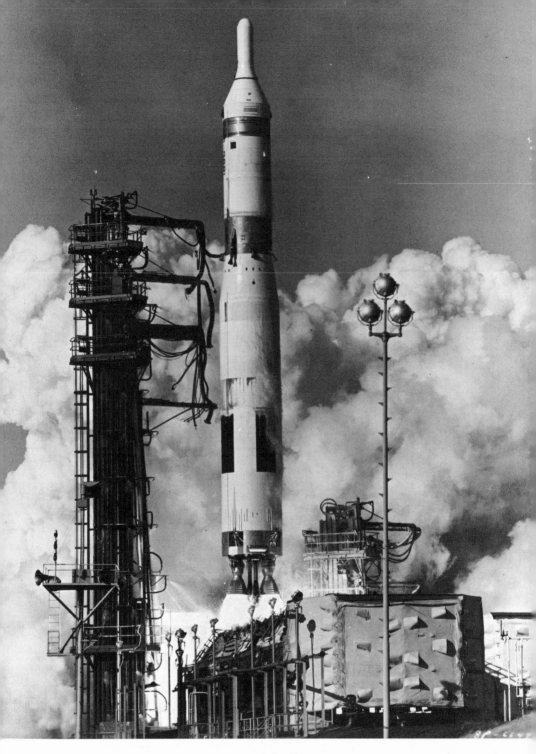

USAF Titan ICBM at liftoff.—MARTIN

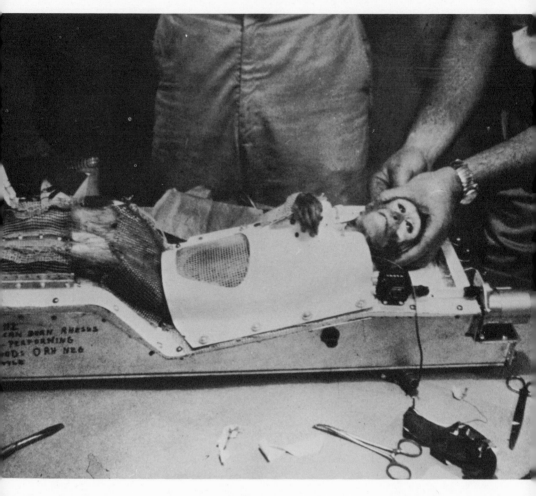

Monkey Able is released from her life-support couch after a 1,500-mile flight through space in the nose cone of a Jupiter rocket. She is aboard the USS *Kiowa* after recovery.—NASA

So much for the background of the famed Cape Canaveral Guided Missile and Rocket Range. Now, let's relate, even if only briefly, some of the high spots of the more vital recent launchings.

— 37 —

ATLAS, SPUTNIK, AND THE SPACE RACE

On December 14, 1958, a Jupiter Rocket carrying a tiny squirrel monkey, named Gordo, was hurled 300 miles into space, in a 1500 mile test, providing valuable data for man's space flights of the future.

The purposes of the experiment, according to the United States Army, were to set the basic requirements for survival and consciousness in the primate family during rocket travel, and to establish a basis for further experimental research involving escape from the earth's gravity.

The information gained from Gordo's brief and fateful ride seemed to give proof to medical authorities that man could probably survive in a similar undertaking. Unfortunately it failed to bring little Gordo back alive because of a technical mishap that has plagued other rocket experiments, and the Jupiter nose cone in which the tiny traveler rode was not recovered.

The little fellow, who had been given the name of "Little Old Reliable" by the people at Cape Canaveral, had all the appearance of an accomplished space traveler, equipped as he was with a helmet of molded electrical clay potting compound over chamois leather, and strapped into the cabin with his tiny knees drawn up. In order to remove the carbon dioxide and moisture from the spaceship, it carried an oxygen flask and air-regeneration kit.

Scientists concerned with the subject of space medicine were convinced that man could make such a trip on the basis of information gained about little Gordo's blood circulation and the monkey's breathing activity while on this 1,500-mile junket. Details of the monkey's physical condition during the 15-minute, 1,500-mile flight were sent back by instruments attached to his body. Gordo's heartbeats proved that he was doing splendidly until the end, when the capsule fell into the brine far out in the South Atlantic.

Then, after a few mishaps during launchings of other missiles and rockets—something that is only natural in such tremendous undertakings—came the perfect launching of a 40-ton 100-foot Convair Atlas by the United States Air Force on its first adventure into space, on December 18, 1958. Launched under the auspices and authority of the Advance Research Projects Agency of the Department of Defense, this Convair rocket, lifted up from Cape Canaveral into the waning rays of the Florida sunset, at 6:02 P.M. (EST), hurtling skyward with a brilliant flash of flame. Struggling aloft atop a huge tail of flame, and rising straight up for some 65 seconds before it arched gracefully high into the starless sky, this huge missile roared toward the southeast. Somewhat later a large, puffy vapor trail became visible, as the missile, guided by a Paoli-built electric brain, hit the cooler air masses high above the earth. This electronic brain, capable of making 10,000 arithmetical calculations in a second, helped keep the Atlas missile on its course toward its orbit.

As revealed by the Defense Department, the Atlas engines burned for 4½ minutes, until the rocket was blasting along at 17,100 miles an hour. And as the Pentagon disclosed, the mighty Atlas' apogee or highest point was 625 miles, while its perigee, or lowest point, was 118 miles, which placed it beyond the major drag effects of the earth's atmosphere.

The propulsion for the huge stainless steel Atlas vehicle was a standard Atlas power plant built by the Rocketdyne Division of the North American Aviation Company. The satellite was guided into orbit by the Atlas radio inertial guidance system built by the General Electric Company.

In connection with the 8-foot high, 16-foot-long electric brain —officially called the Atlas Ground Guidance Computer—the officials of the Burroughs Corporation, which built the computer at its Paoli, Pa., research laboratories, described this marvel of engineering ingenuity as follows: "During the countdown, the computer, housed in the control center, gave the missile its course, and all other instructions. The missile sent back statistics on its actual performance, after which the computer, comparing this information with the prescribed course, flashed back any adjustments necessary in the missile's flight. But once the missile was in orbit, the Mighty Atlas was entirely on its own." Having proved its operational capabilities, that of carrying a hydrogen warhead more than 6,000 miles —its full missile range—this mighty missile was the United States' only fully tested intercontinental ballistic missile at the time, though the 16th fired since June, 1957.

The dramatic announcement of the launching of this Air Force vehicle, together with the history-making broadcast of President Eisenhower's Christmas message and its rebroadcast from the satellite, was made at a White House diplomatic dinner. The President and Mrs. Eisenhower had just finished shaking hands with the dinner guests—representing some 41 foreign countries—when President Eisenhower stepped to the center of the White House's East Room and gave his guests a real conversational morsel, in the form of a dramatic announcement about the powerful high-performance Atlas ICBM from Cape Canaveral's proving ground. And then there came a round of applause.

What made this Atlas missile even more sensational was the fact that it was called the talking satellite, a well-earned name, for it broadcast back to earth the first human voice from space—President Eisenhower's recorded wish for "Peace on earth and goodwill to men everywhere." True, there was peace on earth, all right, but not too much international goodwill. The men who make wars, and who were engaged in preventing them, were busy with palaver, peaceful or tough. However, both Mr. Eisenhower and the Defense Department emphasized the peaceful aspects of the satellite project.

Not wanting this to become too technical, let me simply say that seven teletypewriter messages were beamed to the fast-traveling Atlas, and when the missile had described forty egg-shaped paths around the globe, these messages were sent out as the Atlas made its fortieth pass over the United States. All seven of the messages of the President, recorded and stored on tape inside the rocket, came back simultaneously at Cape Canaveral.

This missile flight also inaugurated earth-to-space communication, and as the Pentagon announced: "This was the first successful, multichannel, teletype transmission on a ground-satellite-ground relay system."

Turning now to further U.S. accomplishments in space conquest, an Army Jupiter rocket was launched in June, 1959, soaring 300 miles high for a 15-minute journey with an arkful of life in an instrument-jammed nose cone. In addition to two female simians, the cargo consisted of what really could sound like an exotic repast —three vials of sea urchins' eggs, pinch of yeast, 200 corn seeds, some purple and yellow onions, 100 fruit fly pupas, and 25 cubic centimeters of human blood. The explanation for this was that the yeast was sent up because it is the lowest specimen on the evolutionary tree, whose single cells divide once every two hours at a temperature of 86 degrees Fahrenheit. Next up the ladder of Darwin's theory were the eggs and sperm of the sea urchins—soft-bodied invertebrates that look like pin cushions and reproduce like human beings. The eggs of these urchins had been placed in sea water-filled vials. In one vial the eggs had already been fertilized, whereas in the other the fertilized eggs and sperm had been kept separate until after the missile's flight had started, when they were permitted to mate in a state of weightlessness. The products of these matings attained the free-swimming larval form later. Thus the first bisexual reproduction in space was consummated by the eggs and sperm inside the Jupiter's nose cone. The plant specimens were primarily used in radiation experiments.

What made this Jupiter rocket flight doubly interesting were the two female monkeys, christened Able and Baker, who, during the flashing, 1,700 mile, 15-minute journey through space from the Cape to Antigua, hit speeds up to 10,000 miles per hour and reached a peak altitude of 300 miles. And for the 9 to 15 minutes in space, the monkeys were not only weightless but exposed to a cosmic ray bombardment. When the buoyant cone, with its fantastic array of life, came down off Antigua, it was fished out of the water and brought to a Navy tug by four navy frogmen, heavily smeared with shark repellant. (The reason for the shark repellant was that the sizzling sound of the hot nose cone in the water might have attracted sharks.)

The monkeys recoverd from the cone were something special. Lady Able was a rhesus monkey weighing all of 7 pounds, whereas Baker was a bright-eyed, long-tailed, white-faced squirrel monkey, weighing one pound, and actually one of the smallest of the primate monkey family. Like the other astronauts—Gagarin, Titov, Shepard, Glenn and the test pilots Crossfield, Walker, and White—they wore molded plastic helmets during their adventure into space. They were strapped onto a fiberglass and rubber contour couch, and lying with their knees drawn up and their backs turned to the front of the cone in order to withstand the shocks of re-entry into the atmosphere of the earth. Whereas Baker merely had come along for the ride, Lady Able was expected to do all the work during the flight into space. Baker was, however, wired completely in order to get her heartbeat, body temperature and respiration.

Monkey Able's darkened compartment was equipped with a tiny telegraph key, and her job now was to press this key whenever a red light flashed on. During the preceding months the monkeys had been conditioned to press the key when the light flashed, and failure to hit the key also meant a slight electric shock. Thus the smart Able soon learned the trick. Inside her helmet were small earphones to pick up each shock, to reassure her of her performance.

When the monkeys were finally picked up after their eventful journey, Able died later on the operating table during the performance of some surgery for the removal of an electrode from under her skin, whereas Baker lived on, to fly another day.

Coming now to another most important event in the race for space, in which the United States and the Soviet Union were competing with one another in achieving more and more daring space adventures, a 142-pound Explorer was launched from the Cape by a three-stage Thor-Able rocket on August 7, 1959. Sponsored by the NASA, this missile had a most extraordinary-looking payload. The size of a medicine ball with strange-looking vanes jutting out from the central sphere, this contraption, whose paddle wheels contained cells to utilize the sun's energy in the satellite's communications apparatus, was accelerated to a speed of 22,000 miles an hour, 4,000 miles faster than was needed to get into orbit. It had been sent farther into space than any earth satellite thus far, and yet came as near as 150 miles to the earth. In its orbit around the earth every 12½ hours, it was estimated that it would last at least one year.

Equipped for some major experiments, it could safely be ranked as the most important scientific payload the United States had launched up to that time. It was ostensibly intended to try to secure more information on size and intensity of the newly-discovered radiation belts that girdle the earth. Its mission also was to try to reveal the dimensions of the earth's magnetic field and the nature of the electrified layer of the earth's atmosphere, known as the ionosphere. Each flat surface of its four paddles, folding back at launching and jutting out and unlocking once in space, was covered with cells that generated electricity from sunlight. Shiny plates below were intended to detect the impact of the tiny meteoric particles.

And so, fifteen minutes after the 90-foot rocket was shot into space, the Space Administration announced that all three stages of the rocket had fired, and the Paddlewheel's signal was picked up four minutes after launching time by the International Telephone and Telegraph Company's station in Southampton, Long Island.

The tiny sphere was expected to provide scientists with vital data that would pave the way for long-distance shots to Mars and Venus. It also carried a very tiny TV camera to send back pictures of the earth's cloud cover.

Among its intricate features was a so-called Space Command system, ingeniously turning on and off its three radio transmitters, one of which was turned off by a ground signal from Cape Canaveral shortly after the satellite had been launched and turned on again by another signal from the famous Jodrell Bank Tracking Station located near Manchester, England.

No less ingenious a device on this *Explorer VI* was the one that maintained temperature in the instrument compartments during the period that the satellite streaked through the heating sunlight and cooling shadow of the earth. This device was a toylike propeller, turning a small patch of black material on the satellite's aluminum shell either to absorb or reflect heat.

With regard to the Russian space achievements, we in America who were already more or less acquainted with the purpose of these satellite rockets, suddenly heard a strange "beep beep," on October 4, 1957, which, as soon became apparent, emanated from the Russian *Sputnik* (a name signifying Fellow Traveler). Circling the earth every 96 minutes, this 184-pound sphere reached a high point, or apogee, of 588 miles and a low point, or perigee, of 142 miles in its orbit around the world. The Russians next sent a dog into space in November, 1957.

One month later, another Russian achievement sparked our imagination, when the Soviet scientists launched a whole menagerie consisting of dogs, a rabbit and other animals for test into the upper strata and brought them back safely to earth. It proved the third flight into space for one of the dogs, named Daring or Otavzhnaya. The other was named Snowflake, or Snezhinka, both dogs being female. Moscow announced that the rocket also carried equipment to study the ultraviolet portion of the solar spectrum, the structure of the ionosphere and the micrometeorite stream. A distinct novelty was having a rabbit on the passenger list.

This aspect of the test was explained by Dr. Douglas Worf of the NASA, with the suggestion that it might have been done to discover what effect such flights might have on the reproductive organs. Science, he said, might thus be able to learn more quickly how pregnancy is affected by weightlessness, cosmic rays, and other phenomena encountered on such space flights, because the gestation period of rabbits is about one month.

Referring to other Russian activities in astronautics, and starting with the works of I. V. Mescherskii on the dynamics of bodies of variable mass, and the publications of K. E. Tsiollovskii, on the principles of rocket flight, that country had had already a very interesting background in astronautics toward the end of the 19th century. And as I brought out in previous chapters, Tsiollovskii, the father, and to the Russians the Patron Saint, of the science of astronautics, has been fairly well represented by rocket historians in western literature.

Soviet rocket developments, and especially those concerned with stratosphere exploration, were openly and freely discussed in his time. Realizing the enormous military potential of the rocket, the Soviet government had organized a government-sponsored rocket research program in 1934, five years after Germany had commenced her own rocket ventures, but eight years before similar systematic, army-sponsored researches began in the United States. When the Russians not only moved much of the Nazis' technical rocket data, but also many of Germany's most eminent rocket experts to Russia after the end of World War II, the Soviets began to exploit rocket power plants in real earnest. They first embarked upon an upper atmosphere rocket research program that involved the recovery by parachutes of test instrument containers. This was followed by experimental shots into space of animals whose body reactions were studied in flight. They then turned their attention to a single-stage rocket, initially launched in May, 1949, to an altitude of 68 miles and with an instrument payload of 286 pounds. After their first satellite triumph came the Soviet's *Sputnik II*, with the dog Laika aboard, on November 3, 1957. During this shot the Russians took measurements of the animal's breathing and heart rate under take-off acceleration and orbital weightlessness. It was more than six months after Laika died—due to lack of oxygen—that the Russians disclosed that the dog's heart had taken three times as long as they had expected to return to normal. They also suggested that weightlessness affected the nerve centers.

On August 19, 1960, the Soviet orbited *Spacecraft II* and

showed increased lifting power with a whole menagerie consisting
of two dogs, rats, mice, flies, seeds and fungi. After 17 circuits
around the world in 24 hours, it was ordered to return to earth to
a predetermined spot. All the animals returned hale and hearty,
and *Isvestia* revealed subsequently that the physical behavior of
the dogs had been checked by cameras located in the space cabin.
Slices of skin donated by volunteers and kept sealed in test tubes
not only had been kept alive, but the slivers of skin had been re-
grafted on these donors, to study their reaction.

With their customary flair for trying to impress the world at
the most unexpected and hectic times, and to prove to the United
States in particular that their possession of ICBM'S was fact and
not fantasy, the Russians followed through with a long series of
flights. Launching several artificial earth satellites in rapid succes-
sion and shooting five unmanned capsules for their man-in-space
program, they finally orbited a 10,000-pound capsule—the first
satellite space ship *Vostok* (meaning East)—with Flight Major Yuri
Alexseyevich Gagarin as that country's first Cosmonaut, and returned him safely to earth on April 12, 1961. This successful launching and safe return after 89 minutes was hailed by Soviet scientists
as one of the great advances in the story of man's age-old quest to
master the forces of nature. This success was achieved, in spite of
the Russian boast, not so much by Russia alone, but as an achievement of mind and spirit regardless of political and geographical
boundaries.

Though the U.S. has been told little regarding the firing se-
quences, we do know that test pilot Gagarin was sent into a 100-
mile high orbit in a 5-ton space ship, that he completed the orbital
path after 89 minutes and that he broke a speed record of 17,000
miles per hour. Nearing the atmosphere after reverse blasts, his
space ship slowed down, after which his parachute opened to carry
the vehicle safely back to earth. The minimum height of Gagarin's
spaceship was 109½ miles, and the maximum 187¾ miles.

For once breaking a tradition of silence that has been one of
the most disturbing elements in the West-East attempts at space
cooperation, Moscow announced that Major Yuri A. Gagarin was
sent into orbit from Baikomar, a place called Cosmodrome by
them, and returned to earth near the village of Smelovka, some 20
miles southeast of Engels in the Saratov regions on the Volga.

All throughout the flight test Gagarin's movements were observed by means of an intricate radio telemetric and television system, not unlike that used later in our own space man Shepard's sub-orbital flight, during which bilateral radio communication was established and successfully maintained. Aloft 1 hour, 48 minutes, of which 1 hour, 29 minutes had been in space orbit, Gagarin experienced weightlessness for more than 70 minutes, scientifically proving man's ability to function and survive under the weightless condition of space.

While this flight undoubtedly marked another milestone in the history of aviation and space conquest, to quote from the N. Y. *Herald Tribune's* editorial of April 13, 1961: "Yet to say that the feat of Gagarin is a triumph for all mankind, is not to deny that it also a triumph for the Union of Soviet Socialist Republics," and again, "That it was a Russian who was the first to make this mighty leap forward will centuries hence seem of no greater moment than that it was an Italian who first sailed to the shores of America," and finally, from the same editorial, "It will be well for us, if, while saluting the Russian accomplishments, as President Kennedy did in his prompt and sincere message yesterday, we recognize that today, as three-and-a-half-years ago when the first Sputnik was launched, we have a tremendous task to fulfill both in strengthening our national defense and in reasserting our traditional leadership in modern man's scientific march."

— 38 —

AMERICA'S SUB-ORBITAL FLIGHTS—
SHEPARD AND GRISSOM

Alan B. Shepard, Jr. whose safe return from his 15-minute excursion through the uncharted regions of space, on May 5, 1961, was hailed throughout the free world, is the first American to have made a sub-orbital flight through the threshold of space. Returning in excellent physical condition to the welcome waters of the Atlantic where a fleet of United States Navy vessels was riding at anchor and some Marine helicopters were flying overhead, 320 miles out, to fish him out of the brine, Commander Shepard had rocketed some 115 miles into the airless heights over Cape Canaveral.

While it was to be regretted that this was not a round-the-world orbital flight, it provided the United States and the free Western World with a much needed morale-building fillip nonetheless.

Before Shepard's historic flight three splendidly-functioning Mercury Redstones had been blasted into space; the first, a heavily-instrumented Mercury production on December 16, 1960, the next, carrying a non-paying passenger, chimpanzee Ham, on January 31, 1961, and finally, a dummy spacecraft, going 400 miles distant and 100 miles up, on March 24, 1961. All was now ready for *Freedom 7*, the Mercury Redstone III, at the Cape, where Alan B. Shepard and the other astronauts had been on pins and needles waiting for the OK signal for Shepard to set out on his hypersonic journey to the fringes of space.

Originally developed by the Army, and now produced by the authority of the NASA, the first large ballistic rocket ever developed in the United States had been launched for the first time from the Army's White Sands Proving Grounds, in New Mexico, in 1955. The Redstone engine had entered development tests in 1950, and became the first rocket engine to produce more than 75,000 pounds of thrust in 1952. Because of its complete reliability, the "Old Faithful" Redstone was finally selected as the powerplant for the training flights of the Project Mercury Astronauts. Produced by Rocketdyne of the North American Aviation Company, and considered as being ready for firings from the Range, it was subsequently moved to Cape Canaveral. Since then this prime launcher for the Mercury suborbital flight series has lifted unmanned capsules and manned Mercury spacecraft for suborbital flights, as a member of the first team of missiles in America's conquest of space.

After Shepard had been selected from a card of seven hand-picked astronauts the first and, of course, the most vital step became that of preparing and outfitting him for his great adventure. First came a special suit of thermal-padded underwear, together with white socks and white canvas slippers. Then the "biomedical sensors," of which there were four, were attached to his body and glued to his chest. Around his neck was a small, taped respirator to test his breathing rate, leaving some wire as well as the respirator free, to be attached to his nostril. The sixth wire ran down to a body temperature probe—the rectal thermometer—intended to record his body temperature on his in-flight or return to earth. All these wires converged upon a small metal plate plugged to his suit. Then came the moment for Shephard to don the upper portion of his underwear, a procedure that took place in the pressure suit room.

Interestingly enough, the space suit itself, made by the B. F. Goodrich Company, like those worn by navy test pilots on all their high-altitude tests, could trace its ancestry back to the 1930s, when the first space suit was made for Wiley Post, "who wanted some kind of rubber suit that would enable him to fly his famous Winnie Mae above the Italian-held altitude record of 47,000 feet. Post then went to Goodrich at General James H. Doolittle's suggestion."

Post's outfit came close to scaring one motorist in the Mojave desert out of his skin, when engine failure forced Post to land in the desert one day in 1934, and he headed toward a nearby highway to look for help. Spotting a car that had pulled up on the roadside, Post waddled up to it in his bulky suit and helmet and grunted a greeting to the driver. First the frightened motorist retreated behind his car, then he took off like a jackrabbit. Post had to chase, catch and hold him before the man could be convinced that he wasn't being attacked by a creature from Mars.

Coming back now to Shepard's suit, which is vital for protection of any human above 45,000 feet, the full pressure suit actually consists of four basic parts—torso, helmet, gloves and boots. The suit's torso is a closely-fitted coverall shielding the entire body with the exception of head and hand. The helmet, attached by a neck ring, contains anti-buffeting protection and a communications system. The gloves are also complex. The "hands" are curved with elaborately-ribbed material—with the exception of the left middle finger. Under pressurization, this finger remained rigid so that Shepard was able to push instrument buttons.

Oxygen was fed to Shepard through a hose at the waist. One hundred per cent oxygen flows throughout the suit to cool it, then circulates in the helmet for breathing. Temperature inside the suit can be controlled at 80 degrees Fahrenheit—even in the intense heat encountered during re-entry into the earth's atmosphere. Ventilation is conducted through the "trilock ducting," a three-dimensional material in the suit, to the wrists, ankles, crotch and periphery of the neck ring. Sheparrd entered the suit by means of a pressure-sealing zipper located diagonally across the chest. He was able to move shoulder, arm and leg by means of a series of pleats and bellows tailored into the suit. The 20-pound suit was of aluminized nylon on the outside and rubberized nylon inside.

An Air Force high-altitude, double-walled, ventilated and insulated garment made up the clothing layer beneath the suit,
whose inner wall was constructed in such a way that its perforations
not only permitted the body pores to breathe, but evaporated the
body perspiration and warmed up or cooled off the oxygen which
controlled the body temperature. During the flight, enough oxygen
was pumped into the suit through a connection at the waist, and
as already said above, finally fed into the helmet for Shepard's
breathing, while the exhaled breath was permitted to escape
through a specially-constructed vent in this helmet. The impurities
were then cleaned from the air, which, once refreshed, circulated
back to Shepard. Should there be a leak in the capsule's wall or
cabin, however, or should the pressure system fail, a monitor
would send the internal pressure up at once, with a 100 per cent
oxygen mixture.

As lack of space prevents me from going into the many other
activities that preceded Shepard's shot into space, suffice to add
that Shepard entered the Mercury spacecraft on Pad V, exactly
31 minutes after countdown, at 5:18 A.M. He was strapped and
linked up, and, with the warning siren sounding across the range,
the capsule's hatch closed and astronaut Shepard was completely
on his own at last.

Silhouetted against the horizon like sentinels standing watch,
were the white, red, orange and green gantries, and the Pershing,
Minuteman, Redstone, Jupiter, Thor, Atlas Centaur and Titan
missiles. All the attention was focused this day, however, on the
Mercury Redstone in which Shepard was to be shot skyward.

Then, at 34 minutes, 13 seconds past nine, the ignition signal
sounded and as a flame beneath the base of the rocket billowed
clouds of red and orange, the powerful rocket with its priceless
traveler rose, carrying with him the blessings and prayers of those
who had been watching and standing with bated breath at Cape
Canaveral, Patrick Air Force Base, Titusville, Cocoa Beach, Eau
Gallie, and elsewhere. They kept their fingers crossed for the safe
return of the first United States astronaut.

The capsule in which Shepard was reclining,—made of titanium, beryllium and nickel-base alloys—was 9 feet high and 74
inches across. Its main sections were a heat shield, a cabin, and
a long cylinder on top which housed the many recovery devices.
The cabin, the very nucleus or heart of the capsule, and the con-

Lt. Commander Alan B. Shepard, Jr., USN, is shown here being fitted for his space suit at the B. F. Goodrich Company, Akron, Ohio, during early preparations for the Project Mercury program.

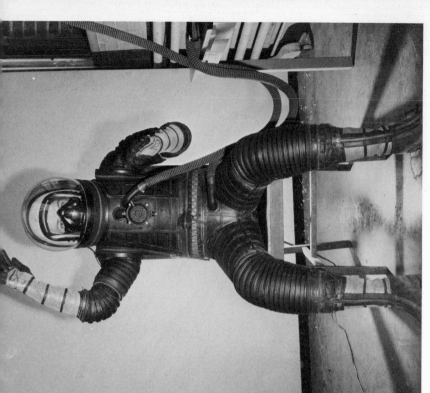

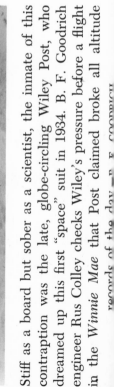

"Man from Mars" was for years the tag for comic strip characters dressed like this. B. F. Goodrich developed this suit for the Navy in 1952. It was the first great breakthrough in space suit design, partially solving the mobility problem while providing enough pressure for infinite altitude.

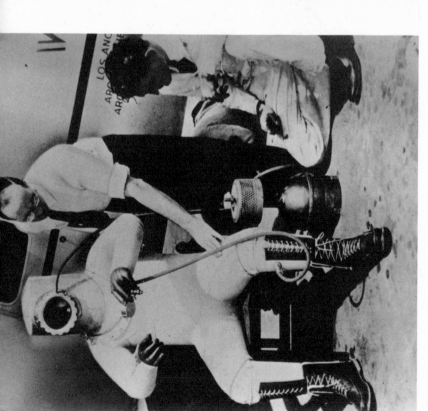

Stiff as a board but sober as a scientist, the inmate of this contraption was the late, globe-circling Wiley Post, who dreamed up this first "space" suit in 1934. B. F. Goodrich engineer Rus Colley checks Wiley's pressure before a flight in the *Winnie Mae* that Post claimed broke all altitude records of the day.—B. F. GOODRICH

An artist's drawing of the Mercury spacecraft, *Freedom 7*, showing the escape tower and retro rockets.—NASA

A skindiver operating as part of the missile recovery team.
—U.S. AIR FORCE

The *Liberty Bell 7* spacecraft gushes water after going under for the first time. Seconds later the Marine helicopter, with astronaut Virgil I. Grissom already aboard, dropped the spacecraft and it sank.—NASA

tour couch on which Shepard was resting protected from all the forces of lift-off and re-entry, was made of crushable, honeycombed aluminum, a fiberglass shell, padded with rubber molded to the contour of Shepard's body. Facing the astronaut two feet in front were the instrument panel and flanking consoles, with some 165 different switches, dials and meters, which enabled him to concentrate on the flight.

The handle on Shepard's right was constructed in such a way that he could control the yaw (or drift angle), pitch, and roll through his wrist motions. This spacecraft had its own propulsion systems, including 16 low-thrust jets, and the retrograde rockets used to retard the forward motion of a satellite. There were, moreover, the posigrade rockets, separating the capsule, once in flight, from the Redstone booster at the proper stage in orbit. There also was the escape tower to be used in case of trouble, as well as a complicated series of explosive bolts to release the capsule and parachute.

The Mercury Capsule itself was actually a space wicker basket, stitched together with seven miles of wiring and serviced by little sprays, or jets of hydrogen peroxide. A porthole—or periscope—permitted Shepard to see the Atlantic. This periscope system was very unusual, as it consisted of an eight-inch viewing screen placed about two feet from his viewing position. It enabled Shepard to see the earth beneath, make measurements of his direction, while an optical altimeter permitted him to measure the capsule's altitude.

The heat shield of the capsule resisted temperatures up to and even beyond 5,000 degrees Fahrenheit, while the temperature of the cabin's interior would never exceed 100 degrees.

The standard airplane barometric-pressure altimeter, so widely used by airplane pilots on short or long hauls, could not be used here, because there was hardly any temperature, and none at all in space.

One of the systems upon whose function Shepard was completely dependent, as it stabilized his spacecraft, controlled maneuvers, prevented tumbling, and helped to survive the shock and heat of re-entry, was the Honeywell Altitude Stabilization and Control System. This unique contraption held the craft in an attitude of separation, yawed or swung it around sideways, so that the "blunt" heat shield end faced forward, and tilted it upward 14 degrees, increasing the tilt to 34 degrees when the retro rockets were fired. The craft then turned, and the heat shield headed downward for re-entry. Then, when the Honeywell system had started the spacecraft revolving at 10 degrees per second, and a drogue chute was released, the Honeywell system was discontinued, and the spacecraft splashed into the ocean, where Shepard was safely picked up.

Another ingenious device, enabling the astronaut to see in the dark, and helping to stabilize the Project Mercury in which Shepard was riding, was the Infra-Red Bolometer, which *senses* infra-red radiation, these waves between visible light and microwaves. Installed in cameras and navigation instruments, and used in earlier ballistic flights, including the one that had carried chimpanzee Ham, these bolometers, placed in the small end of a space capsule, were able to detect the outlines of an object in terms of the heat that it gave off. Knowing which way is down, these sensors signal when correction is necessary. By releasing a little jet of hydrogen peroxide, another instrument then rights the craft.

Incidentally, these bolometers are also part of the observation instruments in the *Tiros* weather satellites, and are being built into the terminal guidance sensors now under development for the Space Probes to Venus and Mars.

When the Shepard Mercury Spacecraft had reached an altitude of 196,000 feet, at which time the Redstone flame had vanished, the craft had separated from the booster rocket, and the capsule's three small rockets had done their job of pushing the craft up and way from the Redstone, only then did Shepard take manual control of the capsule's movements and fire the retro rockets, which allowed the capsule to head back into the earth's atmosphere. Suffering a few minutes of weightlessness or drag of weight as the capsule went through deceleration and reduction of speed, Shepard was pushed more and more back into the contour couch, during this period. Strapped to this form-fitting couch, Shepard performed many duties—27 major tasks and about 70 communications—during the 5 minutes that he was weightless.

As his capsule whirled at a speed of about 5,100 miles an hour through space during descent, during which he suffered the forces of about 11 times his own weight which kept tearing at his body, Shepard came through with flying colors.

Then, as he dropped some 40,000 feet from a height of 115 miles at a speed of 30 feet a second, the first of the two red and white parachutes, which would buffer the fall, opened. Reaching a height of 7,000 feet, he then dumped the fuel peroxide system.

Shepard told the Science Board of the National Academy of Sciences later that the stress had not been "unduly difficult," nor was there anything upsetting about the five minutes of weightlessness in mid flight, although he added that "his vision was blurred by head rattling sensations for 15 seconds, so that he could not see the instruments on which his life depended." The only difficulty he encountered during his 15 minute-22 seconds flight, he reported, happened shortly after lift off when the Mercury Capsule crossed the sound barrier. But, that, too, quickly passed, he said. Aside from losing three pounds and incurring two small bruises from the shoulder straps, Shepard paid a very small physiological price for the rocket ride into space.

Three hundred and two miles out into the Atlantic, a fleet of navy vessels and marine helicopters was waiting. Hauled into a helicopter, while a hook was attached to the capsule, and lifted five feet out of the water, Shepard was taken straight to the carrier *Lake Champlain,* where a touchdown was made on deck at 11:02. Emerging from the helicopter two and a half minutes later, and planting his feet firmly on the carrier's deck, he was rushed below, where the medical team of Doctors Robert Laning and Jerome Strong gave him a preliminary check-up to make sure there were no complications. After this a call was received from the White House, when President Kennedy complimented him on his achievements.

Thence Shepard flew to Grand Bahama Island to undergo exhaustive tests and examinations, and medical experts conceded that "he had lived up to their expectations, as the undertaking had not left any marks." However, at Langley Air Force Base his medical examiners reported that Shepard's heart had beaten at twice the normal rate during his moments of maximum stress.

Later, when he was received at the White House on June 6, and reported in somewhat more detail about his experiences, he said that the experience of space flight had been closely simulated in the two years of training on the ground and as a result it should be possible to shorten the training period for future astronauts. As a more personal suggestion he expressed the hope that "fewer body fluid samples requiring the use of needles would be needed in the future by the physicians."

Two world records had been made by Shepard's flight: for a

manned space flight, altitude without orbit; and the greatest manned mass lifted without orbit, claims that were put at once before the Federation Aeronautique Internationale, in Paris.

Virgil I. "Gus" Grissom, America's second space man, made it on July 21, 1961, flying somewhat higher, somewhat faster, some-farther than Commander Alan Shepard, Jr. However, he ran into some trouble and met with an accident when at the end of his suborbital flight his two-million dollar capsule sank in 2,800 fathoms of Atlantic water.

Blasting away the hatch of his *Liberty Bell* 7 Mercury capsule, the 25-year-old astronaut dove into the water in his cumbersome pressure suit and swam the 70 feet to the Navy helicopter waiting "horsecollar," lowered by the copter 30 feet overhead. Pulled away safely, he was deposited in good health, though tired, on the carrier *Randolph's* deck.

Here is exactly how it happened. In spite of its valiant attempt to save the sinking two-ton capsule, which had become water-logged by light seas flooding through the open hatch, the second helicopter's engine became so overheated due to the water's extra weight that, afraid lest it be pulled down by the weight of the sinking space vehicle, the copter's cable was cut. The *Liberty Bell* 7 went down to its watery grave, together with the motion pictures taken by Captain Grissom throughout his 15-minute adventure on his suborbital flight. Down also went the photographic and other evidence of how this instrument board worked and reacted to the strains and stress of travel through space.

— 39 —

GHERMAN TITOV'S EPIC FLIGHT

On August 7, 1961, 26-year-old Major Gherman Stepanovitch Titov, Russian Air Force officer and son of a Siberian school teacher, went hurtling around the world in a five-ton spaceship on a historic voyage long enough to have carried him far beyond the moon. For 434,000 miles, 17 days, and 17 nights, the spaceship *Vostok II* (the name meaning East), the size of a marble to the naked eye, whirled about the earth every 88.6 minutes. Seen by thousands, it traveled through space at a speed of 17,750 miles per hour.

Titov's route plan of flight for 17 orbits in some 25 hours called for passing over practically every inhabited area on our planet. Each circle of the globe carried him 65 degrees north and south of the equator, and his flight varied from a low altitude of 110.3 miles above the earth to a high of 159.3 miles.

Believed to have been launched from the same spot as Cosmonaut Yuri Gagarin, on April 12, near Oyura Tam in the desert wastes of the Aral Sea southeast of Moscow, Titov landed "exactly in the planned area of the Soviet Union," following his flight. According to Soviet sources, Titov's flight was almost identical to the August 19, 1960 junket of the Soviet spaceship which carried the two dogs Belka and Streika around the earth 17 times, actually the first living beings to return safely from an orbital flight.

The question has been raised by many why Titov had to make 17 whirls around the world before coming down. The fact of the matter is that Titov could either have come down at the end of his first orbit, or he had to wait for his 17th time around, in order to land in the exact selected recovery area in Russia. As the earth makes a complete rotation every 24 hours, this corresponds to the time for the 17 trips around the planet for Titov's capsule. If his return to earth had taken place between the 2nd and 16th orbit he would have landed far from the designated spot.

According to Moscow Radio, *Vostok II* carried living organisms in addition to Titov for the study of their reaction to prolonged radiation exposure, although (as per the Soviet's custom of secrecy) it was not disclosed what these organisms were. In addition to numerous other apparatuses, such as multi-channel telemetric systems, *Vostok* also carried a tape recorder for recording the speech of the cosmonaut, and automatic accelerated readings of recordings on command from the earth, Moscow radio said.

In good condition throughout the flight, Titov reported that his instruments were behaving as they were expected to, and he kept himself busy in the small space cabin making tests, radioing voice greetings to the people of the lands he traveled over, and doing exercise. His first meal was a three course luncheon, which he took at 12:30 P.M. Moscow time and which he digested well. He dined again at 5:00, sleeping well later for 7 and one half hours.

Scheduled to cover nearly half a million miles while circling the earth on man's longest flight, Titov also tried his hand piloting his spaceship, and as he was flying over Soviet territory, the television system relayed messages and films showing his calm and smiling countenance.

Quoting the New York *Times* editorial: "Round and round this now puny globe Major Titov went; he did calisthenics, ate, slept, thanked Premier Khrushchev, broadcast greetings to the continents and nations he was passing over. It was a spectacular demonstration of Soviet technologists' capabilities in space, and of Major Titov's personal bravery and competence. But all this brilliance was marred by the transparent Russian propaganda. He and his vehicle are the products of a society which is still unable to give its citizens a standard of living, good housing, clothing, and the like— equal even to that of Western Europe, let alone the United States. The billions of dollars' worth of effort that have been poured unstintingly these past few years into making this feat possible, could have been used to ease the terrible housing shortage, to provide Soviet citizens with more adequate health care, and for other worth-while, literally mundane purposes. Now the Soviet masses whose sacrifices have paid for this accomplishment are asked by their masters to hail this feat as another proof of the superiority of the Soviet system."

While the subject of weightlessness and gravity has been discussed in one of the other chapters, some answers as to how prolonged weightlessness does affect the human body, and how man can survive the deadly radiation of space, have been given by authorities and specialists in space aviation. For instance Dr. Carmault B. Jackson (in charge of examining and questioning American astronauts Shepard and Grissom on their return from space) said that the first effects would be on Titov's circulatory system. Unless he performed proper exercises, he might experience lightheadedness akin to that people suffer when getting up from a sickbed for the first time.

Professor Boris Kloskovsky of Moscow told Tass News Agency, "In future doctors will send people through space to treat many diseases, and will substantially extend man's lifetime."

Soviet technicians, being interviewed, reported that the pulse rate while Titov was awake remained constant at 88 beats a minute, whereas while he was asleep his pulse rate dropped to 58.

Dr. Sigfried Gerathewohl, staff scientist with the NASA, said the pulse rates announced were reasonable. He explained that "while a human is weightless, his body metabolism slows and the heart action slows accordingly. While awake, Titov did work that quickened his pace, making his pulse more normal. The same work done on earth would have quickened it above the normal resting rate on earth," Dr. Gerathewohl concluded.

Finally, in an interview with the world famous space expert Willy Ley, given to Cyril Egan, Jr. of the New York *Journal,* Mr. Ley said, "The Soviet Union today has the ability to boost man in space capsule around the moon and back to earth. The day-long flight of Cosmonaut Gherman Titov solves two major problems of a moon trip—eating and sleeping in a state of weightlessness. The sole stumbling block left before a manned lunar shot is finding two people psychologically compatible to work well as a team during the week it would take for such a trip. That is why I believe the Russians' next space attempt will be an earth orbit of two or more persons that will last a week or more. One of the passengers probably will be a woman. This will be mainly for propaganda. The Communists make a big play about the equality of the sexes. Besides, a woman cosmonaut has the added advantage of being able to withstand monotony of prolonged weightlessness. Her small stature makes her better suited to standing up under the impact of acceleration and deceleration on take-off and re-entry," Willy Ley concluded.

Bob Considine, in his October 6, 1961, column *On the Line,* refers to "the Russian announcement that Cosmonaut Titov was airsick through most of his weightless day in space," and he suggests "that science must come up with either a foolproof remedy for this avant garde seasickness or develop an engine that speeds up spatial travel." Apropos of this, the Soviet reported that it is considering using artificial gravity in a spaceship if weightlessness should prove to be a problem. This gravity can be simulated by centrifugal force resulting from the rotation of a spaceship around a suitable axis.

— 40 —

HIGH-ALTITUDE BALLOONS
AND WEATHER SATELLITES—*TIROS I, II, III*

The most amazing information about the planet we live on reaches us day by day. Now that man has begun to take a big step into outer space, the accuracy of weather forecasting, and knowledge of how to protect man against the ravaging effects of weather, have become of the utmost importance. It is true that Mark Twain, our country's famed and beloved humorist, once observed that "Everybody talks about the weather, but nobody does anything about it." That is not exactly the case today, as meteorologists and weather experts, together with space scientists, are doing plenty and have devised all sorts of ways and means to foretell the weather. Science, in fact, has never before made such phenomenal progress.

Concerned with such problems as the possible influence of solar events on the weather, the late test pilot Captain Joseph W. Kittinger did some excellent research as he rose to an altitude of 96,000 feet in a balloon capsule. These huge balloons, made of thin but tough plastic material, have been able to take weather instruments to the higher strata of the atmosphere, where they were left for many days at a time, in order to secure a pretty good picture of extra-terrestrial influences on the weather.

A Navy balloon, launched from the deck of the United States carrier *Antietam*, stationed 430 miles southeast of the mouth of the Mississippi, soared to a record height of 21.5 miles in quest of weather information on May 4, 1961. This event would have been crowned with 100 per cent success, had not one member of its two-man crew lost his life during the attempt to rescue him by helicopter from the Mexican Gulf. This dampened the spirits of the Navy men who had been engaged in a project that sent the 411-foot-high, helium-filled balloon 113,000 feet into the air, 12,000 feet higher than any other balloon had attained so far.

Both men—Commander Malcolm Ross, physicist at the Office of Naval Research, in Washington, and Lt. Commander Victor G. Prather, a medical assistant at the National Naval Medical Center, Bethesda, Md.—had been engaged in studying the effects of high altitude and weather on the human body, and helping to test the pressurized suits in temperatures ranging as low as 65 degrees below zero. The forty-story-high balloon, considered the largest of its type, and constructed of polyethylene one-and-one-half thousandths of an inch thick, was filled with 10 million cubic feet of helium.

The aluminum-framed gondola, measuring five by five by six feet, was protected on all sides by what looked like ordinary household-type Venetian blinds, used for temperature control, aluminized on one side and black on the other. The mission itself was primarily concerned with meteorological data, but also with photographing the half-million square mile area of the earth, information used to check the accuracy of similar photos taken by orbiting rockets and satellites. Other tests were also made, and in order to capture the heavy cosmic ray particles to test the direct impact on their bodies, both balloonists had been smeared with body emulsions. The radiation exposure was measured, moreover, by a special Geiger counter. The U.S. carrier *Antietam* (commanded by Captain Paul E. Hartmann) had been maneuvering all during the day in an effort "to make a running catch of the balloon as it came down."

As the balloon finally touched down on the waters of the Gulf where it remained afloat, the fatal accident occurred. Lt. Commander Prather fell from a sling that had been lowered by a helicopter hovering above, and apparently was dragged under water by the heavy weight of his pressurized flying suit. Seeing this happen Lt. Kenneth Benson, a member of the helicopter crew, dived into the water and succeeded in hauling the unfortunate Lt. Prather to the surface. But he died shortly after he had been taken aboard the *Antietam*. As for Commander Ross, he had been lifted safely into the helicopter.

Aside from the part played by weather balloons in high altitude tests, the launching on April 1, 1960, of *Tiros I,* the world's first meteorological, picture-taking satellite to provide cloud pictures, is actually the pioneering effort of a weather observing system in space. It is probably the one source of data that can be used to study the ultimate feasibility of weather control. The purpose of *Tiros* was to search for information about the movement of storms, to take photographs of the earth, to map the stratosphere and ionosphere for practical meteorological purposes, and finally to hunt and scan hurricane formations in the Atlantic and Caribbean. And thus man was provided for the first time with a satellite's-eye view of cloud formations over much of the world.

From the satellite's orbit, 450 miles high, two television cameras relayed more than 22,000 pictures to weather scientists on earth. And, to quote from the information furnished by the National Aeronautics and Space Administration, "Study of these pictures confirmed that they enabled man to identify and locate storms and details of their structure." *Tiros II* was launched on November 23, 1960, and *Tiros III* was launched to coincide with the east Coast hurricanes, although, according to NASA's scientist, William G.

Stroud, "*Tiros III* is not to be used to track hurricanes in the same manner as the Weather Bureau's hurricane hunter airplanes, although it is to be hoped they will aid in detection of storms, and perhaps—in their control."

Mr. Stroud further indicated that, "if a hurricane develops during the life of *Tiros III*, we will assemble all pictures taken in the days immediately before, and by studying these pictures may be able to discover how clouds in hurricane belt areas are formed, providing maybe a clue to what type of conditions must exist for a hurricane to form."

Shaped like a giant pill-box, 42 inches in diameter, *Tiros I* weighed 270 pounds and stood 19 inches high. Its top and sides were covered with 9,200 solar cells which transformed the sun's light into electricity for recharging the satellite's batteries. Computers predicted the path of *Tiros I*. Using the information, the cameras were programmed to turn on only when the satellite was facing the earth, and only when the area over which *Tiros I* was passing was in sunlight.

To remain stable in orbit, *Tiros I* maintained a spin rate of of about nine revolutions per minutes. When spin rate dropped, a pair of tiny rockets were fired through radio command by ground stations. The two cameras in *Tiros I* were designed to supplement each other. The one, a wide angle camera, took a strip of overlapping pictures each covering an area of 800 square miles. The smaller camera covered an area about 70 miles square, showing more detail. Connected to each camera was a magnetic tape recorder that could store signals representing up to 32 photographs. When *Tiros I* came within range of the two ground stations located at Fort Monmouth, N.J., and Kaena Point, Hawaii, picture signals were transmitted from the tapes or directly from the cameras. At the ground stations both a photographic and a magnetic tape were made. Meteorologists identified the photograph locations through a combination of tracking reports, which showed the course *Tiros I* was taking when the pictures were taken, and major landmarks which were visible on the photographs.

Tiros III, a glistening hat-box contraption carrying a pair of television cameras the size of water glasses, was placed in the bulbous nose of a three-stage Douglas Thor-Delta Air Force rocket, as it left its launching pad at the Cape. Immediately after its firing, on July 12, 1961, *Tiros III* went into action, photographing the

A Douglas Thor Delta launches the *Tiros II* satellite from
Cape Canaveral.—DOUGLAS AIRCRAFT

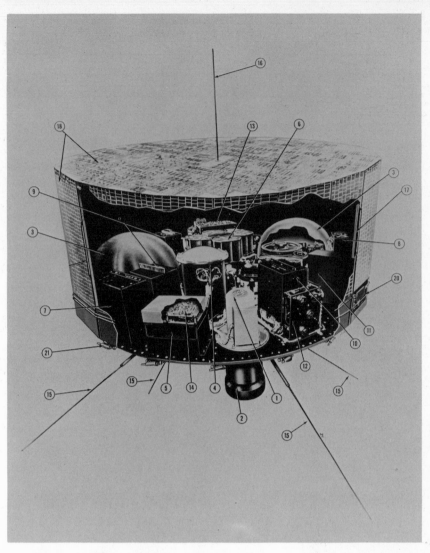

The *Tiros* weather satellite, shown here in a cutaway view identifying the principal elements of the system as follows: 1) one of the two half-inch Vidicon cameras; 2) wide-angle camera lens; 3) television tape recorders; 4) electronic "clock" for controlling sequence of operations; 5) television transmitter; 6) storage batteries; 7) camera electronics; 8) tape recorder electronics; 9) control circuits; 10) auxiliary controls; 11) power converter for tape motor; 12) voltage regulator; 13) battery charging regulator; 14) auxiliary synchronizing generator for TV; 15) transmitting antenna; 16) receiving antenna; 17) solar sensor to measure position of satellite with respect to sun; 18) solar cells; 19) precession damper to eliminate "wobble" after satellite is in orbit; 20) de-spin "yo-yo" mechanism; 21) spin-up rockets.—NASA

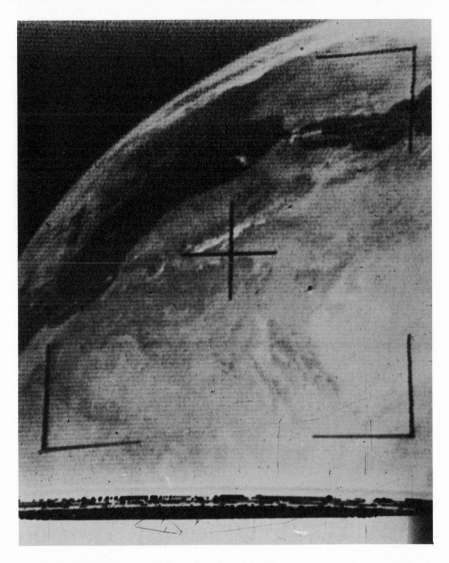

This photograph was taken by *Tiros III* as it passed over North Africa with its lens pointed northwest. In the upper right corner are the Iberian Peninsula, the Strait of Gibraltar and a portion of the Mediterranean Sea. The land mass shown in the foreground includes Algeria and Morocco.—NASA

A "paddlewheel" satellite. The purpose of the solar cells on the paddles is to provide a continuous source of power for the radiation and magnetic field measuring devices in the spacecraft.—NASA

The Nimbus satellite, which is being developed to serve in a standard satellite system that can provide valuable data for day-to-day weather analyses. In this case, too, solar cells provide the power source.—NASA

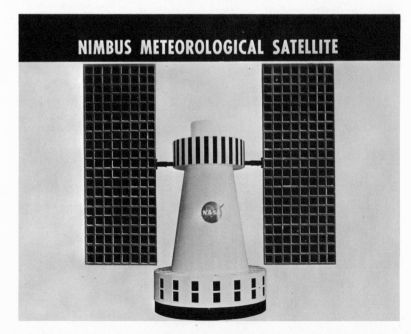

earth's weather from an orbit 400 miles high. It took 32 pictures on the very first of its passes around the earth, which were transmitted on a radio command from Wallop's Island, Virginia. Here, as well as at the St. Nicholas Islands, off California, the pictures are developed by meteorologists who establish location and analyze information, after which the more useful information is forwarded to the United States Weather Bureau's Meteorological analysis center in Suitland, Md., to be incorporated into the weather maps and distributed far and wide over civilian and military weather networks. Should *Tiros III* happen to spot a hurricane, warnings would be sent out immediately to the Caribbean islands and the mainland.

This was dramatically shown in connection with Hurricane Esther, the first hurricane or storm detected by *Tiros III*, on September 10, as it was forming over the Middle Atlantic. the Bureau said: "Without the pictures that were transmitted to earth by the weather eye satellite, it is possible that the tropical storm might have remained undetected for several days, until reported by a passing ship. The *Tiros III* feat was said to be one of the best demonstrations thus far of the potential meteorological satellites for revolutionizing forecasting."

It will be possible soon to obtain simultaneous pictures of upper air as well as of atmospheric conditions on the earth's surface over the entire globe with the more advanced weather eye, *Nimbus*. This one will carry improved instruments that will take more detailed pictures of clouds over larger areas, estimate the heights of their tops, and possibly identify the area of rain or snow. A system of such satellites will provide data on weather conditions over the entire globe several times a day. Under the increased space budget proposed by President Kennedy, it is planned to keep at least one *Tiros* satellite in orbit through 1962, when the more powerful, better equipped *Nimbus* will be launched, which, unlike the *Tiros* series, will keep its cameras constantly directed at the earth on a round-the-clock basis.

Because events in the Arctic atmosphere also play an important role in the generation of weather over the United States and Canada, a large, eighty-five-foot dish antenna has been set up at Gilmore Creek, some fifteen miles north of Fairbanks, Alaska, to receive polar weather pictures from the *Nimbus* satellites. Further north, on Axel Heiberg Island, way beyond the North American and Canadian frontiers, an unmanned, atomic-powered weather station has been operating for some time now, sending reports every three hours to a manned station at Resolute Bay, on Cornwallis Island, 300 miles to the south.

The latest member to have joined the Weather Satellite Club is the Republic of Israel. Israel launched from a barren area of sand dunes an Israeli-made, solid fuel, multi-stage weather rocket on June 5, 1961. This was the first rocket to have been successfully fired by a Middle Eastern country, and the seventh country to have launched such a rocket. Besides the United States and Soviet Russia, the others have been France, Britain, Italy and Japan. The 550-pound, solid-fuel rocket, *Shavit-Shtayim* (the Hebrew word for Comet Number 2) soared more than fifty miles high. Launched at a secret Mediterranean seacoast site, it was the brainchild of Israeli scientists.

— 41 —

COMMUNICATIONS SATELLITES—*ECHO*

The successful launching of *Echo I*, on the night of August 12, 1960, inaugurated the first experiment testing the feasibility of passive communication satellites.

"This earth satellite," to quote the National Aeronautics and Space Administration's statement, "may eventually make possible worldwide radio and telephone systems permitting instant communication between points anywhere in the world . . . television also may be profoundly affected by such communication satellites. With the use of a number of reflective satellites such as *Echo I*, television or radio programs might be transmitted around the globe for local reception. Many radio signals have been *bounced* from one point on earth to *Echo I*, then back from the passive satellite to another point on earth."

Echo I is an inflatable aluminized plastic sphere, 100 feet in diameter, half the thickness (.0005 inch) of the cellophane on a package of cigarettes. The sphere's exterior is coated with vapor-deposited aluminum which reflects about 98 per cent of the radio waves broadcast to it, up to frequencies of 20,000 megacycles. *Echo I* was lifted into orbit by the Thor Delta, a launch vehicle which stands 92 feet high and develops 150,000 pounds of thrust.

An intermediate size vehicle, it will be used for a variety of satellite and deep space missions during the next few years. Unlike other satellites, *Echo I* carries no instruments to gather information and send it back to earth.

The sphere has become a world-wide laboratory tool for researchers in communication fields. It is showing what one of the earliest feasible and practical applications of space research can be in the field of communications. Already our long-distance telephone and telegraph lines are overcrowded, or overloaded. Our trans-oceanic telephone cables will soon be inadequate. From the United States to the rest of the world, some 340 voice circuits are available. In fact, "it is estimated that international telephone calls," to quote from the report of the General Telephone and Electronics Corporation, "will increase from 4 million in 1961 to more than 10 million in 1970, and 100 million by 1980. The only way that the communications industry will be able to carry this greatly increased traffic will be to go to outer space."

"Answering the needs of the future will require a truly global communications system," the General Telephone and Electronics Corporation says. And as President Kennedy has stressed, all of the countries of the world, large and small nations alike, must be able to communicate with one another. To meet these goals, General Telephone and Electronics has proposed to the government the adoption of what is known as a "high altitude stationary synchronous satellite system," which would provide 3,000 two-way communication channels by means of three satellites placed equidistantly in orbit around the equator at an altitude of 22,300 miles. Ground transmitting stations in key locations throughout the world would transmit messages to one of the three satellites which would in turn send each message to a receiving station in some far-off destination. In other words, the signals would leapfrog enormous land and ocean areas, rather than go by cable or conventional radio.

The satellites would orbit in fixed position in relation to a point on the earth, rather than moving across the sky. This would be accomplished by launching the three satellites along a path directly over the equator. When the satellites reached the altitude of 22,300 miles, they would be given the required eastward velocity to push them in orbit along the equator. They would travel at the same angular velocity as the earth's rotation. Thus the satellites would occupy a fixed position over the same point on the earth, although they would actually be moving through space at about 6,900 miles per hour.

Bearing in mind that the satellites will be placed 22,300 miles above the equator, the time required for the signal to go from the New York transmitting station to the satellite and then to the European receiving station, a distance of about 50,000 miles, would be about three-tenths of a second.

The U.S. Government announced on June 5, 1961, that the Administration was considering giving research subsidies to private industry to hasten the start of an operational system of communications satellites. It was also revealed that the NASA would enter into an agreement with the American Telephone and Telegraph Company to provide launching facilities and a network for tracking the communication satellite in orbit. Agreeing to reimburse NASA for the cost of the firing of the satellite the Telephone Company proposed to build an "active repeater" communications 130-pound satellite, which would be fired into orbit 5,000 miles away from the earth. This satellite then would be in position to receive and retransmit a large number of phone calls or one television program between Europe and the United States. The United States would have two experimental communications satellites in orbit by the summer of 1962, while the Radio Corporation of America would have a relay satellite under contract with the NASA, as a government-financed undertaking.

— 42 —

MILITARY PERSPECTIVES—*MIDAS* AND *NIKE ZEUS*

While a preceding chapter has attempted to convey information about satellite weather mapping and sleuthing, let's now focus our attention on what has been accomplished in satellite photography, and the tracking of satellites and rockets and their military perspectives.

When the photographic art was about to become a tool of great practicality, inquisitive and ingenious man not only used his eyes, but commenced to take pictures—however crude in the beginning—from balloons, mountain tops, towers and, in more recent days, from airplanes, helicopters and rockets.

When ballooning became a popular pastime, and every Tom, Dick and Harry was doing it, the French balloonist and photographer Nadar (nickname for Gaspar Feliz Tournachon), a pioneer in aerial photography, took the first aerial photograph of a Paris rooftop scene with a successful daguerretype in 1858. Two years later, J. W. Black, of Boston, joining Professor Sam A. King, well-known aerialist of those days, took a photograph from a balloon from a height of 1,200 feet, for many years considered the most successful aerial photograph on record.

Anticipating the role of aerial observers for artillery adjustment by about 50 years, General George B. McClellan had photographs taken from balloons in many Civil War battles. Today, now that man has overcome the pull of earth's gravity and satellites are shot into space with increasing frequency, photograph-taking rockets and satellites are widely used, and observation can be carried out in many ways. For this purpose sensors do their work in different sections of the electro-magnetic spectrum, with the staellites, acting as components of a communication and photographing system, relaying signals from one point on or near the earth's surface to another.

Of singular interest is the so-called "24 satellite" which, as its name implies, completes an orbital revolution in 24 hours. If its motion is therefore in the same direction as the earth's rotation, it will remain within line of sight of a fixed region on the earth's surface. Properly-placed satellites could provide virtually complete global photographic and communication coverage at all times. Passing from horizon to horizon in roughly 95 minutes, a 4,000-mile satellite would be within line of sight of only about 25 per cent of the earth's surface at any one time, so that at least four such satellites would be needed to provide world-wide photographic coverage.

From the invention of the bow and arrow to the splitting of the atom, warfare, historically, has taken on a new dimension. Predicting all sorts of military functions in the future for man in space, the time may even come that outer space craft may be used to win wars on earth. No one, however, is able to safely predict what the future in space flight will bring. The first thing is to make sure that man can exist as well as function under all the difficulties inherent in manned space flights; in other words, to determine man's ability to sustain the rigors of space travel and what apparatus will be needed to ensure his safety. Once all these difficulties have been overcome, the issue, now obscure, may become clearer, and military authorities may then foresee the day when enemy satellites and rockets may be intercepted by properly-equipped space fighters. However, no matter how one looks at what still is "unknown," the ground work, begun with the orbital flights of Gagarin, Titov, Glenn and Carpenter, has been laid.

Of course, looking at it from a military standpoint, space had already been encroached upon during World War II, when the buzz bombs, or German V-2 projectiles, traveled part of their cross-channel shots well outside the atmosphere.

Meanwhile, since space undoubtedly has definite military implications *Midas III*, the so-called United States spy satellite traveling a record, all-seeing high orbit, 1,850 miles above the earth over the Poles, took its missile hunting payload from Point Arguello, California, over the USSR on July 12, 1961. It consumes 160 minutes for each pass around the earth in an almost circular orbit.

On this excursion into space, *Midas'* photographic or television equipment was reported to be so sensitive that it could detect a glowing cigaret in the dark 10 miles away. Best guess was that it could probably cross some area of the Soviet Union every other day. Once operational, it is reported, a network of Midas satellites will circle the earth at the same time, and all of the globe will come under the satellites' infra-red scrutiny. *Midas III* (short for *M*issile *D*efense *A*larm *S*ystem) is therefore an experimental forerunner of a satellite system that "could detect the hot exhaust of a missile launched anywhere on earth, thus giving it near-distant warning of an attack."

However, there may be some political implications and unfavorable Soviet reaction to a military satellite orbiting over its territory, despite the fact that the United States Air Force stresses the defensive nature of the *Midas* project.

The intention is to provide for the United States and the Free World the capability of detecting the launchings of aggressor ballistic missiles seconds after they have been launched. As elaborated by the United States Air Force further, "*Midas III* is to gather information on the ability of its infra-red sensors to detect the heat given off by missile exhaust and to distinguish the rocket flame from other heat sources on earth."

Tucked in the nose of the 3500-pound cylindrical, 30-foot long

The 100-foot diameter *Echo* satellite during inflation tests. The giant balloon is made of a micro-thin film of plastic coated with a vacuum-deposited film of aluminum.—NASA

A cutaway diagram of the Delta rocket and its payload, *Echo*.

—NASA

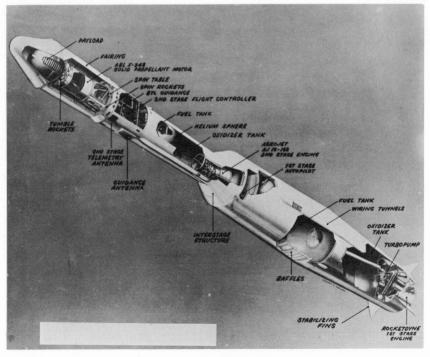

The U.S. Army's Nike-Zeus anti-missile missile is launched.
—DOUGLAS AIRCRAFT

A Bomarc missile is launched at Patrick Air Force Base.—U.S. AIR FORCE

A Nike Ajax installation.—DOUGLAS AIRCRAFT

The Terrier anti-aircraft missile in operational use with the U.S. Sixth Fleet.—GENERAL DYNAMICS

An army of Nikes in readiness—DOUGLAS AIRCRAFT

satellite are the infra-red sensors (built by the Aerojet General Corporation) and the instruments and transmitter for relaying information on the satellite's performance back to earth. Picking up infra-red waves generated by heat, the *Midas III* circles the earth in its Polar orbit, 1,850 miles up.

Midas III may not only have a look-see at Soviet territory— including Tyura Tam, Russia's big missile base in the Ural Mountains, north of Lake Ural—but also be able to restart the satellite's engine in space. This very feat was achieved earlier in the same kind of vehicle atop Discoverer 21's Thor Booster. "This restart ability means," the Air Force asserts, "that future space vehicles can get away from missiles or armed satellites sent up to intercept them, by changing direction with small Vernier rockets."

While *Midas,* and its sister satellite *Samos,* are expected to provide our country's defenses with an early warning against attack, by giving us 30 minutes in which to retaliate after they have transmitted information about missiles launchings as soon as they leave their pad, the Distant Early Warning or DEW Line, inside the Arctic circle, gives us only 15 minutes warning at the moment, picking up Soviet launchings only after the weapons are already airborne.

Considering that the most powerful United States Military rocket—the 100-ton, 25-foot missile improved Atlas—was sent forth on July 7, 1961, on the longest military rocket flight then on record, some 9,050 miles through space from Cape Canaveral to the Indian Ocean (nearly half way around the world), we may have some idea as to the importance of the military rocket business. Traveling along a ballistic trajectory which carried it nearly 1,000 miles high at peak speed of 17,000 miles per hour, it crossed on its all-over-water course the tip of Brazil and passed south of the Union of South Africa. Fifty-three minutes after launching, two tracking planes and a vessel followed the cone's path as it dived back into the heat barrier of the earth's atmosphere on a target about 1,000 miles southeast of Capetown.

Having thus successfully cracked the distance mark for a military rocket with this flight, an official of the General Dynamics-Astronautics Co., which makes the Atlas, hoped "this shot marked the end of the missile problem." But the only real defense against Russian ICBMs this country has, according to people in the know, may be the Army's Nike Zeus, a solid-fueled, three-stage, 48-foot rocket, brainchild of the retired General John Medaris, who had started Nike Zeus on its way in 1956.

General Medaris is said to have estimated that a Nike Zeus defense could destroy 80 per cent of incoming Russian ICBMs, and General Lawrence S. Kuter, as head of the North American Defense Command, also is pleading for such anti-missile missile at the earliest possible moment.

Finally, General Bernard A. Schriever, head of the Air Force Systems Command, at a recent American Rocket Society meeting, called for development of satellite interceptors, large rocket boosters and manned space stations, saying that "America's conquest of space with man and machinery may well be the key to our national survival." He also stressed "that the nation that dominates space might, if it chooses, dominate the world."

In his program what General Schriever chose for special emphasis was Dyna-Soar, a winged space craft that would be sent into orbit by rockets and glide back to earth. Major General John B. Medaris, former head of the nation's space program, said on October 25, 1961, that he "had no doubt that the Soviet Union had solved the missile defense problem, as Marshal Rodion Malinovsky had claimed." However, in the retired General's opinion "our own anti-missile system with Nike Zeus also constitutes a solution."

Hailed as one of our nation's nearest defenses, two stages of the extremely swift missile interceptor have been fired successfully. The first test firing of all three solid-fuel rocket motors of the Army's Nike Zeus anti-missile was successfully completed at White Sands Missile Range, N.M., on November 30, 1961. Ignition of the relatively small third-stage reaction motor was carried out as planned. The successful test may prove Nike Zeus can get upstairs fast enough to intercept an enemy warhead streaking in at 20,000 miles an hour.

The U.S. Army announced on December 21, 1961, that its Nike Zeus anti-missile missile had successfully intercepted a missile in flight for the first time. The Army released at the same time photographs of the Nike Zeus weapon intercepting a Nike Hercules anti-aircraft missile in a test over the White Sands Missile Range in New Mexico. The Nike Zeus still faced a much more critical test during the summer of 1962, when it "will be pitted against an Atlas intercontinental missile, which travels up to 17,000 miles an hour. The Hercules has a speed in excess of 3,000 miles an hour. In this

White Sands test, the Zeus did not make physical contact with the Hercules weapon in the air, the Army said, but it had "soared well within the lethal radius" of the nuclear warhead it was designed to carry.

Of course, to be effective, this anti-missile system must also find the incoming warhead and determine its speed and direction. It also must determine which is the warhead and which are decoys. Then the warhead has to be destroyed either by detonation or, if possible, by disarming it so that it cannot explode.

— 43 —

AN ATOM-POWERED SATELLITE

While the United States Navy was busy creating the almost unbelievable wonders of atomic ships below the sea, atomic energy was being pioneered in a new avenue in space exploration by the first nuclear energy satellite, on June 29, 1961.

On that day, a 79-foot Thor-Able-Star rocket was fired from Cape Canaveral, with three satellites in its nose cone: the 175-pound experimental *Transit IV-A* (with a small atomic battery), the first powered by nuclear energy, and two smaller scientific satellites. The first of these, named *Injun*, has the purpose of investigating the radiation in the Van Allen Belts, while the purpose of the other, the 55-pound *Greb*, developed by the Naval Research Laboratory, is to study the X-ray radiation from the sun and its effect in causing ionospheric disturbances and radio blackouts on earth. Once in space, these two were separated by springs, from the *Transit IV-A*, and were said to be operating excellently. This Navy Transit Navigational Satellite, *Transit IV-A*, could actually be said to be the experimental forerunner for a Space Navigational System, permitting ships at sea to navigate with unusual accuracy. Officials of the U.S. Navy and the Atomic Energy Commission pointed out that the launching of these three satellites not only "proved the feasibility of placing several satellites into orbit with one launching rocket, but also that they will become of importance in establishing a multiple-satellite system, such as a communications network in space."

The atomic power devices have demonstrated, as is now reported, "psychologically and technically their value in providing a reliable, long-lived source of electricity for powering instruments in satellites." This would overcome the chance of breakdown encountered with the conventional storage batteries. The tiny atomic power source in this *Transit IV-A* satellite is one of a series of SNAPs (meaning: Systems for Nuclear Auxiliary Power) developed by the Atomic Energy Commission for applications in space, as well as on earth. Developed and built by the Martin Company of Baltimore, this 4.7 pound SNAP device, producing 2.7 watts of electricity for at least 5 years, does not depend on sunlight, as do the solar cells now used in the satellites.

Thus this historic, three-for-one rocket heralds a new era in the conquest of space.

— 44 —

TRACKING SATELLITES AND MISSILES

The tracking of satellites, guided missiles and manned rockets is no easy task. As it is one of the most vital operations connected with space science, an extensive world-wide tracking system has been set up. With each shot into space of rockets and satellites, when ground requirements also have to be met, virtually all tracking stations, here and abroad, get into the act.

As new missiles are being developed, new and ever-growing ground support requirements go hand in hand with them. New tests also require mobile tracking sites at launching areas, together with complex electronic tracking and recording gear for use after missiles and rockets have been fired. Data then are collected, processed, and reports are made.

Though all active stations in connection with the launching of United States missiles and satellites are manned by or operated under the supervision of NASA personnel, active tracking stations abroad—those located in Bermuda, Mexico, the Canary Islands, Nigeria, Zanzibar, in addition to Jodrell Bank tracking station in England, the Australian ones of Muchea and Woomera, Canton Island and with the exception of the huge Thule Air Force Base in Greenland—are staffed mainly with foreign personnel.

In the actual recovery of capsules, which is no easy task either, units from U.S. fleet and Marine Corps groups, together with land vehicles, helicopters, aircraft carriers, patrol and warning aircraft, are assigned their respective tasks to make locating capsules possible.

Among the many vital and successful tracking stations located around the world, the largest steerable radio telescope is the 250-foot diameter dish at Jodrell Bank, Cheshire, England, intended originally to poke its nose into the far reaches of the universe and listen for signals from distant galaxies. It is playing a large part in tracking both American and Russian space probes. Its famous astronomer director and one of the most outstanding authorities on radio telescopes is Professor Sir Bernard Lovell, the brain and guiding spirit behind the tracking, identifying and recording of satellites, rockets, and general space programs. Until not very long ago the largest one in the world, the Jodrell Bank radio telescope does yeoman duty in listening to signals from distant places. In some cases it has even reached out 23 million miles from the earth. For instance, after the Soviets launched *Sputnik VIII* toward Venus on February 12, 1961, the mighty Jodrell Bank bowl picked up some radio signals on June 11, purportedly having come from this Soviet Venus rocket. Sir Bernard Lovell, together with the Soviet's woman head of the Russian tracking network, and Dr. Khodarve, an expert on the Venus probe, who had been sent to the radio laboratory, were able to identify the signals immediately as having come from the rocket, when its tape recordings were analyzed. This Venus probe was to have passed within 60,000 miles of the planet Venus and while radio contact was lost on March 2, Jodrell Bank had begun picking up signals again on the rocket's wave length on May 17, 1961.

Another memorable tracking achievement—actually a trailblazing exploit in deep space probes—occurred in connection with the launching of the United States' *Pioneer V* which, leaving its launching pad on March 11, 1960, sent data back to earth from a point some 22,500,000 miles out in space. It still holds the communication distance record. When *Pioneer V* had left its launching pad at the Cape on its way to the vast distance of nearly 23,000,000 miles from the earth, and was streaking over the English horizon twelve minutes after lift-off, its signals were located almost at once by Sir Bernard's Jodrell telescope. Less than ten minutes later a coded signal was sent into space through a transmitter mounted on the gigantic telescope. In less than a second it was decoded, indicating that the payload was to be released from the carrier rocket.

Traveling deeper into space for a two and a half month period, *Pioneer V* continued to receive coded signals sent to it by the gigantic Jodrell bowl, and kept sending Jodrell the scientific data that had accumulated. By the time that its signals and batteries had finally deteriorated, *Pioneer V* had furnished Jodrell, nonetheless, with all sorts of information concerning these vast spaces on its 22,500,000 junket through the interplanetary system.

Among the great many tracking stations that exist here and abroad, one very large dish telescope now being erected is the 600-foot telescope built by the U.S. Naval Research Laboratory at Sugar Grove, West Virginia. A 240-foot space tracking antenna was announced in August, 1961, for Goldstone, California, by the NASA, and by Dr Eberhardt Rechtlin, Director of the Deep Space Instrumentation Facility (DSIF), which is operated for the NASA by the California Institute of Technology Jet Propulsion Laboratory. The DSIF presently consists of three tracking stations, located approximately 120 degrees apart around the world in order to insure that one of the stations is always in position to maintain radio contact with a spacecraft. These stations, equipped with two space tracking antennas each 85 feet in diameter, are at Goldstone, Cal., at Woomera, Australia, and another one near Johannesburg, South Africa. The planning schedule calls for the 240-foot antenna to be operational at Goldstone by January 1, 1965.

In addition to the devices mentioned above, there is the Ballistic Missile Warning System, a primary radar locating device for missiles, making use of dishes or radio telescopes of about 140-feet in diameter and probing out to distances of a few thousand miles.

Another installation is the BMEWS, or *Ballistic Missile Early Warning System* at Thule Air Force Base, Greenland, established there under treaty with Denmark. This one is a veritable missile-age eye in the Arctic, situated 931 miles from the North Pole, and 1,750 miles from the nearest point in the United States. With its radio beams reaching some 3,000 miles into Siberia, it ought to make it the largest installation in this or in any other country.

Thule's greatest value lies, of course, in the fact that it may mean a gain of at least 15 minutes warning of a missile in flight. While it cannot arrest the missile, it can tell where it came from and where it is heading. This information is then relayed to the respective command centers in the United States, permitting decisions to be made and action taken.

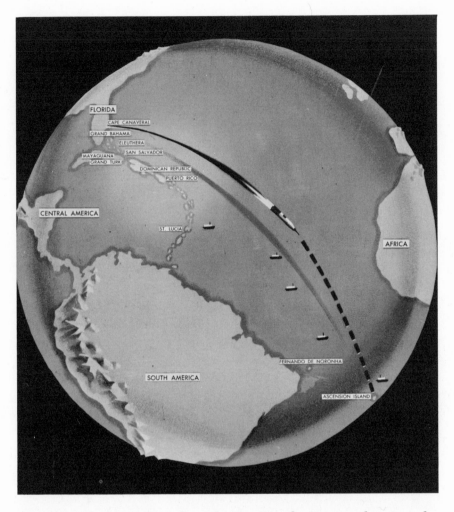

Diagram of the 5,000-mile Atlantic Missile Range showing the
locations of tracking vessels and land-based tracking stations.

—U.S. AIR FORCE

The guided missiles Range Control Center at Cape Canaveral.

—U.S. AIR FORCE

The world's largest radio telescope, at Jodrell Bank, Cheshire, England. Its reflector bowl is 83 yards across.—BRITISH INFORMATION SERVICES

The giant radio telescope at Parks, New South Wales, Australia.
—BRITISH INFORMATION SERVICES

America's largest radio telescope "dish," a 70-ton, 150-feet-in-diameter steel and aluminum parabolic antenna, is being built on the Stanford University Campus. This $350,000 research installation, built by Stanford Research Institute scientists with support of the Air Force Office of Aerospace Research and the Defense Atomic Support Agency, will produce a 300-400 kilowatt radar probe with which the sun, moon and interplanetary gases will be probed.

A device which is the only one of its kind in the Southern Hemisphere is the very important tracking installation, said to be the world's farthest hearing "ear" on the universe, at Parkes, New South Wales, 200 miles west of Sydney, Australia. Forty feet shorter in diameter than the huge one at Jodrell Bank, this Australian, 210-foot antenna listens in on radio sources ten times farther off in space. The range and location of this gigantic installation will insure it an important role in tracking the scientific probes that are being sent into interplanetary space. It will be used, for instance, for a detailed mapping of our Milky Way galaxy, and of similar features in the clouds of Magellan, and the Andromeda Nebula. It will also search for new radio sources in space and chart their distribution. What is even more important, it may also help to solve the problem, according to Dr. E. C. Bowen, pioneer in the development of radar and Chief of the Division of Radiophysics of the Commonwealth Scientific and Industrial Research Organization, whether the universe had a beginning, or has always been in existence, surviving by a constant birth and dying of matter. Finally, Dr. Bowen said: "The range would be about 1,000,000,000 light years, or 6 billion trillion miles, and the huge antenna will be steerable over most of the visible sky." Initial and partial contributions for the erection of this powerful Australian telescope have come from the Carnegie Corporation and the Rockefeller Foundation.

As for life existing on other worlds, scientists have been trying very hard for the first time in human history to intercept radio signals from "living beings" on other worlds. No such signal has been received during the experiment. However, according to a scientific report appearing in the November 18 issue of the British journal *Nature* (and according to Dr. George Claus, a microbiologist of New York University Medical Center, and Dr. Bartholomew Nagy of the Fordham University, Dept. of Chemistry), "tiny one-celled organisms that resembled fossil algae but are different from any organisms known to have lived on the surface of the earth have been found in meteorites by these two Hungarian scientists working together. The finding is interpreted by the two as strong evidence for, but not proof of, the existence of a form of life outside the earth."

Last March Dr. Nagy, and Dr. Douglas J. Hennessey of Fordham, and Dr. Warren G. Meinscheim, of the Esso Research and Engineering Company, of Linden, New Jersey, reported that they had found in one meteorite chemical compounds closely akin to the chemicals involved in the life processes of plants and animals on earth.

One popular theory is that the meteorites are the debris of a demolished planet that once circled the sun not too far from earth. If so, the new evidence is that conditions on such a planet were not too much different from the condition on the earth, and that they were conditions that would allow a form of life to develop.

— 45 —

RADIATION IN SPACE

With each further penetration into the limitless regions of space, added impetus is given to the study of such deep space phenomena as cosmic and gamma rays, ultra violet and other solar radiations, the Van Allen Belt, and magnetic fields in the ionosphere and beyond, all of which affect spacemen, of course.

It has been established that our earth is surrounded by a great radiation belt—electrical ring—referred to as the Van Allen Belt. This lethal barrier, or barriers, discovered only in 1958, must be avoided by spacecraft for fear of exposure to deadly electric particles. (Since then, it has been disclosed that only one ring of this belt is to be avoided as being hazardous, and to which I shall refer later.)

This two-part belt, ringing the earth like two giant doughnuts and extending from 4,000 to 24,000 miles, has baffled our scientists. Subsequent information has come to light after the exploits of our satellite *Pioneer V* launched on March 11, 1960, and of the 83-pound *Explorer XII*, launched on August 15, 1961, indicating that a huge disturbing magnetic field may exist at distances ranging from 40,000 to 60,000 miles. Scientists have been engaged in studying these cosmic rays for more than half a century by the use of high-flying balloons. As these balloons soared to ever higher regions, Geiger counters kept going up, giving added proof that there were more and more cosmic rays in these higher regions. Hence the questions arose, where did these rays originate, and what was their mission in the cosmos?

Seeking the answer to these riddles, scientists kept probing, until Dr. James Van Allen, Chairman of the Department of Physics at the State University of Iowa and top level adviser of the NASA, came up with the answer. Having turned his attention at the end of World War II first to the study of rockets, and subsequently to high altitude research, Dr. Van Allen and his colleagues became aware of a very sizable zone or belt of radiation around the earth in 1958. This huge belt or halo, winding itself like a "slightly flattened innertube" around the world, was christened the Van Allen Radiation Belt. It is this name that keeps cropping up in all reports and technical papers, with which astronomers, scientists and spacemen are now so vitally concerned.

It should cause no surprise that researchers, scientists, and all others exploring these secrets in the sun's path have found that venturing into space portends hidden dangers. They have also become increasingly aware that these two Van Allen Belts must surely create a hazard and constitute a barrier to all spacemen shooting into deep space. Once these barriers—replete with radiation storms, hail of deathly rays, cosmic dust pellets—have been overcome, they may then enter upon the trackless wastes of interplanetary space. In order to peer into these unexplored reaches of the universe, NASA has shot a satellite into the sky provided with large, specially equipped astronomical telescopes, to measure the previously undetectable cosmic gamma rays. These rays, which race through the universe with the fantastic speed of light—or 186,000 miles a second —are in reality some form of electro-magnetic radiation, like our invisible X-rays, and ultra-violet light.

Launched from a four-stage Juno II rocket, seeking an orbit ranging from 300-700, or maybe 1100 miles above the earth, the main objective of this astronomical satellite telescope, shaped like an old street lamp, is to detect and map the distribution of gamma rays generated in our own and neighboring galaxies, as for instance in the Milky Way. Through these discoveries and measurements, scientists and astronomers try to discover newer clues for solving the mystery of the creation and universal distribution of these rays.

This astronomical satellite, whose two radio transmitters are controlled from the ground, and developed and built at the Massachusetts Institute of Technology by Doctors Kraushaar and George Clark, tumbles end-over-end ten times an hour once in orbit. This enables the gamma-ray telescope to explore a portion of the heavens every six minutes. The telescope's heart, or center, consists of a sandwich of crystal layers, composed of sodium iodide and cesium iodine. Once a gamma ray hits these crystals, it produces through emission of electrons and positrons (the latter positively charged electrons) certain scintillations, which are then transmitted to scientists and observers on the earth below.

It is expected that this giant—the first astronomical space telescope—may remain orbited around the earth for at least three years, so that it may give a fundamental insight into the origin of the universe and forces that keep all of it going.

It would not be out of place here to refer once more to the trail-blazing exploits of the *Pioneer V* satellite, which has sent us so much valuable data from at least 20,000,000 miles out in space. As it kept broadcasting, it has signalled us one discovery after another. It had passed, according to the May, 1961, communique from B. V. Berkner, Chairman of the Space Science Board of the National Academy of Science, through the Van Allen radiation belts discovered some years previous. "Once *Pioneer V* had reached the 40,000 mile mark," Dr. Berkner disclosed, "it discovered a third immense ring current surrounding the earth at some eight to ten earth radii, or roughly 80,000 miles."

Pioneer V not only found that the magnetic field of the earth was bounded by the plasmas of space, but also discovered an interplanetary magnetic field of such scientific importance that it clarified the picture of the sun's controlling influence on the earth. "Just as *Pioneer V* reached the 6,000,000-mile point in the universe," Dr. Berkner concluded," "the sun erupted in a violent solar flare, so that scientists got their first glimpse of events taking place way deep in interplanetary space as a result of such a monstrous eruption."

In addition to the information given in previous pages about the magnetic and other belts that encircle the earth, it was disclosed late in December, 1961, that the earth has been discovered to have a "corona of helium forming a 900-mile-thick layer in the upper atmosphere." The discovery of this helium layer, extending from about 600 to 1,500 miles above the surface of the earth "was the product of international scientific collaboration in space research." The theory was first suggested by Professor Marcel Nicolet, Director of the Centre National des Recherches de l' Espace in Brussels, Belgium, and was subsequently substantiated by American scientists from the *Explorer VIII* scientific satellite.

To summarize what has been learned about the atmosphere in the last few years, Dr. Robert Jastrow of NASA, director of the theoretical division of NASA's Goddard Space Center in Greenbelt, Md., disclosed that "up to about 72 miles the atmosphere is composed primarily of a mixture of nitrogen and oxygen. Then there is a layer consisting predominantly of oxygen extending to around 600 miles. Above this, there is an intervening level of helium, which is the second lightest element. And from the latest information it appears that the hydrogen layer begins around 1,500 miles, and extends with decreasing density out to around 6,000 miles, where the density of the earth's atmosphere merges into that of interplanetary gas. The average temperature in the upper atmosphere," Dr. Jastrow reported, "is estimated at 2,025 degrees Fahrenheit." And "it has been determined that the density and temperature of the upper atmosphere is greatly affected by the cycles of the sun." And "as the sun moves from a period of maximum to minimum sunspot activity in an eleven year cycle, the temperature in the upper atmosphere tends to drop. Thus in 1964 the low point in solar activity, the pre-dawn temperature in upper atmosphere is expected to reach a low point of about 470 degrees Fahrenheit."

— 46 —

COLLECTING DUST FROM COSMIC SPACE

It must have become clear from preceding pages that a study of radiation belts surrounding the earth and an intimate knowledge of the potentially hazardous radiation of at least one of these belts is most essential to manned space travel. However, a knowledge of this radiation is not enough, as there are other hazards facing astronauts, such as dust from space.

To explore this phase of the space picture, the United States

Air Force disclosed that its Venus Flytrap Rocket had succeeded in collecting what space scientists believed were the first samples of space dust, on June 21, 1961. On its trip into deep space the Venus rocket ran into a band of space dust, or micrometeorites, which appeared to be 100 times as dense as had been predicted.

While the extent of hazard may be mainly psychological, the hundreds of thousands of dust particles swirling through the solar system may not only provide new clues to their own origin, but possibly to the genesis of our earth as well. Though much of this matter has been identified on earth, space scientists have not yet been able to discover its real connection with other terrestrial matter. Aiming, therefore, at a further study of these tiny dust projectiles (possibly the remnants of an exploded planet) NASA announced on August 25, 1961, that the 72-foot four-stage Scout Rocket Explorer placed a satellite into orbit with the intention of studying the lethal effect that such space dust might have on astronauts. Within two hours after launching from Wallops Island on the Virginia Coast, the satellite began sending back information. Hurtling through space at speeds of 45 miles a second, these particles could erode or puncture an astronaut-carrying space vehicle.

There are two types of hazards in connection with space dust that have so far puzzled space scientists. One is physical, because as the micrometeorites streak through space at the fantastic speeds claimed by the Air Force, they could be just as lethal as bullets. The other is psychological because, even if these particles were not to succeed in penetrating the space ship (as suggested by Dr. Fred L. Whipple, professor of Astronomy) the sound created by their banging against the rocket or spaceship might be greatly unnerving.

In the first attempt to capture this dust in space and bring it back to earth, an Air Force Aerobee-High Experimental Rocket streaked through space 101 miles above the White Sands Proving Ground on June 6, 1961, and was brought down again by parachute 55 miles from its launching pad. This rocket was equipped with a contraption similar almost to a Venus Flytrap plant, which folds its petals around insects and slowly devours them.

The Air Force device consisted of eight metal leaves, with space dust traps affixed to the leaves. At the time when the rocket was shot into space the leaves were folded in, but once the rocket had attained an altitude of a definite number of miles, the leaves, through some highly ingenious mechanism, would open up and ensnare the slower traveling dust particles.

According to Dr. Robert K. Soberman of the Air Force Cambridge Research Laboratory at L. G. Hanscom Field, Bedford, Mass., the experiment proved that these fly traps were struck by ten particles per square centimeter every second, and that about one million particles, or fragments, may have been retrieved even though most of them proved too small to be studied.

— 47 —

SPACE MEDICINE

To be able to support human life in the vacuum or near-vacuum of space, in which man's body fluids may reach the boiling point, his breathing process impaired, and the vehicle in which space-man travels into space at times may be heated red hot, measures must be taken that are far more complex than what we are able to imagine. And the space man's housing vehicle must be far more elaborately equipped and much more complex in structure than what we have learned already about existing probe instruments.

Friction and compression, both of which increase with the rocket's speed, also generate an enormous amount of aerodynamic heat and if it were not for special metals and other materials that are able to withstand high temperatures, one is apt to wonder why spacemen and test pilots are not being cooked in their own cockpits.

Little Gordo's ride on December 14, 1958, during which the tiny squirrel monkey was hurled 300 miles into space aboard the Jupiter rocket, furnished inescapable proof to the medical authorities that a spaceman could stand and survive similar space undertakings. This has been conclusively proved by Gagarin's, Titov's, Glenn's and Carpenter's orbital flights. However, the hunt for metals, and, of course, food that will meet requirements of this new era of the universe is high on the list of space scientists. It has also become quite clear that the heat problem vis-a-vis use of protective metals is, of course, greatest in the missile field, because as the speed of missiles increases the temperature also rises in geometric progression. Heating becomes especially acute when the space vehicle returns to the atmosphere of the earth, hence the existence of several cooling systems such as ablation cooling involving coating the missile with a substance that vaporizes during heating.

According to the North American Aviation Space and Information Systems Division: "If man is long to survive beyond his atmosphere, he will require a total life support system which will protect him against space while satisfying both his biological and psychological needs. However, before this system can be devised, man's space requirements must be anticipated and defined."

Turning now to space medicine, of prime importance in man's travel through space, extensive studies of how man can survive the perils in space have become an indispensable phase of research undertaken by medical space scientists. Previous chapters have already shown that man has to be well supplied with oxygen, food, as well as protected from unseen dangers encountered from radiation, meteors and other space hazards.

Life can exist only when conditions are such as to provide the proper kind of temperature, light and sustenance for growth and reproduction. The prerequisites, as we all know, are oxygen, carbon, hydrogen and nitrogen. Reference has already been made to yeast, which was placed in the Army Jupiter satellite's cargo, in 1959, to study its reproduction under space conditions and to discover whether it might be developed as a space food. Another possibility, both as an air and a food source, appears to be the algae, single-celled plants which absorb carbon dioxide and release oxygen. In connection with this, Dr. Dean Burk, researcher on algae at the National Institute of Health, referred to a discovery made at Yellowstone Park of a special species of algae that not only proved to be a fast grower, but was able to withstand a temperature as high as 86 degrees Fahrenheit, and provide oxygen and food. Asserting that these algae recycled the space vehicle's air supply, removed the carbon dioxide, and controlled the oxygen, Dr. Burk added that if these algae were grown on human wastes they could also furnish the necessary foods in the space cabin.

In the evolution of space training, we have already been told that animals make space flights safer for man. The Russians used dogs, rabbits and other animal species, whereas, according to Colonel Harry A. Gorman, Chief of the Veterinary Service of the Aerospace Medical Center at Brooks Air Force Base, in San An-

An assembled Saturn C-1 in a shop at the NASA Marshall Space Flight Center, Huntsville, Ala. The rocket is 162 feet long, with a maximum diameter of 21½ feet.—NASA

The Saturn barge *Compromise*, carrying the first Saturn flight booster, inert second stage and payload, passes through the lock at Wilson Dam on the Tennessee River on its way to Cape Canaveral.—NASA

The Saturn flight booster is raised onto its launch pedestal at Cape
Canaveral. The 310-foot-tall gantry used in erecting the vehicle
will be removed shortly before launch.—NASA

A view of the Saturn C-1, the first to be launched, taken during the three-second interval between ignition of the engines and lift-off. The launching took place on October 27, 1961.—NASA

An artist's conception of a lunar base of the future.. A nuclear-powered space vehicle, one of a series of shuttle rockets ferrying astronauts and supplies from Earth to Moon, rises from the dust-covered surface. Solar energy provides the heat, light and power for the pressurized, dome-covered base.—DOUGLAS AIRCRAFT

tonio, the United States space authorities use mice, frogs, hamsters, opossums, and simians in their researches to help make flights safer for spacemen. After their basic training, or after undergoing bio-medical tests, these animal pioneers are sent into space, to solve many of man's health problems encountered there. Selected with the utmost care, and after receiving the best kind of treatment, often denied to a great many people on earth, the smallest animals are picked first. Then the hospital's research is extended to the larger species, until enough has been learned from them to apply the same to man in space. Not unlike human beings animals have, of course, traits, whims and fancies that render them adaptable to certain experiments under conditions prevalent in space. Brooks Hospital prides itself on the possession of an operating room, X-ray machines, and the sort of equipment usually found in the best equipped institutions catering to human beings. After a period of quarantine to safeguard them from disease, most animals are first measured, classified, given blood tests, and, if necessary, also receive surgery. Of all the animals coming to Brooks Hospital, Colonel Gorman disclosed, monkeys are considered the cleverest and most pliable animals to work with, a fact that had been so conclusively shown by the small rhesus monkey, Sam, by the first class "astronaut" monkey Ham who, after his ride in the Mercury rocket, became a patient or inmate of Hollman Air Force Base in New Mexico, and by Able, of the space flight team Able and Baker.

While on the subject of monkeys and their use in space experimentation, a small rhesus monkey at this time of writing is to go on a 6,000-mile ride aboard an Atlas missile, with a tiny radio transmitter embedded in its tummy. The purpose of this newest of space animal experiments was to find out how the monkey's heart reacted to the rigors of space flight. These data were then to be radioed from the monkey's stomach to a receiver on the couch on which the monkey was reclining. Once the tests proved to be of practical use, similar experiments with surgically-embedded instruments would be tried on astronauts. Incidentally, the transmitter already had been inserted some time ago, and had been found completely workable in ground tests. Also embedded in the monkey's body was a small grid, which not only picked up the heart signals, but sent them over a tiny wire to the internal transmitter. The final result would be an electro cardiogram, together with data on the monkey's respiration, and a record of the heart sounds.

Adding its name also to the space honor role was the tiny, six-inch tall squirrel monkey Goliath, who was killed on November 11, 1961, when a mighty Atlas missile in which the poor simian had its last ride was destroyed in flight, some 100 yards off Cape Canaveral. On a 5,000-mile-course test, with the intention of attaining an altitude of 650 miles, the Atlas, about half a minute after launching, veered suddenly—possibly due to a faulty mechanism—and scientists blew it up. While the cause of mishap was still a mystery, some sources reported that the missile lost thrust in one of the Atlas' five engines.

Little Goliath had been placed inside the rocket's nose Tuesday morning, having been trained to go for 80-hour periods without food or water. Scientists had installed a water fountain inside the nose cone, and had trained Goliath to quench his thirst from this fountain during the ride. However, the test's main purpose was to determine the effect of the 20 minutes of weightlessness. The other cargo, incidentally, consisted of fruit flies, bread mold, eggs and viruses.

— 48 —

MISSILES OF THE FUTURE—
SATURN AND DYNA-SOAR

Marking the biggest steps the United States has taken toward the conquest of space are the 40-ton, 85-foot Atlas, which has already proved its operational capabilities, and the Titan, of the United States Air Force, both designed to deliver a thermonuclear warhead to a range of about 5-6,000 miles. The gross weight of the missiles is in the 200,000-pound class, with take-off thrust of in excess of 360,000 pounds, and Atlas also has the unique quality of being able to place itself with its military load, tank and all, in a satellite orbit, at an altitude of 400 miles. In the planning stage with an Atlas is Project Surveyor for 1963, a spaceship for softlanding instruments on the moon to explore its surface. In this project an Atlas B for first stage and a Centaur liquid oxygen engine for the second stage are to be used.

Then there is the monstrous, three stage Saturn Rocket (162 feet tall, the size of a 16-story building) with its cluster of eight

engines, with a total of 1,300,000 pounds of thrust, and with a capsule weight including 600,000 lbs of fuel, estimated at about 925,000
pounds. Made at Huntsville, Alabama, and said to be twice as large
as the booster, it is probably the first in a series of six liquid fuel
rockets which, scientists hope, will eventually land an American
astronaut on the moon. The gantry for this Saturn monster (which
is also a tremendous engineering and construction object) may be
said to be the largest moving object in the world, standing as high
as a 31-story skyscraper. This gigantic missile, which, as I said before, was constructed at Huntsville, Ala., was so monstrous in size
that it proved too bulky and large to ship by rail, air, or road, so
the ingenious engineers conceived the plan of shipping it by barge
by a round-about, 2,200-mile route to its launching pad at Cape
Canaveral, 600 miles away. But then there arose another problem,
because some 60 miles from the construction post at Huntsville,
they had to contend with a broken lock in the Tennessee River. So
they first shipped the huge rocket to that place, and then transferred
it to a roadway of one mile built by the Tennessee Valley Authority
all around the broken lock. Once it was around, the monster was
again transferred to another barge, which the engineers-construc-
tors had to build on the other side of the lock. After this it became
somewhat easier sailing.

According to the NASA, the three rockets of the future are the
earth orbit Saturn C-I, the circumlunar Saturn C-2, and the lunar
landing Nova.

Saturn II is designed to orbit payloads of more than 22 tons
around the earth, land a ton-and-a-half on the moon, or put instruments on Mars and Venus, whereas Saturn III, having two kerosene
engines, each developing 1.5 million pounds of thrust, and capable
of putting 50 tons into orbit, is expected to fly a multiple crew
around the moon, or send 12 tons on a one-way trip to Mars.

According to an announcement by the United States Air Force,
the 102-foot Titan II—the powerful intercontinental ballistic missile
—develops 430,000 pounds of thrust, 70,000 pounds more than the
Atlas, at a speed of 15,000 miles per hour, whereas the Nova, now
being developed as a vehicle for a manned flight to the moon and
return, with a cluster of eight engines, is said to develop a total of
12,000,000 pounds of thrust.

Finally, there is now being developed a Rover Nuclear engine,
powered by atomic energy, with twice the weight lifting capacity

of any chemically-fueled rocket of similar size. This will function, it is expected, as the power plant in a space ship known as the Nerva, which may already be in the production stage. This leaves the Dyna-Soar, or Space Glider.

As I wrote about three years ago, the United States Air Force had ordered the development of a Space Glider boosted by powerful rockets that would soar around the earth at near-satellite speeds. This project, then, represented the most ambitious step yet undertaken by the United States toward manned space flight. This glider would be in reality a combination of a ballistic missile and a winged plane. The centrifugal force given it by the rocket boosters, together with the dynamic lift of its wings, ought to enable it to soar around the world at hypersonic speeds. In the first phase of this boost-glide flight, or dynamic soaring, the glider would be lofted to an altitude of forty miles by a long-range military ballistic missile. It then would travel in the thin air of the atmosphere for 8,000 to 12,000 miles at a speed of around 10,000 miles an hour, while its wings should enable it to land like a plane.

The military authorities explained at that time, that, "As a weapon this Dyna-Soar could be used for reconnaissance, for strategic bombing, searching out targets on first pass, directing bombs on them on the second, and then come back to friendly territory. It is, however, expected that it will take some years before the first such vehicle can be flown." This is what I referred to in 1959.

And now, according to the United States Air Force reports of July, 1961, "a pool of qualified test pilots would be created from which to draw the men who would eventually man and fly the Dyna-Soar, the United States Air Force's first manned spacecraft, now under development." It further disclosed that "some fifty Air Force test pilots have been chosen who, after rigid, and similar vigorous selection processes used in chosing the seven Mercury astronauts, will fly the future military spacecraft, such as the Dyna-Soar."

These Air Force test pilots have already been given intensive medical examinations at the Lovelace Clinic in Albuquerque, New Mexico, and have been subjected to a variety of stress tests, such as centrifuges, heat chambers, and pressure chambers, at Wright Patterson Air Force Base in Dayton, Ohio. From this pool, the U.S. Air Force now intends to draw those for the first manned spacecraft who are to fly the Dyna-Soar.

The fuselage of this Dyna-Soar research spacecraft is said to have a flat bottom and stubby wings, which will provide the aerodynamic lift. This would enable the craft, unlike the Mercury capsule, to maneuver in the outer fringes of the earth's atmosphere and to select its own landing place when on the way down. For the Dyna-Soar's boost into space, it would have the help of Titan II, after which it would be on its own and coast on its momentum at an altitude of 100 miles or more.

Some of the pilots, it has been reported, have already been working closely with the designers, contractors or manufacturers of this vehicle. It has also been disclosed that four of the test pilots have been sent as consultants to the Boeing Company, in order to offer some of their own suggestions, which, as top flight pilots, they certainly are qualified to do.

On October 27, 1961, the black and white, eight-engined Saturn rocket was successfully sent on its way, on what was its first test flight. The NASA reported that the 162-foot missile reached a peak altitude of 84.813 miles, at a top speed of 3,607 miles an hour, before it took a nose dive into the Atlantic 214.72 miles down the range, only 8 minutes, 3.6 seconds after firing.

The eight engines, building up 1,296,000 pounds of thrust after lift-off, increased this thrust to 1,515,000 pounds just before engine cut-off. Its mission: Simply to prove to all concerned that it could fly. And it surely did. And whereas the scientists would have been just as pleased if the Saturn Giant had flown but one single minute, they were overjoyed now that the missile had completed its intended task of flying the full eight minutes. No wonder that Dr. von Braun's statement was to the point, when he said that the shot showed "we are right on time," while Dr. Robert Seamons, assistant administrator of the Federal Space Agency, termed the shot "a very significant step for manned space exploration." Dr. Kurt Debus, one of the many scientists who had a hand in the launching of America's very first satellite, and who together with Dr. von Braun and Dr. Seamons was present at the firing, said that "the rocket's thrust was equal to the horsepower to drive 300,000 conventional automobiles," and "if all the tankage capacity of the Saturn were filled with gasoline, there would be enough to run the average automobile for 250 years."

Finally, though it must be acknowledged that technical data often are dull and to many readers of little import, it still may be enlightening to compare the major United States rockets. For example, the Redstone rocket has a thrust of 75,000 pounds, the Thor 150,000 pounds, the Atlas, 360,000 pounds, and today's Saturn, as already referred to has 1,300,000 pounds of thrust.

— 49 —

MAN IN THE MOON—
HOW HE WILL GET THERE AND LIVE THERE

With the United States and Russia in a race to the moon, there now exists little doubt that many of us will witness moon landings, if not in the sixties surely in the seventies, and similar "landfalls" on some of the other planets undoubtedly later.

According to the international authority on the structure of the atom and Nobel Prize Winner, Dr. Harold C. Urey, "Men will go to the moon, regardless of what doubters may say. In the near future this will occur, and it will be recorded in histories to come as an enormously great exploit." To the question, "Why go to the moon particularly?" Dr. Urey's answer was, "In the first place, it is our closest neighbor in space. Secondly, the origin and history of the moon have remained a mystery, despite intensive study during the last century and a half." To quote the scientist and former President of the British Interplanetary Society, Arthur C. Clarke, "The moon is now closer, in fact of travel time, than were Europe and America fifty years ago. And though journeys to Mars and Venus will naturally take longer than lunar flights, several months, instead of a few days, they will consume little more fuel. The nearer planets will all be within range well before the end of this century, for once a space craft has escaped from the earth, it can travel indefinitely without using its rockets again."

When the great Persian astronomer, Nassir Eddin Al Tusi, uttered his prophetic words seven hundred years ago of *Quo vadis et quo auxilio* (Wither goest thou, and by what guidance) to the Venetian explorer Marco Polo, as the latter announced his adventure to the Far East, the astronomer's advice of "know thou the stars" was as much to the point as it is to this very day. Because now that space is being explored and the moon is to be the next port of call, men are fast learning where they are going, how to get there, and how to take care of themselves.

Turning once more to Dr. Harold C. Urey, the questions are asked: "Why the moon, what is the moon, and where did it come from? Sir Charles Darwin claimed that the moon was torn from the earth by solar tides, and it was this theory that had been accepted far and wide for many years. This theory was not considered physically feasible, although it has not been finally established that such an event did not actually happen. However, if the moon did not escape from the earth where did it escape from, or where did it come from?"

In this connection, Dr. Urey suggests the possibility that "two bodies like the earth and the moon could have accumulated near each other in space from debris of some kind, and have markedly different densities." He said, further, "so far as we know there is no reason why the more dense material should prefer to accumulate in the small object. Thus accumulation for two planets so near each other appears to us today to be very improbable." Then, Dr. Urey mentions a third possibility, "that the moon was captured by the earth. This means that the two objects must have moved in very special orbits relative to each other, and that sufficient energy was dissipated by tidal friction to cause the two to remain in the neighborhood of each other." This event, Dr. Urey said, "would be very improbable if there had been only one moon. It seems likely that if one moon were captured by the earth during the formation of the solar system, there should have been many more such objects present at that time."

While I am not able to go into a further discourse on the origin of the moon, let me add this, that Dr. Urey said that "perhaps the planets were formed at a later stage in the history of the solar system from materials which had been 'sorted out' in some way, while the moon is a relict of the earliest stages, which escaped during the sorting process. Thus the moon may be a very primitive object of some kind, much more primitive than the earth." Throughout the ages all sorts of fantasies have been expounded about exploration of the moon, as well as of the planets. And the systems suggested to take man to such places in the universe were just as fantastic, though many, of course, had a great basis of truth. Writing on the history of astronautics, Dr. Carsbie C. Adams specifically noted that the "main stream of progress required three tributaries: man's speculations on interplanetary space, and how it might be traversed, the development of the notion of reactive force, and the evolution of the rocket through experiment and trial."

Three years ago I referred to the plans formulated by scientists of NASA for the first moon ship. On the basis of blueprints, this monstrous ship probably would weigh 2,500 tons, generate more thrust than 16 Atlas Intercontinental Missiles, and, according to D. Wyatt, then assistant director of Space Flight Development for NASA, should be just about able to put one man on the moon and return him. Wyatt informed a House Appropriations Subcommittee, then headed by Texas Representative Albert Thomas, that the moon trip might be achieved in ten or fifteen years, and that the ship itself would be ready in about seven.

Now let's see what has happened since 1958, and let's begin by referring to President Kennedy's bill, passed by Congress on July 20, 1961, within a mere few hours after Captain Virgil Grissom's suborbital flight. This bill authorized NASA to spend $1,784,300,000 on a vastly-expanded space program, including a start toward sending a man to the moon "before this decade is out." In his second State of the Union Message, President Kennedy made it clear that, while he advocated a man-to-moon program within this decade, our "eagerness to share the meaning of space" was definitely "not governed by the efforts of others."

It has been estimated that it would cost the United States at least 40 billion dollars, or an average of about $225 per person, to send a man to the moon. In order to land a manned missile or rocket, or whatever it will be, on the moon, according to the estimate furnished to the Senate Committee by the NASA, it will require a rocket more than 300 feet tall, weighing some 5,000 tons, and capable of generating at least 12 million pounds of thrust on blast off.

Major General Don R. Ostrander, director of the Space Agency's office of launch vehicle programs, said that design work on the massive rocket, known as Nova, was scheduled to begin before the end of 1962. It is estimated that the Nova will be 360 to 375 feet tall, taller than the spire on St. Patrick's cathedral, and one quarter the height of the Empire State Building including the building's television tower. This five-stage rocket, more powerful than any missile ever used in this country, would have fifteen times more thrust than the space launching rocket of the U.S.S.R.

One of the most difficult phases of an expedition to the moon, Dr. Abe Silverstein, director of the Space Flight program, explained to the Senate Committee, may well be the return launching of the missile from the moon, due to the many major problems that will arise, although the problem of creating a lunar capsule able to withstand the almost exorbitant temperatures resulting from its re-entry into the atmosphere of the earth, seems to have been solved.

There are, of course, other hazards and problems facing the scientists, such as providing the right sort of guiding devices for steering the moonship through space, for landing it without difficulty on the moon, and for ensuring its safe return journey to the earth. There have to be, besides, sufficient protective devices to protect the moon ship not only against the radiations existing in at least one of the Van Allen Belts around the earth, but against the powerful radiations from the sun on the moon itself. As the moon travelers also have to cope with the situation of being without atmosphere on the moon upon landing, they will have to live in a a capsule, providing them with oxygen, water, as well as food, and devices to enable waste products elimination. Moreover, the capsule in which moon travelers will be obliged to make their "home" for the length of their stay, must contain equipment that will enable them to explore the moon. They will also need retro-rockets, rather than parachutes, to make a landing on the moon possible, as parachutes, due to lack of air, cannot be used.

All available indications point to the fact that the temperature on the moon fluctuates between 250 degrees at noon and minus 215 degrees Fahrenheit at night, a variation of almost 500 degrees.

According to the information furnished by the American Rocket Society's Life in Space and Space Flight Report, together with the particulars furnished by the Martin Company of Baltimore, Maryland, the moon is probably barren of vegetation, covered in many places with low mountain ranges and pockmarked with craters. Thus, when man reaches the moon he will find himself in a world of dimensions different from his own. Each lunar period of dark and light occupies the equivalent of half a month on Earth.

Since the pull of lunar gravity will be only one-sixth that of earth, man will be able to cover about 18 feet in a single stride, and a casual jump will take him six to ten feet high. With the same amount of effort needed for lifting 50 pounds on earth, he will be able to lift 300 pounds on the moon. Said the Martin Company: "The effects of reduced gravity may thus be both exhilarating and helpful."

An over-all view of a possible lunar colony, as detailed by the Rocket Society and the Martin Company, would include a cluster of large balloon-like shelters, the entrance to an underground installation, an underground storage hangar, a launch pad with space ship erected ready for return to earth, a vehicle repair and maintenance hangar, a lunar surface vehicle and exploratory teams. To protect members of the future lunar expedition against solar radiation and extreme temperature ranges, several shelters would have to be built, consisting of above ground spheres, tunnels, trenches and bunkers.

Another type of housing will be like a cluster of large balloons whose spherical shape will be practical because the walls, made of a pliable membrane material brought from the earth, would be inflated and pressurized. The entrance will have an airlock chamber with a decontamination system to keep dangerous radiation from invading the building. The completely functioning lunar base will be powered by a nuclear reactor, which is to be installed in a crater, and the power cabled to a distribution center. Inside the spherical control building, operations personnel will record data from an orbiting lunar communications satellite passing over. Outside, antennas will pick up and relay messages from earth, other planets and vehicles in space.

From underground passages, men in pressurized suits will emerge on the lunar surface for exploratory missions. As sound does not carry on the moon, the men must speak to each other with portable radios or light wave devices.

An advantage of the tunnel shelter lies in the more stable temperature which begins a few feet below the surface, where it will remain constant somewhere between minus 25 and minus 40 degrees. Also underground, it is proposed that a retractable observatory with a powerful telescope will rise from a covered silo.

As for the preservation and continuation of life, or life systems, algae colonies grown in tanks will provide oxygen and some food for man's use on the moon. Algae, as we have already learned, are a simple species of green plant which, through the chemical process of photosynthesis, absorbs light and carbon dioxide, and produces oxygen and an edible bulk high in protein. In this complex system the smaller tanks will siphon off the oxygen and introduce it into the lunar base's air-conditioning equipment.

Alongside the tanks will be an underground farm, where it is proposed to raise fowl, other small animals and vegetables with artificial light. This brings us to the qusetion of water. This will be extracted, above ground, from the crystalline structure of rock. Of course the importance of water to the astronaut is patent, as he must either transport enormous quantities with him into space or uncover a celestial source. The latter, as North American Aviation's Space and Information Systems divulges, is not as incredible as it appears. Chemists, they say, have long known that water combines with most compounds and can be extracted by several methods. The problem lies in collecting a quantity sufficient to meet man's needs. Paradoxically, they say, man's first planetary outpost, the moon, may contain appreciable amounts of water in its most abundant raw material—rock. This water can be released by the simple process of crushing and heating. A huge furnace powered by concentrated heat will break down rock crystals, after which a still-like device will trap and separate water from the other gases.

Extracting ore or other lunar material is to be accomplished by underground, self-contained mining equipment. Transport vehicles then are expected to carry the ore back through the shaft to a processing plant. As a matter of added interest on the subject of water, volcanic rock contains from one to 12 per cent water by weight; meteorites contain as little as one-tenth of one per cent. If the rock on the lunar surface is primarily volcanic (a theory supported by several geologists) water in the most hydrous types could be released at the rate of one gallon per cubic foot of rock.

According to additional information furnished by the North American Aviation's Space and Information Division, the necessary temperatures for the rock processing range from 700 degrees Celcius, for which plastic Fresnel lenses are used. The lightweight solar furnaces used for the extraction process can be readily transported to the moon, where a vacuum, a cold trap, and high solar energy will make the extraction process of the rocks relatively simple.

While all the aforegoing is so far based on preliminary investigation and research, it is understandable that the construction of a lunar base will depend to a great degree upon the topography and geology of the lunar site selected. These factors, of course, cannot be precisely determined until American space men have had a chance to explore the surface, as well as the sub-surface, partly by means of telescopic observations. The choice of site will result from various phases that precede the actual landing. Hence, during the first phase, unmanned, exploratory vehicles, such as the Ranger, Surveyor and Prospector, will do the actual pioneering work of transmitting geological data back to earth for analysis and evaluation.

Then will follow the second phase (after a manned round-trip circumnavigation of the moon), a manned landing and return to earth which will also place a booster tank in a crevasse for temporary housing. Manned expeditions might then also break ground, and subsequent expeditions could start building on this simple beginning.

Now with regard to science's attempts at moon probes, it is significant that in the first American attempt, in 1958, the payload was thoroughly sterilized to avert contamination of the moon by earth bacteria. On this particular space attempt, a lethal emulsified liquid was injected into the sealed compartment within the rocket's nose cone. This practice has been kept up, like that of the Soviet scientists, whose package that hit the moon in 1959 was also completely sterilized. In other words, contamination of outer space worlds is, or has become, an important problem, and each time that a space probe is lofted it becomes a potential carrier of earthy microbes. Biologists believe that these microbes not only could seriously change the pattern of native life on a planet, but would destroy evidence of value to the understanding of life's origins on this planet and elsewhere. The well-known geneticist and Nobel Prize winner, Dr. Joshua Lederberg, disclosed recently that "some of our own earth's microorganisms are very likely capable of surviving in the climate of Mars." He further stated that "if microbes from the earth found conditions congenial on another planet they could conceivably sweep across that entire world in days or weeks."

No wonder, then, that before our astronauts land elsewhere in the solar system, each such landing will have been preceded by a decontaminated space probe.

Let's discuss the development of rockets and missiles that will eventually land our spacemen on the moon.

So far, as already stated in previous chapters, the most formidable rocket developed by the United States is the Saturn. The Nova, a vehicle also on the list for the manned trip to the moon and return, will be a cluster of eight F-I engines with a total of 12 million pounds of thrust. For the round trip a manned moon flight will need a rocket engine able to lift a total of 6.7 million pounds from this earth at a velocity of seven miles a second, or around 25,000 miles an hour. This velocity, actually known as escape velocity, is essential to overcome the earth's gravitational pull.

The Ranger project is part of the NASA program to explore the moon, planets and interplanetary space. On August 23, 1961, Ranger I was launched from the Atlantic Missile Range, Cape Canaveral, by an Atlas Agena B rocket, the launch combination to be used in all of the firings. It was the first of the nine firings planned in the Ranger series. There are three phases to the Ranger project: Rangers 1-2's primary purpose was to develop and test basic elements of spacecraft technology for lunar and interplanetary missions. It was decided not to aim these early Rangers at the moon. Rangers 3-5 (the second phase of the project) started early in 1962, and is designed to place a capsule containing a seismometer and transmitter on the moon's surface. Prior to impact, these Rangers will send back readings from a gamma-ray spectrometer, and will take successive photos of the lunar impact area. Rangers 6-9 (the third phase of the project) will send back to earth stations high-resolution television pictures of the lunar surface up to the moment the spacecraft impacts the moon.

Of course, United States scientists have been pressing plans to land robots on the moon some time soon, whereas the NASA announced plans some time ago for a three-man moon-ship to be sent on a round-the-moon trip in five years, with the added hope that landing would be made on the lunar surface about 1969.

At the same time the NASA called for bids on the Apollo Craft, giving the following particulars about the crew, who will travel in the cone-shaped forward area, while the bed itself will be a net couch standing upright against the rear wall. Announcing that the ship will carry provisions for two weeks in flight and for the sojourn on the moon, NASA also disclosed that one or more seats will contain a built-in toilet; it will also have an airlock, set in the nose of the airship (which will be not unlike a torpedo tube) that will permit the astronauts to disembark.

First test flights of the Apollo (carrying instruments only) are scheduled for 1963-1964. The spaceship, as blueprinted, will be shot into space by a Saturn multi-stage booster in its early flight around the earth, and then by a Nova rocket having a thrust of 12 million pounds, many times more powerful than the biggest American-made rocket today, and weighing between 50 and 75 tons. After getting rid of the boosters during the flight, it will have reversing rockets that would slow it down considerably for what is called a soft landing. It is then that the prospective astronauts will disembark and collect samples of lunar crust. After a week of a so-called "vacation" on the moon's craters, the manned spaceship section will rid itself of the burnt-out reversing rocket and head earthward, at a mere 25,000 miles a minute, aided by another set of reversing rockets. Jettisoning all extraneous rockets and equipment, the moon-ship will then enter the earth's atmosphere, which also shall be the signal for the opening of the large parachutes that will cushion the ship for a final landing.

All this, according to the estimates of the NASA, will cost the tidy sum of $20 billion.

Actually signalling the start of a new phase in moon exploration, a test version of the ship that is to land the nation's first instruments on the moon was put into orbit on August 26, 1961, from Cape Canaveral. It was only partly successful. According to plan, the 765-pound tower of instruments was to have been hurled into an extremely elongated orbit, to have soared to a high point or apogee of 685,000 miles, and to have been swung back to a low point or perigee of 37,500 miles.

Instead, the Atlas-Agena B rocket booster put it into a close-in orbit of 312 miles and 105 miles respectively, where the 300 pound robot (actually designed to eavesdrop on possible moon quakes), got stalled. Preliminary studies of radio signals from the orbiting vehicle indicated that the "moon bus" positioned itself exactly the way it would have to travel when the real moon trip is attempted. One set of the moon-ship's "eyes" was directed at the sun, in order that the ship's batteries could profit as much as possible from the solar rays, whereas the other set of "eyes" was turned toward the earth, so that the tail antenna, continually focussed at the ground, would have most effective long-distance communication.

Once the robot, or an instrumented package shot featuring a seismograph, is ejected on the moon it is expected to radio back information of any possible moon quakes or anything else it may detect, until it is worn out. Hoping then to continue with other lunar robot landings, and turning its attention to a bigger "moon bus" landing, called Surveyor, to work out selections for the best landing sites for landing manned lunar adventures, the NASA has a most ambitious goal in the years ahead, the very goal envisioned some months ago by President Kennedy—that of a manned lunar landing with a three-man capsule.

— 50 —

THE ROCKET BELT

For the first time man has used a rocket—carried on his back— to fly over the ground. More than 30 flights have been made with this man-rocket, manufactured by Textron's Bell Aerosystems Company, of Buffalo, for the United States Army. Bell test engineer Harold M. Graham has flown with the rocket over ground distances up to 360 feet. Engineer Graham has also flown to the top of 30-foot high hills using the rocket belt, at an average speed estimated at 20 miles per hour. Graham is believed to be the first man to fly over the earth's surface supported only by portable rocket equipment.

According to Wendell F. Moore, who directs Bell's man-rocket research program, the current device "is strictly a feasibility model designed to prove that lightweight rocket power can lift a man and transport him over the ground in controlled flight." The most frequently mentioned military use of man-rockets would be to transport foot-soldiers over surface obstacles such as streams, rivers, ravines, barbed wire and mine fields. Rocket belts may be employed during amphibious operations permitting assault troops to fly from ship to shore. Rocket belts also could be used to reach the top of vertical obstacles such as cliffs and steep hills.

Basically the Bell man-rocket consists of a twin-jet hydrogen peroxide propulsion system mounted on a fibreglass corset which has been moulded to fit the back and hips of the operator. The operator slips his arms through padded lift rings attached to the corset. Then he secures the unit with two quick-release safety belts that pass around his abdomen. Metal control tubes, attached to the lift rings, extend forward on each side of the operator. A control stick on one tube permits him to change his flight direction. A motorcycle type hand throttle mounted on the other tube allows him to regulate rocket thrust levels, thus controlling his rate of climb and descent. The device has proven so stable in flight that pitch and roll are easily controlled by movements of the operator's body. The rocket propulsion system is fully throttleable. When activated by the pilot's controls, hydrogen peroxide is forced under pressure into a gas generator where it contacts a catalyst and decomposes into steam. The steam escapes through two rocket nozzles providing thrust. Main thrust from the nozzles is directed toward the ground while jet deflectors provide thrust for yaw control when activated by the operator.

It all looks easy, but it has required about seven years of thought, research, design and tests, and many hundreds of thousands of dollars of outlay (some of it provided by the army) to put man with the portable rocket in test flight. The ultimate range, height and speed will be determined by developments in the device and in fuel. However, for security reasons, officials have been prevented from describing the range and flight duration abilities, as well as the weight of the system and performance details such as maximum thrust levels of the rocket belt.

— 51 —

THE FLIGHT OF ENOS, THE ASTRO-CHIMP

On November 29, 1961, at 10:07 A.M., a freckle-faced Chimp, in a bell-shaped capsule atop a thundering Atlas, arched over in the almost cloudless sky and headed out to sea slightly to the north of east. Thus it was that a 37½-pound, dead-panned primate, named Enos, zipped away from Pad 14 at the north end of Cape Canaveral to blaze the space trail.

Model of a robot lunar vehicle which could be controlled from Earth.—CUTLER-HAMMER

An operator on Earth sees the lunar surface on the television screen. Signals between the Earth controller and the lunar vehicle would take 1.3 seconds to pass in either direction.—CUTLER-HAMMER

Flying through the air with the greatest of ease—and a rocket strapped to his back.—BELL AEROSYSTEMS

Enos the chimpanzee is fitted into his pressure couch prior to his three-orbit flight around the world.—NASA

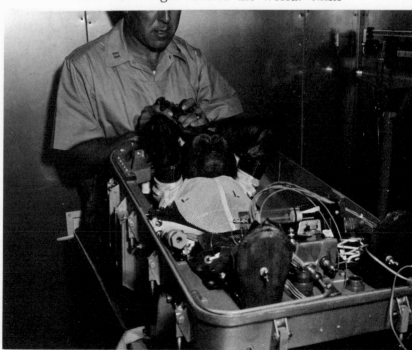

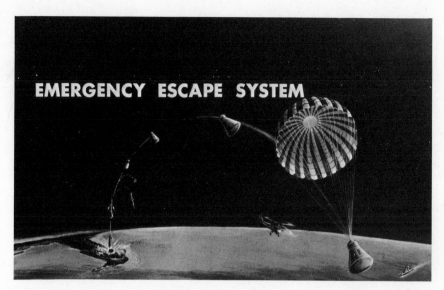

Artist's conception of the Mercury-Atlas 5 emergency escape
system.—NASA

The orbital flight path of the Mercury-Atlas 5, showing the sequence
of events on launch and recovery of the spacecraft.—NASA

Astronaut John H. Glenn, Jr., and Space Flight Equipment Specialist Joe W. Schmitt perform suiting-up preparations shortly before MA-6 launch time.—NASA

The huge U.S. Air Force Atlas rose smoothly into the clear Florida sky on a 360,000-pound thrust generated by the missile's three engines, amidst a roar that was deafening more than a mile away.

The launching was perfect. About two seconds after lift-off the capsule's escape tower was jettisoned. The Atlas dropped its booster stage as planned two and a half minutes later, and two minutes later hurled the capsule loose on its intended trajectory. In point of fact the capsule carrying Enos was aimed on a course that repeatedly cut the equator at an angle of 32 degrees in a generally west-to-east direction.

By 10:14 the capsule, automatically firing small jets of hydrogen peroxide, turned itself around in space so that it flew with its blunt end forward. In the next minute it had achieved its orbit at 17,500 miles per hour. Its peak altitude was 147.5 miles, its minimum 99.5 miles. All in all it took exactly 88.5 minutes to go around the earth once. The Space Agency's press officer, Lt. Colonel John A. Powers, announced that the missile was performing perfectly.

About 15 minutes after the lift-off official watchers signaled that the capsule had been blasted into orbit and began registering vital data, mainly as to the functioning of its life support system, which furnished heat and oxygen to Enos.

By 10:35 EST the capsule had been picked up by trackers on Bermuda, a ship in the Atlantic, on the Canary Islands, Zanzibar, at Kano, Nigeria, and an Indian Ocean ship, all of whom reported that the capsule and its occupant were doing splendidly.

As the vehicle sped the simian from the French Cameroons on his merry way around the world, our human astronauts listened in to the progress and activities of the Astro-Monk. Space pilots Alan Shepard and Virgil I. Grissom, together with the other five astronauts, were busy monitoring Enos' orbital adventure at stations located at various tracking points around the world. Commander Shepard followed its progress on instruments at the Bermuda tracking station. Grissom and John H. Glenn were both doing their stint at the capsule communications post in the Mercury Control Center at the Cape. At the Muchea, Australia, station was Walter Schirra. Leroy Cooper did his listening at Point Arguello, California, Donald Slayton kept a tab at Guaymas, Mexico, and Scott Carpenter was keeping alert on the missile countdown in the blockhouse at the Cape. All seven were, of course, in line and eligible for the first orbital jaunt around the world, although after Enos had whirled around this planet twice in 3 hours, 21 minutes, John H. Glenn was to be picked to take an American space ship into orbit.

In point of fact, less than an hour after VIP Enos had emerged from his capsule safe and was aboard the U.S. destroyer *Stormes*, NASA announced that the freckle-faced, forty-year-old Marine Lieutenant-Colonel Glenn had been chosen to perform that task.

Coming back now to the simian astronaut Enos, he had not gone along just for the ride. He had entered upon his task with a great sense of responsibility, even before he was shot into space. Enos' strenuous work had really begun at 2:20 in the morning of November 29.

At that hour the diapered VIP was dresed in a nylon mesh space suit, which was zippered into the domed couch on which the little fellow was lying during his space journey. Incidentally, Enos was not just one chimpanzee picked at random. Not at all. He had been picked from five other simians, one of whom was monkey Ham, the one that had taken a 200-mile sub-orbital ride some time before. Another was a chimp called Rocky, so named because of a very fine set of cauliflower ears and a generally pugnacious nature.

When Enos was finally attired and ready for his adventure into space, he was given a free ride in a special van to the Atlas launching pad 14. At four minutes past four on this early morning Cape technicians placed his airtight couch compartment into the Mercury capsule, on top of the Atlas booster. And thus the scientific chimp, who had been plucked from the African French Cameroons, was wired so that he could send back to the Cape his every reaction from his whirlwind ride through space twice around the world.

Before the launch the Cape technicians had turned on what is known as a sequencer, that confronted the chimpanzee with an intricate series of tests designed to determine how much the prolonged weightlessness and other flight stresses affected the simian's ability to perform all the tasks that he had been taught on the ground. Enos spent the time from two minutes before the launch until after the splash into the Atlantic Ocean performing a complex series of "psychomotor" tests, which he had learned during the many weeks before of ground preparation. These tests had been worked out along the lines designed by the famed Russian physiologist Ivan Pavlov. These aided our scientists to determine how well a human being—in fact any living being—could perform under prolonged weightlessness.

Enos had four main tasks to perform with six-minute rest periods. His work panel in the capsule consisted essentially of black, white and red levers placed side by side, and one-inch-square windows above each of them. The system had been arranged so that the cycle of tasks could be started again once he had run the course. And if the mission had gone the three orbits instead of the two, Enos would have had 69 minutes of work to do during the flight.

In *Task 1* a red light went on above the red handle, and was to remain on for 15 minutes, and Enos was required to push down the lever (shaped somewhat like a bicycle handle) once every 20 seconds. If he failed to do so, he would get a slight electric shock in his foot. As part of the same test, a blue light appeared over the left handle once every 2 minutes. He had 5 seconds to depress the lever and turn off the light.

In *Task 2* (after 6 minutes of rest) Enos would get rewards rather than shocks, because when the green light went on over the right window, he had to wait 20 seconds, and then push the lever down. If he did this a green light would go on over the nipple panel at the right of his head, and his reward would be a sip of water.

In *Task 3* a yellow light would go on over the center window, and he was required to depress the center handle fifty times. After he had performed this chore, his reward would be a small banana-flavored pellet, which would appear in a little slot on the panel, and which Enos would grab. (The Indian Ocean tracking ship reported that Enos had earned ten pellets.)

In the final *Task 4* the system reverted to the shock treatment again. When a triangle, circle, or square would show up in each of the three windows Enos had been taught that he had to push the lever down under the "something else" window, or else he would receive a shock. Enos had learned his lessons well, and a great deal of credit should go to the scientists and trainer for the tremendous patience they must have had in getting Enos (and, of course, all other simians) to do these tasks so well. Enos kept on tripping levers from the control panel in spite of the brutal pressure of acceleration and the confusing sense of weightlessness during his flight. His ability to function was not hindered in any way by the crushing force of blastoff or the initial entry into the world of weightlessness, in which he would be for all but a few minutes of the space ride.

As had been the original intention, Enos was to have gone three times around the world, and the decision to bring the capsule down after the second orbit around, officials disclosed was "to save the chimp's life and to save the capsule." According to Mr. Walter Williams, operations director at Cape Canaveral, the first evidence that something was wrong came when the capsule was over the Muchea, Australia tracking station on its second orbit. The decision then to bring it down was made under the same criteria that would have governed had there been a Shepard, Grissom or Glenn on board. The main trouble had been with the reaction jets, which squirt sprays of hydrogen peroxide to turn the capsule about any of its three axes and keep it properly positioned.

The trouble on November 3 over Muchea developed "because one of the three jets used to control the capsule's rolling motion either stuck open or closed." This actually meant that more powerful stabilization jets had to take over. Hence the decision to terminate the orbital flight at completion of the second orbit was made at the Cape by the flight director Christopher Kraft. Reverse rockets then were fired and the capsule headed for landing 500 miles south of Bermuda in the Atlantic.

Now followed the most critical performance, of course, after this 50,000-mile trip—the parachute descent back to earth and Enos' pickup after 3 hours and 21 minutes, when the little fellow's adventure ended. An impressive force of 18 Navy vessels and dozens of aircraft had already been positioned in the Atlantic, ranging over a wide area about 800 miles southeast of Florida.

At 1:28 P.M. the recovery parachute deposited the capsule on the ocean waves 250 miles south of Bermuda, virtually in the center of the target area, where the U.S. destroyer *Stormes*—which had taken about an hour to steam up to the impact—plucked him from the Atlantic. A message from the *Stormes* said that "when the capsule hatch was opened on the destroyer's deck, the animal appeared to be excitable but in good shape." The capsule was aboard the ship's deck an hour and 25 minutes after hitting the water. As the little fellow must have been hungry (having been fed synthetic food) he was given an added food bonus of two oranges and two apples, the first non-synthetic food he had had since being locked up into the capsule at 4:41.

First Enos was taken to Bermuda, and after being checked out physically, he was flown to the Cape. And while he was getting rid of his space and sea legs by walking up and down in the hospital room, his capsule was loaded aboard a C-124 transport plane, and flown to Patrick Air Force Base.

As for the simian's physical comfort or discomfort, Woomera, Australia, had reported that the 37½-pound, 38-inch high chimp's heart beats had advanced to between 115 and 120 beats a minute, reaching a peak of 150 during blastoff. On the first orbit his heart ranged between 105 and 120 beats a minute, while the peak was reached around 150 at a point of maximum acceleration in the rocket's initial climb. Enos' respiration was 20-25, with one peak at 30, and his temperature obtained with a rectal thermometer remained close to 98 degrees. On the second orbit the heartbeat range was 120-150, and his temperature ranged between 98 and 99.

As evidence of the great interest evinced in Enos' space flight, NASA's Spacecraft Center (Hampton, Va.) referred to the receipt of fan mail from all over the world addressed to ENOS THE CHIMP. One letter, in fact, covered part of the wall in the Public Affairs office of NASA. It was almost six feet high, and the words in large black crayon read: "Dear Enos, we are happy that you had a good ride. We want to know how to say your name. We would like to have some pictures of you. We would like to see a banana pellet. We are proud of you." This letter was signed by the first grade of Bakerfield elementary school, at Aberdeen, Md. with 24 carefully scrawled signatures of the pupils in room I.

Thus ends the saga of dapper astro-monk Enos, who went through all this like the real little he-man he was, except for some "minor display of temper put up with the ceaseless popping of photographers' flash bulbs. He did not act at all like a fellow who had had a great weightlessness lifted from his tiny shoulders." And according to Captain Finneg, "he showed no appreciable weight loss," in spite of the fact that "he had been rammed back into his couch with a force about 8 times his own weight, as the capsule in which he was riding decelerated from the top speed of 17,500 miles an hour to 1,350 in slightly over 3 minutes."

— 52 —

PROJECT APOLLO'S PROGRESS

The NASA disclosed on December 15, 1961, that a contract for development of a 2,500-ton rocket, to be used to send a three-man expedition to the moon, had been given to the Boeing Company. This company had been selected to develop and build twenty-four of the Super-Saturn rockets, which, in size and power, would dwarf any now being used or developed by the civilian space agency or by the military.

In its first stage the rocket will cluster four or five F-I rocket engines, each producing 1,500,000 pounds of thrust. This booster, or first stage, will be 33 feet in diameter, 70 to 80 feet high, weighing 5,000,000 pounds at lift-off. On top of this will be a second stage, powered by high-energy liquid hydrogen, and each producing 200,000 pounds of thrust. The third stage will be powered by one or more liquid hydrogen rockets. With its three stages, the rocket will be capable of lifting about 100 tons into a low earth orbit, or of sending forty tons on an escape mission to the moon or the planets.

This rocket, the NASA reports, is "likely to play the key role in achieving the Administration's new objective of landing a manned expedition on the moon before the end of the decade." The rocket's first mission will be to send a 15-ton Apollo capsule carrying three men on a trip around the moon and back to earth. This mission is scheduled for around 1966.

On December 27, 1961, the United States announced that it aims to send three robots to the moon during 1962, to serve as advance scouts for manned expeditions. They "will televise (sometimes in color) X ray, drill, plow and pummel the moon before the first American astronaut sets foot on it—hopefully in 1970. From such a lunar 'physical' American scientists hope to find out how deep is the moon dust, and how hard the crust beneath it—so that humans who follow can be guided accordingly.

"Also how radioactive the moon is, whether it has any useful minerals, if any water can be wrung from its rocks and whether any lunar materials could be used to fuel rockets taking off from there for Mars and other planets."

All these plans were disclosed by N. W. Cunningham, head of the lunar sciences program for the NASA and a physicist and meteorologist at the annual meeting of the American Association for the Advancement of Science. He said that "the first robot will measure radiation hazards it encounters on its 2½-day journey, televise its descent to the lunar surface and jump out onto the moon just before its 'bus' crash-lands. It will start taking pictures of the moon from 2,500 miles away and telecast them to a special NASA receiver in California, almost a quarter-million miles off. About 100 pictures, spaced 13 seconds apart, are to be transmitted. A 350-pound instrumented capsule will be ejected just before the crash-landing. It will be equipped to detect possible moonquakes for one to three months afterward," Mr. Cunningham disclosed.

Finally, on January 5, 1962, the NASA made public drawings of the Apollo spacecraft from which man may get his first close-up look at the moon.

NASA also released three drawings, showing the technique of launching a manned space craft into earth orbit, launching a powerful booster rocket and supply vehicle into orbit close behind, and joining them in space for the long journey to the moon.

"The huge orbiting booster rocket, starting its motors in the near vacuum of space after hooking onto the Apollo vehicle, would drop away after accelerating the Apollo to escape velocity. The Apollo craft then would proceed around the moon, come back into earth orbit, and then be slowed so as to re-enter the atmosphere and return the crew to earth." The NASA sketch of the Apollo showed its three occupants seated side by side in the nose cone. NASA also disclosed that "while the astronauts would be seated for the launching, they would have considerable room in which to move about in flight."

— 53 —

JOHN GLENN—AMERICA'S NEWEST HERO

"You fear the least what you know the most about." Thus spoke the sturdy, sandy-haired Lt. Colonel John Hershel Glenn, Jr. recently, after going over the intensive preparations for his historic flight.

A former combat and test pilot, and 40-year-old Marine Corps officer, "the old man" of the team of seven astronauts, who for two-and-a-half years had trained for this space venture, Colonel Glenn had flown 59 missions in the Pacific in World War II, and 90 missions in Korea. He was awarded five Distinguished Flying Crosses, and the Air Medal with eighteen clusters, not forgetting the U.S. Medal President Kennedy pinned on him after the completion of his Mercury flight.

That his earlier experience proved to be of undeniable value he explained as follows: "Experience in dangerous and unexpected situations is even more valuable than good conditioning. If you have successfully controlled your airplane in an emergency, or dealt with an enemy pilot whose prime object is to destroy you, your chances of making the proper decision next time are increased." And he continued, "The space traveler, alone where no one has been before, will need a confidence only experience can give him."

There was a lively atmosphere all along the Banana River and at the beach at Cocoa Beach, where I had arrived to register at the NASA control desk at the Starlight Auditorium to pick up my press and police identification pass from Cocoa Beach. Thousands of "bird watchers" had spent this night and many nights before on the beach, and many thousands more had joined them every morning in the expectation that the launch would take place, to witness what they hoped would be the most momentous, panoramic view of the Mercury-Atlas rising from its launching pad, and finally sending the courageous colonel into orbit.

The excitement was intense. The whole resembled a carnival scene. Countless cars were parked. Dozens of trailers, many beach tents were set up for the long nights. Hot dog stands were doing a whale of a business. Women were sizzling steaks and chops over charcoal broilers. People had scarcely been able to sleep on the beaches, as parties around bonfires had kept them awake. Bongo drums had gone on all night. There was a holiday mood. The luckier ones had found a haven in some of the 24 motels all along the long stretch from Cocoa to Cape Canaveral, whose 1,500 rooms had been sold out many weeks before.

The Cape Canaveral District in Brevard County—73 miles long and less than 20 miles wide on the Atlantic side of the State—has been booming ever since King Rocket took over in what now has become the fastest growing county in all America. It has been said that "it is the home of the population explosion," because while the 1950 Census listed 23,653 people in Brevard, the figure had risen to 111,425 people in 1960, and the swampy, sandy earth had been turned into well-made roads, canals, pastel-colored ranch houses. This area seemed to have gone up faster than Colonel Glenn, and that is surely saying something.

Land prices have risen equally dramatically. After NASA announced last August that Cape Canaveral would be its primary launching site for the "new generation of space rockets and for the effort to reach the moon," the price of ocean-front property increased almost at once tenfold. For example, tracts farther inland, that had sold for $300 an acre, rose in price to $1000 an acre. In one municipality, Cocoa Beach, building permits for 1961 totaled more than $6 million, twice the record figure of the previous year. Here, too, land is being cleared for a 100-unit apartment house.

Several motels are being built. An attraction is a 90-foot high observation tower at the nearby space centers. Also a large hospital is now being built. In 1950 there were only 1,163 military, civil service and construction workers employed by the government in Brevard County. This year 25,200 workers (whose average pay in the Atlantic Missile Range is now about 7,000 dollars a year) had a total payroll of $25,200,000. The current official estimate is that it will rise to $41 million next fiscal year. Almost everything here reflects the new space economy. The motels even bear such names as Polaris, Vanguard, Satellite, Sea Missile. It is almost unbelievable that this section, that once probably had as many rattlesnakes as people, so quickly turned into what might be compared to a booming oil town, with its missile gantries much resembling oil derricks.

As I picked up my press pass at NASA Headquarters in the Starlight Auditorium, I was handed a great deal of material that provided a background against which to evaluate Glenn's flight into space. In point of fact NASA had not overlooked one iota of information that could prove of interest to the outsider.

To begin with, the training program of all the seven astronauts was stressed. The brochure disclosed that they had been first given lectures in the vehicle systems by NASA and by several of the contracting companies. NASA Langley Research Center also gave them a 50-hour course in astronautics, where the McDonnell Aircraft Corporation had talked to them on the Mercury subsystems.

Dr. William K. Douglas lectured them on aeromedical programs of space flight, whereas at the Navy centrifuge in Johnsville, Pa., were flown the Mercury acceleration profiles. They flew brief zero-gravity flight paths at several Air Force bases. At the Navy Air Crew Equipment Laboratory in Philadelphia the astronauts became acquainted with the checkout of the Mercury environmental system, and they also became familiar with the physiological effects of high CO_2 content in the environment at the Naval Medical Research Institute. They furthermore received indoctrination on the Redstone by the Army Ballistic Missile Division, and the Air Force Space Systems Division finally told them about the Atlas launch vehicle.

Each astronaut received concentrated personal instruction on the elements of celestial navigation and star recognition at the Moorhead Planetarium, Chapel Hill, N. C. At the USAF Training Command Survival School at Stead Air Force Base in Nevada, they received a 5½-day course in desert survival training. During March and April, 1960, open water normal egress training was conducted off Pensacola, in the Gulf of Mexico, when each astronaut made at least two egresses through the upper hatch, when up to 10-foot swells were experienced. Each of the astronauts also made underwater egresses, some of which were made in the Mercury pressure suit.

During the flight the mission pilot had the following tasks: to secure maximum data on spacecraft performance, of his own reactions to weightlessness and stress, and to study the characteristics of the earth and stars from his vantage point over 100 miles above the earth's surface.

These tasks consisted furthermore in managing the operation of all spacecraft systems, the attitude control system in particular, the environmental control system and communications systems. Also to observe and correct any discrepancies in systems operation, which discrepencies would be correlated with telemetered observations received at ground stations. To monitor critical events during launch and to terminate the mission if found necessary. To maintain complete navigation log during flight, that would enable him to compute his retro-fire if ground communications were to fail. This on-board navigation would also include periscope ground sightings, which would indicate position over the ground and altitude. The ground communications would then receive retro-fire information

Glenn leaves Hangar S en route to the space capsule. He is carrying a portable air conditioner attached to his space suit.—NASA

Climbing into the *Friendship 7.*—NASA

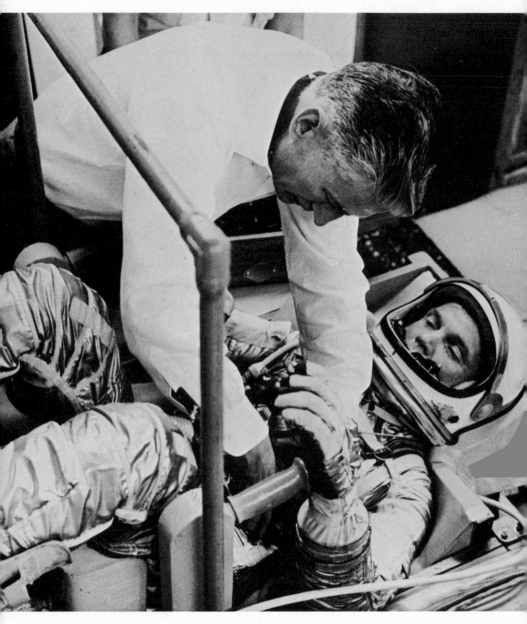

Joe W. Schmitt makes adjustments to Astronaut Glenn's suit before
launching.—NASA

The Mercury Atlas 6 carrying the *Friendship 7* spacecraft with John Glenn aboard rises from its launching pad at Cape Canaveral.

—NASA

After his historic orbital flight, Glenn's spacecraft is brought alongside a recovery ship in the Atlantic.

and receive detailed behavior of spacecraft systems as determined from ground telemetry. Finally to evaluate his physical condition to augment the biomedical data which were telemetered to the ground.

About every 30 minutes the astronaut would make detailed voice reports on spacecraft systems and operations conditions. His own transmissions would include critical information as to mode of control, precise attitude, planned retro-fire time, control system fuel, oxygen and coolant.

The MA-6 Mercury spacecraft was similar to those used in previous Mercury flights. About as high as a phone booth, the interior looked much like the cockpit of a high performance airplane, but smaller. Confronting Colonel Glenn were the following major items: the instrument panel, whose instruments were located on a main instrument panel, a left and a right console. The main panel was directly in front of Colonel Glenn. The navigational and control instruments were located in the left and center sections of the panel, and the periscope was located in the center. The right section of the main panel was composed of environmental system gauges and controls, electrical switches, indicators and communication system controls.

The attitude of the Mercury space craft was changed by the release of short bursts of hydrogen peroxide from 18 thrust nozzles located on the conical and cylindrical portions of the craft's surface. The timing and force of these bursts were controlled by one of the following: 1: automatic stabilization and control system, or "auto pilot"; 2: Rate stabilization and control system, or "Rate command system"; 3: The manual proportional control, a manual-mechanical system; and 4: The Fly-by-Wire, or manual electrical system.

The left console included sequencing telelights and a warning panel, indicators and controls for the spacecraft's automatic pilot, environmental controls and landing systems. Altogether there were over 100 lights, fuses, switches and miscellaneous controls and displays to be handled.

To the left of Glenn's head was a 16-mm. camera to photograph the instrument panel display from launch through recovery. A pilot observer camera was also mounted in the main instrument panel to be operated from launch through recovery.

And then there was the periscope, an earth periscope, located approximately two feet in front of Glenn, which gave a 360-degree view of the horizon. Glenn was able to manually adjust it for "low" or "high" magnification. On low he had a view of the earth of about 1,900 miles in diameter, and on high the field of view would be reduced to about 80 miles, whereas the altitude could be measured within plus or minus 10 nautical miles. This Mercury Earth Periscope also served as a navigational aid.

Glenn's support couch was made of a crushable honeycomb material bonded to a fiberglass shell lined with rubber padding. This couch was designed to support Glenn's body load during all phases of the flight, and to protect him, too, from the acceleration forces of launch and re-entry.

The environmental control system gave the MA-6 spacecraft cabin a 100 percent oxygen environment providing the breathing, ventilation and pressurization gas required during the flight. This system was completely automatic, but in the event that the automatic control failed, and should the situation require it, there was a command receiver or a telegraph code key. As for food, *Friendship 7* carried about 3,000 calories of food—beef and mixed vegetables—and about six pounds of water. The water was carried in two flat bottles, each provided with a tube. The food itself was contained in two tubes, about the size of tooth paste tubes. There were some quick-energy sugar tablets besides. In addition there was the survival equipment package, consisting of a one-man life raft, a de-salting kit, shark repellant, dye markers, first aid kit, distress signals, a signal mirror, portable radio, survival rations, matches, a whistle, and ten feet of nylon cord. There were moreover a new lightweight, radar reflective life raft, fabricated of Mylar, for air retention, and nylon, for strength. The three-pound, four-ounce raft featured three water ballast buckets for flotation stability and a deflatable boarding, which could be reinflated by an oral inflation tube after the boarding. The raft, made of the same material as used in the Echo satellite balloon, was of an international orange color.

But that was not all. There also was a pilot's map, a small cardboard diagram of the MA-6 flight path with recovery forces indicated, contained within a bag suspended beneath the periscope. On the reverse side, Glenn's view through the periscope from maximum altitude was shown. Also the last-minute information in cloud formation and water phenomena were marked by Mercury weather experts.

The hatch of the capsule itself was secured by explosive bolts, just as the pilot's canopy is secured in a high performance aircraft. Glenn was able to jettison the hatch by pushing a plunger inside the spacecraft or by pulling a cable. Three parachutes were installed in the spacecraft.

The Drogue Chute had a six-foot diameter, conical, ribbon type canopy with approximately six-foot-long ribbon suspension lines, and a 30-foot-long riser made of dacron to minimize the elasticity effects during employment of the drogue at an altitude of 21,000 feet. This drogue parachute was packed in a protective bag and stowed in the drogue mortar tube on top of a light-weight sabot. This sabot worked or functioned as a piston to eject the parachute pack, when pressured from below by gasses generated by a pyrotechnic charge.

On landing, an impact switch would jettison the landing parachute and initiate the remaining location and recovery aids. This includes release of sea-marker dye with the reserve parachute if it has not previously been deployed, triggering a high intensity flashing light, extension of a 16-foot whip antenna and the initiation of the operation of a high frequency radio beacon. If, after landing, the spacecraft should have sprung a leak or if the life support system should have become fouled after landing, Glenn could have escaped through this upper neck section or through the side hatch.

And now something about the Atlas launch vehicle itself. The launch vehicle used for Glenn's flight, for the Mercury Atlas 6 test, was an Atlas D model, a vehicle that developed 360,000 pounds of thrust and burned what was known as Rp-1, a kerosene-like fuel, and liquid oxygen. The Mercury Atlas measured 65 feet from its base to the Mercury adapter section, and was 10 feet in diameter at the tank section, and with adapter section, spacecraft and escape tower stood 93 feet tall. It was constructed of a thin gauge metal and maintained structural rigidity through pressurization of its fuel tanks. All five engines were ignited at the time of launch—the sustainer (60,000 pounds of thrust), the two booster engines (150,000 pounds thrust each), which were outboard of the sustainer at the base of the vehicle, and two small vernier engines which were used for minor course corrections during powered flight. Interestingly enough, during the first minute of flight, the vehicle consumed more fuel than a commercial jet airliner during a transcontinental run.

At staging, about two minutes after lift-off, the two booster engines would drop off and the sustainer and vernier engines would continue to accelerate the vehicle. During the first 2½ minutes of flight, an electronic brain called the Abort Sensing and Implementation System was capable of sensing impending trouble in the rocket and triggering the escape rocket. Glenn then could also trigger the Mercury escape rocket to pull the spacecraft away from the Atlas. About 20 seconds after staging, and assuming that the flight was proceeding as planned, the 16 foot escape tower and rocket would be jettisoned. Landing systems would be armed. And the Mercury Atlas vehicle would continue to accelerate toward the orbit insertion point guided by ground command guidance.

In the actual flight of Glenn all seven of Project Mercury's team of astronauts participated in the MA-6 orbital mission, some even as flight controllers from far-flung vantage points around the globe. Hence with John H. Glenn, Jr. as prime pilot, M. Scott Carpenter was the back-up pilot, and Alan B. Shepard Jr. technical advisor at Cape Canaveral. Astronaut Walter M. Schirra, Jr. stationed at the Mercury Site at Pt. Arguello, Cal. and Astronaut L. Gordon Cooper, Jr. from the Mercury tracking station in Muchea, Australia, participated. Astronaut Virgil I. "Gus" Grissom monitored launch, insertion, landing and recovery from Mercury's Bermuda station, while Donald K. Slayton performed spacecraft checkout prior to insertion of the mission pilot.

As for the tracking stations and world tracking network, these observed Glenn's flight almost continuously. Six of them were equipped to take over control of the capsule and bring it back to earth, if situations warranted it. These stations were Cape Canaveral, Bermuda, Muchea, Australia, Kauai Island, Hawaii, Point Arguello, Cal., and Guaymas, Mexico.

This world-wide Mercury tracking station complex, including ships in the Indian and Atlantic Ocean, monitoring the MA-6 flight, included the following: aside from Cape Canaveral, also Grand Bahama Island, Grand Turk Island, Bermuda, Grand Canary Island, Atlantic ship, Kano, Nigeria, Zanzibar, Point Arguello, Guayamas, Mexico, White Sands, New Mexico, Corpus Christi, Texas, Eglin, Florida. In addition to these there was the Space Computing Center of the NASA Goddard Space Flight Center, in Greenbelt, Maryland, which also made trajectory computations. During Glenn's flight, information poured into the Space computing center from tracking and ground instrumentation points around the globe at the rate, in some cases, of more than 1,000 bits per second. Upon almost instantaneous analysis the information was relayed to the Cape for action.

This tracking network consisted of 18 nations. The system spanned three continents and three oceans, interconnected by a global communications network. It utilized landlines, undersea cables, and radio circuits. Also special communication equipment, installed at commercial switching stations in both the Eastern and Western hemispheres, was utilized.

Altogether the Mercury system involved approximately 60,000 route miles of communication facilities to assure an integrated network with world-wide capability for handling satellite data. It comprised 140,000 actual circuit miles—100,000 miles of teletype, 35,000 miles of telephones, and over 5,000 miles of high speed data circuits. There were also two radar picket ships. The Atlantic ship *Rose Knott* was stationed on the equator near the West African coast, whereas the Indian Ocean ship *Coastal Sentry* was located midway between Zanzibar and Muchea, Australia.

One function of the computer was to transmit information regarding the spacecraft's position to Mercury Control Center at the Cape, where it was displayed on the world map in the Operations room.

According to the mass of information supplied by NASA to the Press, during the major Mercury launch, the attention of some 15 NASA flight controllers was focussed on dozens of consoles and wall displays in the Mercury Control Center Operations room. This room was the control point for all information that flowed through the world-wide tracking and communications system. In this room NASA Flight controllers made all vital decisions required, and issued or delegated all commands. In this 50-foot square room, about 100 types of information registered at various times on the indicators of the consoles and the high range status map. Of these 100 quantities, 10 showed biomedical condition, approximately 30 related to life support facilities, and about 60 gave readings on spacecraft equipment. This information flew in on high-speed data circuits from computers at the Goddard Center, on direct teletype circuits from remote sites, and by booster and spacecraft telemetry relayed over radio and wire circuits.

For the recovery of the capsule, more than 20 ships were deployed in the Atlantic alone to take care of prime and contingency recovery areas. These recovery forces were under the command of Rear Admiral John L. Chew, Commander of Destroyer Flotilla Four. In addition, ships and rescue planes around the world were to go into action in the event of an emergency landing. More than 15,000 men had a hand in the recovery, search and rescue effort. Responsibility for Project Mercury, the nation's first manned space flight research project, was vested in National Aeronautics and Space Administration, a civilian agency of the Government, charged with the exploration of space for peaceful and scientific purposes. Technical project direction for Mercury was supplied by NASA's Manned Spacecraft Center, directed by Robert R. Gilruth, at Langley Field, Virginia, and which at this moment of writing was soon to be moved to Houston, Texas. The Department of Defense, largely through the Air Force and the Navy, provided vital support. DOD support was directed by Major General Leighton I. Davis, USAF, Commander of the Atlantic Missile Range. In all, more than 30,000 persons had a part in this mission, including government and industry.

About five minutes after lift-off of Glenn's missile, the guidance ground command shut down the sustainer and vernier engines. And as the engines shut down, the spacecraft-to-booster clamp ring was released automatically and posigrade rockets were fired to separate the craft from the Atlas.

After a few seconds of automatic damping—getting rid of any unusual motions—the spacecraft swung 180 degrees so that the blunt face of the craft was turned forward and upward 34 degrees above the horizontal. From that point on during orbital flight, the spacecraft could be controlled in proper attitude automatically or manually by Glenn.

As all went well, the Mercury Spacecraft *Friendship* 7 was inserted into orbit in the vicinity of Bermuda. By that time the vehicle was at an altitude of approximately 100 miles and traveling at a speed of about 17,500 miles per hour. At engine cut-off the craft was subjected to more than 7½ "G." Re-entry "G" also reached 7½. A three orbit flight lasted approximately 4¾ hours, a two orbit flight took 3¼, and one orbit would have lasted about 1¾ hrs. The Mercury Friendship craft reached a peak altitude of about 150 statute miles off the West Coast of Australia, and a low point of about 100 miles at the insertion point near Bermuda. Once it reentered the atmosphere, after the desired number of orbits, as the craft approached the west coast of North America, retro or braking rockets were fired to initiate re-entry.

Friendship 7 began to encounter more dense atmosphere of the earth approximately over the east coast at an altitude of about 55 miles. At this point temperatures began mounting on the spacecraft's ablation heat shield. Peak re-entry atmosphere of about 3,000 degrees Fahrenheit occurred at 25 miles altitude, while the craft was moving at nearly 15,000 miles per hour. The craft would sustain temperatures in this neighborhood for about two minutes.

Almost coincident with the heat pulse was a dramatic reduction in capsule speed. Between 55 miles and 12 miles altitude—covering a distance of 760 miles—the craft's velocity went down from 17,500 miles per hour to 270 miles in a little over five minutes. At about 21,000 feet, a six-foot diameter drogue parachute was opened to stabilize the craft. At about 10,000 feet, a 63-foot main landing parachute unfurled from the neck of the craft. On touchdown the main chute was jettisoned, and on board the electrical equipment was shut down, and the location aids were activated.

Incidentally, there actually had been three forces waiting to snatch astronaut Glenn from the Atlantic sea waters the moment he returned from his globe-circling journey through space. This Armada, labeled Project Mercury Recovery Force, was spaced from the watery edge of the launch area across the Atlantic to the Canary Islands. Led by three aircraft carriers it included 24 ships, 60 aircraft and 15,000 men.

Aside from the carriers *Forrestal, Antietam* and *Randolph,* the fleet included destroyers, minesweepers, salvage ships, fleet oilers, and even three Army LARC's or Light amphibious vehicles. Stationed between Bermuda and the mid Atlantic—the landing spot for a single orbit—was a force led by Rear Admiral R. D. Hogle, in the *Forrestal,* south of Bermuda; at a site selected at the end of the second orbit was a force under Captain J. H. Armstrong in the *Antietam.* The third orbital landing force was located 200 miles northwest of Puerto Rico, led by Rear Admiral E. R. Eastwold, in the *Randolph.*

And now, before chronicling Glenn's experiences during his three orbital flight, it might not be amiss to cite a few more particulars about this 180-pound, five-foot-ten-inch officer, ruggedly handsome with close-cropped hair, green eyes and ready grin, a man who displayed a quiet confidence and who appeared at all times to be in perfect command of himself. A marine corps officer who served with Glenn for four years was quoted as saying that he knew all along that the space people were holding "Glenn back to ride the big one." And he added: "He could ride a cookstove back if they could find a way to throw it up there."

This wise "old man" of the seven-man team, a Presbyterian, who once said that "religion should not be a sometime thing, handy only for emergencies," was born in Cambridge, Ohio. Attending Muskingum College, and leaving in the junior year to become a naval air cadet, Glenn made headlines in 1957 when he was the first man to fly at supersonic speed from Los Angeles to New York. He was married to the former Margaret Castor, of New Concord, Ohio, daughter of Dr. and Mrs. Homer Castor, and they now have two teen-age children, Dave 16, and Lynn Ann 14.

And so this hope and pride of the nation, after ten postponements that had bedeviled his schedule, finally roared toward the Heavens on the 11th attempt to keep his "Rendezvous with Destiny."

On this memorable day thousands of people had again massed on the beaches and along the Banana River, to the north and south of the spot from which Glenn's spacecraft Friendship had streaked skyward on the awesome power of several million horses. Invading the limitless universe in the full glare of world-wide publicity, the Colonel's flight marked the end of the beginning chapter in United States space flight.

Now in order to make this chronicle a little more complete, although volumes have already been written about Glenn's feat, it would not be amiss to include a short resume of the actual happening on Glenn's historic flight.

To begin with, Glenn was awakened by his personal physician at 2:20 A.M., on February 20, 1962, and after a hearty breakfast consisting of two scrambled eggs, filet mignon, orange juice, toast, jelly and a coffee substitute, he submitted at 3:00 A.M. to a final physical examination, during which the scientists attached sensors to his body. At 4:30 Glenn donned his silvery, form-fitting space suit, and the pressure was checked by technicians. At 5:02 he left his quarters at Hangar 8, and walked 14 steps to the waiting transfer van for the launching pad. He entered *Friendship 7* space capsule at 6:03, having ridden the elevator up his triangular gantry at launching pad 14. Then came the moment for which all had waited. At 9:47, belching smoke and fire, the Atlas rose from the pad and shot straight up into the clear blue sky atop an orange ball of flame. It then leveled off toward the East.

At 10:00 the missile was traveling about 17,545 miles per hour, between 100 to 160 miles above the earth. As he was soaring over Kano, Nigeria, Glenn tried his first food in space at 10:25. He was then in a weightless condition, as he squirted the food into his mouth from the tube. His menu consisted of beef, vegetable mixture and applesauce. The food was semi-solid, much like baby food, with adult seasoning and sugar added.

Flying over the darkened, far side of the globe, he sighted the bright lights of Perth, Australia, at 10:38. This pleased him no end, so that he asked the ground stations to thank everybody for having turned the lights on and for this graceful gesture. Glenn's heartbeat and respiration were found completely normal at 10:50, and he said he was "having no problems." At 11:09 he passed over Guyamas, Mexico, heading back across the North American continent, still in voice contact with the ground stations.

He had completed the first orbit of the earth at 11:20 and by 11:28 reported some minor difficulties with the attitude control system—the one used to keep the capsule in the right position during orbit. And by 11:32 he switched to the fly-by-wire manual control system, making second contact with Kano, Nigeria, control station at 11:42. He told the ground stations at that time he was "a little warm," as the sun was streaming through the window of his space capsule. Ground station said at 11:50 that Col. Glenn had reported seeing thousands of luminous particles in space outside the capsule and that beside control difficulties, these were "the only really unusual problems" of his first orbit.

He passed at 12:02 into darkness over the Indian Ocean for the second time, and he saw the third sunrise of the day at 12:28, as his capsule hailed the dawn near Canton Island in the Pacific. Three hours after lift-off, he reported himself still in excellent physical condition. He passed over Point Arguello, Mexico, at 12:46, and then discussed the pros and cons of the attitude control systems with fellow astronaut Walter M. Schirra.

Three hours and six minutes after launch (at 12:54 to be exact) he completed the second orbit, and then was sent on a third orbit by the space agency. As he chatted with the Bermuda tracking station at 12:56, he said that he could see "the whole State of Florida laid out like a map."

Once again over the African Coast at 1:18, he saw his third

sunset within four hours. He cracked a joke with astronaut Leroy
Cooper at 1:31, about military flight pay, as he neared Australia on
the final leg of his 81,000-mile journey. He quipped: "Have four
hours flight time, request flight chit for me."

Then at 1:55 the spacecraft's retro-fire time clock was checked
by the Australian ground station in preparation for descent. And at
2:20 P.M., the three speedbreaking retro-rockets started firing to
take him out of orbit, and then the capsule began its plunge through
the atmosphere immediately.

By 2:28 he had completed his three orbits—four hours 41 minutes after launch. The capsule was still largely under manual control
at 2:28. Ten minutes later, at 2:38, the main parachute opened and
the capsule faced temperatures of 3,000 degrees Fahrenheit on the
way down. It was of this that Glenn said, "Boy, that was a real fire-
ball." Five minutes later, at 2:43, the capsule landed in the ocean
about six miles from destroyer *Noa,* in the recovery fleet, so that
his three orbits had taken exactly four hours and 56 minutes. The
destroyer reported it understood his condition to be "excellent." The
space capsule was recovered from the Atlantic at 3:01, and was
safely on the deck of the *Noa* at 3:04. And sixteen minutes later, at
3:20 P.M., Colonel Glenn emerged from the capsule.

The question has recently been posed, how much it cost the
American taxpayer to put Glenn in orbit. Let's begin by saying that
some thirty thousand Americans, who stood by at the Cape and at
tracking stations around the world, had a direct hand in this space
ride. Another 500,000 Americans had an indirect hand in it. These
people held jobs with more than 5,000 companies that helped to
make parts for the space capsule, the Atlas rocket and the tracking
system. Of the 30,000 persons who played direct roles in the Glenn
flight, 10,000 were employed by private industry, and 20,000 by
Uncle Sam, including those technicians with the NASA and Navy
personnel on ships in the Atlantic.

In considering that this flight was the climax to Project Mercury, which started 3½ years ago, the estimated figure would be
$400 million, or about $2.15 for each man, woman and child in the
United States. Of this amount some $160 million went to the Mc-
Donnell Co., of St. Louis, 95 million for tracking operations, 85 million on rockets to boost the astronauts into space, 25 million on
recovery operations and 35 million on supporting research and other
areas. This does not include the cost of the cake—shaped like a

Mercury capsule—which an enterprising baker had prepared for the event, and which had been made ready to be consumed after the first try and had been kept in storage all throughout the ten tries. This cake was so huge in size, that it had to be made into 125 layers, and with no bakery large enough for the job, it had to be made on a large truck. It was nine feet high, six feet wide, was reportedly made of 300 pounds of sugar, 190 pounds of butter, 250 pounds of flour, 1,200 eggs, 100 quarts of milk, 60 pounds of mixed fruit, 160 pounds of powdered sugar, 60 pounds of margarine, 65 pounds of egg white, one quart of mocha flavor, two quarts of vanilla, and weighed in all 900 pounds. This cake then was driven to the Cape, where the baker had intended everybody who took part in Glenn's orbital flight to get a slice. And there is where the cake story ends, for no one knows what happened to this concoction afterwards—whether it was too stale to eat, or whether there was anyone who took a chance eating it.

And thus it was that the bronzed marine lieutenant colonel Glenn, trained to the litheness of a Greek athlete and spiritually well prepared to make this jaunt around the earth, rode his fiery Mercury spacecraft screaming back through the atmosphere in a triumphal climax to his triple orbit of the earth. It had been a wonderful day—a perfect mission—marred only by minor headaches, an historic occasion, to which all here and abroad had looked forward for more than three years.

As the N. Y. *Herald Tribune's* editorial so well put it: "The astronauts have come closer than any to the ancient Biblical vision of the day, when the morning stars sang together, and all the sons of God shouted for joy. Not since Lindbergh disappeared in the mists over the North Atlantic 35 years ago had there been such a prayerful, single-minded concentration on the fate of one man." The hopes and the fears of countless millions, here, as well as abroad, traveled with Glenn—America's newest national hero—in that small space capsule these 80,000 miles, three times around, climaxed by a mass sigh of relief when he was safe and hearty aboard the destroyer's deck.

And now the long preparation to land a man on the moon begins. When that will be no one knows. That it will come there seems to be no doubt. The dream of Jules Verne will have been realized sooner than we know.

This mission to the moon will probably begin as early as 1968.

Two advanced Saturn rockets will be used. The first will carry an unmanned "escape rocket" into orbit around the earth. The second will then carry the 75-ton Apollo space ship with its three-man crew into the same orbit, where, using the rendezvous technique, the Apollo will overtake and move ahead of the escape rocket. After the two are properly joined, the escape rocket will fire for seven minutes and then fall away, starting the Apollo on its two-and-a-half-day journey to the moon.

The Apollo ship is 50 feet long and has three sections. In front is the command section carrying the astronauts, controls and instruments. Behind this is the service section which carries life support equipment plus rocket power needed to return the astronauts at any time in case of trouble. The third section has rockets to put the ship into a low-altitude orbit around the moon and to back it down onto the lunar surface. The astronauts will then leave the ship to collect samples of the moon's surface, take photographs and make scientific measurements.

After a day on the moon the Apollo's crew will be ready to return. Using its back section as a launching pad, the vessel will lift itself free of the moon's gravity by means of rockets in the second section. This section will then be jettisoned, leaving only the forward section containing the astronauts to complete the last leg of the trip.

When entering the earth's atmosphere the ship will experience temperatures of up to 3,000 degrees Fahrenheit and extreme vibrations. Then, at 10,000 feet, three parachutes will open and lower the ship gently to its landing spot, probably somewhere in the middle west. Thus will end the first Apollo moon mission.

— 54 —

THE TELSTAR STORY

Although this book has already gone to press, the story of Telstar is so world-shaking that I decided to include a few lines even at this belated hour.

Telstar actually marks the historic first step toward a worldwide space communication system, in which satellites, orbiting thousands of miles above the earth, will serve as a network of microwave radio relay stations for the transmitting and receiving of tele-

phone, teletype, photograph, facsimile and other types of instantaneous communications.

What really is Telstar? It is an experimental communications
satellite, which was rocketed into orbit by a Thor Delta rocket on
July 10, establishing a new global communications system in space.
In some respects it is a joint undertaking of government and industry, as the NASA furnished the Thor Delta rocket that launched
the complex satellite into orbit from Cape Canaveral, and the
American Telephone and Telegraph Company, which had sunk
$50 million into the project so far, paid the government for the
cost of launching. To get the green light from the government, the
A.T.&T. had to agree, among other things, that any inventions growing out of the communications satellite work at Bell Laboratories
would be made available on a royalty fee basis to all companies. In
other words the Administration is seeking to prevent domination by
any one company. Telstar itself cost about $1 million, and reimburs-
ing NASA for launching and tracking approaches the sum of $3
million.

Telstar rivals in significance the first telegraphed transmission
of Samuel F. B. Morse's flash of over a century ago, "What has God
wrought?," and Alexander Graham Bell's telephonic: "Mr. Watson,
come here, I need you." It also rivals the laying of the first Atlantic
cable in 1858 and the sending of the first radio signal across the
Atlantic in 1901, the first intelligible signal ever transmitted from
shore to shore in the development of transoceanic radio telegraphy.

Thirty years later, on July 21, 1931, to be exact, the first regular
schedule of television broadcasts was inaugurated by the Columbia
Broadcasting System in New York to a small audience within twenty
miles of the antenna. The medium first reached across the continent
on September 4, 1951, when President Truman's addressing the
Japanese Peace Treaty Conference in San Francisco was heard and
seen simultaneously in New York. Next President Eisenhower's
peace message to the world took place on December 18, 1958,
through the communications satellite in "Project Score" which received and rebroadcast messages from the earth either instantly
or after some time elapsed.

Then, of course, to set the historical aspect of this straight,
came another communications satellite, *Echo I*, a passive satellite,
which only serves as a reflective medium, bouncing signals from one
ground station to another.

As for the Telstar satellite itself, it is a sapphire-studded object, with a 34½-inch sphere base. It was this that established a new communication link between America and Europe. Hope was expressed that it would continue to serve for two years, after which it would be shut off, according to the Bell Telephone people, who designed and developed it. The sphere itself weighs 170 pounds, and is composed of 15,000 parts.

Its orbit's apogee is 3,502 miles, its perigee 593 miles, and its orbiting period 158 minutes. Its capability is to receive 600 telephone channels or one television channel. Its chief function is to receive a radio signal from the ground, amplify it by a factor of 10 billion, and retransmit the signal on another frequency. It is designed to handle voice, picture and coded data. The satellite's planned orbit would keep it at altitudes ranging between 600 miles and 3,500 miles above the earth's surface, which would give Telstar the ability to relay television messages between continents.

Telstar is only roughly spherical in shape, having 72 flat facets. Solar cells, transforming the light from the sun into electrical current, are mounted on sixty of these facets. These facets are coated with man-made sapphires to protect them from bombardment by some of the potentially damaging components of radiation in space. These solar cells also recharge the satellite's batteries and provide Telstar with the power needed to function. Initially these cells are expected to produce 15 watts of electricity.

Receiving and transmitting antennas girdle the satellite's midsection and therefore are called equatorial. These antennas carry out Telstar's basic communications functions, and also transmit a beacon signal used for tracking from the ground. Another antenna— a corkscrew shaped wire—is located on top of the satellite which serves telemetry command and tracking-beacon functions.

As to how it works, the principal ground station at Andover, Maine, for example, will send a signal to the satellite on a frequency of 6,390 megacycles. The satellite then broadcasts this at 4,170 megacycles. And the satellite's output will be held nearly constant at about 2¼ watts regardless of the strength of the signal it receives.

Much of the equipment in Telstar is devoted to experimentation and measurement, rather than communication functions. Still the Telstar satellite serves as a relay station some 3,000 miles above the North Atlantic, and clear television pictures were transmitted on July 10 from the station in Andover, Maine, to a station in Brittany, Pleumeur Bodou, and also to England's Goonhilly station on the coast of Wales. Engineers have indicated that it would take from 20 to 25 Telstar-like satellites in random orbit to provide complete coverage.

NASA is also working on its own experimental satellite programs, one of which is a relay project similar in many respects to Telstar. The relay is being built for the National Space Agency at RCA-Astro Electronics Division at Princeton, and is expected to be launched this year. Another project is the Syncom, being handled for NASA by the Hughes Aircraft Company, and which is due in early 1963. This one is a synchronous orbit, the satellite being placed 22,300 miles above and parallel to the equator.

Thus Telstar, Relay, Syncom and Echo are magic names already for America's pronged attack to shrink the world with a satellite-borne communications system. All these four are satellite relays, each with its special area of attention. Basically these satellite relay systems are divided into two classes: the active class consisting of spheres which pick up signals, amplify them and relay them back to earth, and the passive ones, which simply bounce signals back from their shiny surfaces.

Telstar, Relay and Syncom are the active satellites, more complex because they carry radio equipment, and more useful in the long run. *Echo* is a passive one, and is basically a huge aluminum-covered balloon. It is simpler, it is true, but requires much more powerful ground equipment to transmit signals.

These space communication systems have come at a time when the problems of transocean communication have become increasingly complex, and in the case of television virtually insoluble. In point of fact, television cannot be sent by cable, for it requires channels of great frequency and band width. A single television program requires an electric channel wide enough to carry 600 separate telephone conversations. The Bell system alone at this moment operates nearly 700 voice circuits by cable and radio for overseas communication, and by 1965 it is conservatively estimated twice that many will be needed. According to the Bell scientists it would take 50 undersea cables similar to the three in use in the North Atlantic to handle just the estimated 1980 requirements for telephone and other services. The transmission of a great volume of messages and of television requires trans-ocean use of microwave broadband beams that have a tremendous capacity and that can handle all types of communication. This is the system widely used in overland communication, and a large number of long distance messages are handled by microwave. But microwaves, like light, travel in straight lines, and numerous relay towers have to be built on land to intercept and amplify signals repeatedly and send them on in a straight line. Transmission of microwaves across the Atlantic has not been practical because signals sent across wide bodies of water would soar off into space, and could not follow the earth's curvature to a receiving station. To relay a live signal from the U.S.A. to Europe would require a mid-Atlantic tower more than 145 miles high, which would be an impossible height.

Television cannot be bounced off the ionosphere in the manner of short radio waves. Hence there is no way to relay television overseas, except by satellite, and Telstar is doing this trick ideally. At the extremely high frequencies necessary for TV, signals, as already said, must travel in straight lines. A satellite bounces them around the horizon in two straight lines, one up to the satellite, another down to earth. Any two places within a line of sight then can communicate if they have the right equipment.

Telstar's most dramatic moment came on July 10, when at 7:33 on a remote but no longer quiet hill in the wooded mountains of Maine, the first call from the earth station was made through Telstar. The French ground station reported it was clearly receiving the first transatlantic television broadcast—a live shot of the Andover station and another of Vice President Johnson in Washington. The British station at Goonhilly, in southwestern England, on the other hand, had some difficulty with the first transmission, but received another one on a subsequent orbit.

The Andover installation is in a rustic, 1,000-acre site, a shallow bowl rimmed by mountains about 15 miles south of Rumford, informally known as Space Hill. The Andover Dome, possibly the world's largest inflated shelter, is held rigidly against Maine's strongest winter gales by air pressure of less than one-tenth of a pound per square inch. It has a minimum of interference from other radio installations, and the rim of the mountain is extremely protective.

What is probably the greatest tribute to the persuasiveness and immediacy of Telstar's transmission, may well have been the result of President Kennedy's first assurance in his Telstar televised press conference, on Monday, July 23, 1962, that the United States would not devalue the dollar, and would not cut back its selling of gold. The result was that next morning on London's Stock Exchange almost $45 million was knocked off the listed value of stocks in gold companies, and gold bullion, too, lost some of its lustre as prices began sliding downward that day.

And so Telstar, Relay, Syncom and Echo are magic names that initiate a new era in relaying international television and broadcasting—whose goal, according to President Kennedy, "is the linking of the whole world in telegraph, telephone, radio and television." It may be that some day, perhaps sooner than we think, one will be able to flick on a television set and catch programs live from, say, Paris, Amsterdam, or even Delhi, India.

INDEX